Essentials of Biological Anthropology

Noel T. Boaz

International Institute for Human Evolutionary Research

Alan J. Almquist

California State University–Hayward

Prentice Hall

Upper Saddle River, New Jersey 07458

Library of Congress Cataloging-in-Publication Data

BOAZ, NOEL THOMAS.
    Essentials of biological anthropology / Noel T. Boaz, Alan J.
Almquist.
        p.   cm.
    Includes bibliographical references and index.
    ISBN   0–13-080793–1
    1. Physical anthropology.   2. Human evolution.   I. Almquist, Alan
J. II. Title
GN60.B674   1999
599.9—dc21   98–25732
                                                              CIP

Editorial director: *Charlyce Jones Owen*
Acquisitions editor: *Nancy Roberts*
Development editor-in-chief: *Susanna Lesan*
Development editor: *Elaine Silverstein*
Director of production and manufacturing: *Barbara Kittle*
Project manager: *Joan Stone*
Manufacturing manager: *Nick Sklitsis*
Prepress and manufacturing buyer: *Lynn Pearlman*
Creative design director: *Leslie Osher*
Interior design: *Carole Anson and Levavi & Levavi*

Cover design: *Carole Anson*
Cover art: *Michael Maydak/Conrad Represents, Inc.*
Line art coordinator: *Guy Ruggiero*
Artist: *Maria Piper*
Director, Image Resource Center: *Lorinda Morris-Nantz*
Photo research supervisor: *Melinda Lee Reo*
Image permission supervisor: *Kay Dellosa*
Photo researcher: *Diane Austin*
Copy editor: *Virginia Rubens*
Editorial assistant: *Maureen Diana*
Marketing manager: *Christopher DeJohn*

This book was set in 10/12 ITC Garamond Light by TSI Graphics and was printed and bound by RR Donnelley & Sons Company. The cover was printed by Phoenix Color Corp.

© 1999 by Prentice-Hall, Inc.
Simon & Schuster/A Viacom Company
Upper Saddle River, New Jersey 07458

Printed in the United States of America

10   9   8   7   6   5   4   3   2

ISBN 0-13-080793-1

Prentice-Hall International (UK) Limited, *London*
Prentice-Hall of Australia Pty. Limited, *Sydney*
Prentice-Hall Canada Inc., *Toronto*
Prentice-Hall Hispanoamericana, S.A., *Mexico*
Prentice-Hall of India Private Limited, *New Delhi*
Prentice-Hall of Japan, Inc., *Tokyo*
Simon & Schuster Asia Pte. Ltd., *Singapore*
Editora Prentice-Hall do Brasil, Ltda., *Rio de Janeiro*

To our children

Lydia, Peter, and Alexander

Christopher and Emily

Brief Contents

Contents

Frontiers Boxes

Preface

Essentials of Biological Anthropology is an abbreviated version of our longer work, *Biological Anthropology,* which first appeared in 1997. One might imagine an abbreviated version to be rather simple to produce. It wasn't. Many difficult decisions had to be made as to what to leave out, what to modify, and what to enhance. Many favorite passages fell by the wayside. In the end, though, *Essentials* retains the overall structure and organizational flow of the original version—perhaps the single most important ingredient in making that version a good book.

ABOUT THE BOOK

In a field as fast paced as biological anthropology, we welcomed the opportunity to revise and update the original text. New insights into old problems, new fossil finds, new people working in the field—all require comment. Every chapter in *Essentials* has been revised. The outcome of the combined efforts of reviewers, students who had used the original text, and our second look at what we had done is a thoroughly updated condensed text. Yet our efforts are humbled almost daily by new discoveries in the field. For example, researchers recently found that a region of the brain (the planum temporale) thought to control language is larger in the left hemisphere in both chimpanzees and humans, disproving the notion that this area was asymmetrical only in humans. The human planum temporale of the left hemisphere is normally larger than in the right, but 94% of the brains of chimpanzees showed the same asymmetry. These findings affect our continuing studies of the origin of human language and will be discussed in the next edition. Thus goes the field of biological anthropology—exciting, challenging, ever changing.

Above all else, this is a book of ideas. Students will find this text stimulating as well as challenging, factors that characterize the field as a whole. This version is more user-friendly, with important concepts better illustrated, thanks to the artists at Prentice Hall. Explanations of difficult concepts and numerous examples help the student to thoroughly understand the message. In other words, instructors do not have to spend valuable class time explaining the text to students.

The volume provides the "essentials" without so simplifying or condensing them that the excitement of discovery that hallmarks the field is lost. It represents both a useful approach to the teaching of human evolution at the introductory college and university level and a restatement of the coherency and fundamental compatibility of the many subdisciplines that contribute to biological anthropology. Throughout the book is the unifying thread of evolution by natural selection that forms the basic paradigm of the discipline. As scientists we believe that every question should remain open to the possibility of a new answer; however, Charles Darwin's formulations of evolution and its modifications continue to be the best explanation for our presence and for the world around us. We hope our exposition does justice to his elegant theoretical framework, on which modern biological anthropology is based.

This book is organized along lines of increasing organismal complexity, leading from prebiotic replicating molecules through to modern *Homo sapiens*. Following this organization, the text proceeds generally from very early time to the present, and from broad taxonomic categories that include human beings to progressively more specific categories, ending with *Homo sapiens sapiens*. We have used available paleoecological data to set the stage and provide the context of the morphological and behavioral adaptations characterizing our ancestors at each major time period. We believe that this organization serves to build students' understanding of the biological, genetic, and anatomical basics of biological anthropology so that the complex questions of hominid phylogeny, human sociocultural behavior, human variability, and modern-day adaptation to our increasingly demanding environment can be approached in more meaningful ways.

SUPPLEMENTS

The supplements package for this text is of exceptional quality. It is intended to give the instructor the resources needed to teach the course and the student the tools needed to successfully complete the course.

Instructor's Resource Manual: This essential instructor's tool includes detailed chapter outlines, teaching objectives, discussion questions, classroom activities, and additional resources.

Test Item File: This carefully prepared manual consists of over 1000 questions in multiple-choice, true/false, fill-in, and essay formats. Each question is page referenced to the text.

Prentice Hall Custom Test: This computerized test item file allows you to create your own personalized exams, edit existing questions, import questions, and print multiple versions of the same test. It is available in Windows, DOS, and Macintosh formats.

Study Guide: This carefully written guide helps students better understand the material presented in the text. Each chapter consists of chapter summaries, definitions of key terms and concepts, critical thinking exercises geared to the questions in the text, and self-test questions page referenced to the text.

Boaz Companion Website, at http://www.prenhall.com/boaz: This site allows students using the text to fully access the power of the World Wide Web. Students can challenge themselves through this online study guide by working with multiple choice, true/false, and essay questions keyed to each chapter. The online study guide quiz sections provide immediate feedback to the student, with specific page references in the text. The links contained within this site will introduce students to a new world of physical anthropology.

Anthropology on the Internet: 1998–1999:   This brief guide introduces students to the origin and innovations behind the Internet and provides clear strategies for navigating the complexity of the Internet and World Wide Web. Exercises within and at the end of the chapters allow students to practice searching for the myriad of resources available to the student of anthropology. This supplementary book is free to students when packaged with this text. Local Prentice Hall representatives can explain shrink-wrap options.

Prentice Hall Color Transparencies: Physical Anthropology, Series I: Full-color illustrations, charts, and other visual materials have been selected to help amplify lecture topics.

Videos: A selection of high quality, award-winning videos that show students the world of anthropology are available from Films for the Humanities and Sciences as well as Filmmaker's Library. Prentice Hall sales representatives can provide more information.

New York Times/**Prentice Hall Themes of the Times: Anthropology:**   The *New York Times* and Prentice Hall are sponsoring *Themes of the Times,* a program designed to enhance student access to current information relevant to the classroom. Through this program, the core subject matter provided in the text is supplemented by a collection of timely articles from one of the world's most distinguished newspapers, the *New York Times*. These articles demonstrate the vital, ongoing connection between what is learned in the classroom and what is happening in the world around us. To enjoy a wealth of information provided by the *New York Times* daily, a reduced subscription rate is available. For information, call toll-free: 1-800-631-1222.

Prentice Hall and the *New York Times* are proud to co-sponsor *Themes of the Times*. We hope it will make the reading of both textbooks and newspapers a more dynamic, involving process.

ACKNOWLEDGMENTS

Many individuals have shaped this book. Sherwood Washburn and Jane Lancaster were instrumental in developing our ideas of a text that brought together fossils and behavior. Joe Birdsell was an important influence in our incorporation of ecology and population perspectives. Jack Cronin deserves credit for contributing the concept of a textbook that fully integrated molecular and fossil approaches. We are indebted to the authors of the text's Frontiers boxes who agreed to share their perspectives and insights: Eugenie C. Scott, Lloyd H. Burckle, Matt Cartmill, Linda D. Wolfe, David R. Begun, Alan Walker, Craig B. Stanford, Kenneth K. Kidd, Judith R. Kidd, and S. Boyd Eaton.

Essentials is a reality because one individual at Prentice Hall made it so. For this reason, we are indebted to Nancy Roberts, Editor in Chief of the Social Sciences. She has always believed in the book and encouraged us onward. Within the scope of Nancy's vision came the other creative people we worked with on a day-to-day basis. The efforts of Sabina Johnson and Barbara Reilly, editors for the first book, remain apparent in this edition. For *Essentials,* the careful and painstaking work of Elaine Silverstein, development editor, and Joan Stone, project manager, can only be described as monumental. All of these people, in addition to Joyce Rosinger, who obtained the necessary permissions, and the artists at Prentice Hall, who created new art often from nothing more than crudely drawn sketches, did a truly magnificent job. We gratefully thank all of you for your efforts.

Readers and reviewers have helped immensely in refining passages and editing muddled text. We particularly wish to thank Marc Feldesman, John Fleagle, Paris Pavlakis, and Sue Parker for their help in preparing the first book; their efforts have been retained in *Essentials.* Reviewers whose comments were invariably helpful to *Essentials* were Mark Fleischman, Syracuse University; Leonard Greenfield, Temple University; Lawrence A. Kuznar, Indiana University–Purdue University Fort Wayne; and Robert Shanafelt, Florida State University.

Our students contributed to the development of the book by their many questions and careful reading. Particular thanks for this round of student reviews go to Beth Bedrin and Nancy Cassquero. The excellent work of Leslie Khayatpoor and Margaret Kring on the study guide and instructor's resource manual, respectively, measures up to the task.

For much of the research in biological anthropology that has been conducted and reported in this volume we wish to thank the L. S. B. Leakey Foundation for their program of grants and awards and Dr. Karla Savage, grants officer for the Foundation, for her untiring efforts in this regard. Toward the support of new research in the field (and, thus, assuring that we will have something to write about in the future), a portion of the royalties from the sale of this book is being donated to the Foundation.

Finally, the forbearance, support, and encouragement of Barbara Almquist and Meleisa McDonell ensured that *Essentials* did not take the decade to complete that the first book did. For that we are all most grateful.

About the Authors

Noel T. Boaz is Director of the International Institute for Human Evolutionary Research at Central Oregon University Center in Bend, Oregon. A paleoanthropologist with many years of field experience in Africa, he was trained at the University of Virginia and the University of California, Berkeley, where he received his Ph.D. in Anthropology in 1977. Dr. Boaz's current research interests are in the earliest origins of the hominid lineage, ecological change and human evolution, and biomedical anthropology. Recent publications include *Quarry: Closing in on the Missing Link* (1993) and *Eco Homo,* an ecological history of the human species (1997).

Alan J. Almquist is Professor of Anthropology at California State University, Hayward. Dr. Almquist received his Ph.D. in Anthropology in 1972 at the University of California, Berkeley. A dedicated teacher, he has also headed the Clarence Smith Museum of Anthropology at Hayward and has undertaken fieldwork at early hominid sites in the Middle Awash, Ethiopia. Current research interests include the evolution of human sexual behavior and paleoanthropology. Recent publications include *Milestones in Human Evolution* (1993) edited with Ann Manyak, and a reader, *Human Sexuality* (1995) with Andrei Simic and Patricia Omidian.

CHAPTER 1

Evolutionary Perspectives on Human Biology and Behavior

Biological Anthropology is about humankind's place in nature, how we came to be, how and why our bodies and brains are built the way they are, and why we behave as we do. Portions of these subjects are studied by scientists in many diverse disciplines, but the general, or holistic, study of them is the domain of **biological anthropology.** This broad-based understanding of the human organism is the strength of biological anthropology, and in today's increasingly specialized world of science, it is an important perspective.

The basic scientific framework of modern biological anthropology is *evolution by natural selection,* Charles Darwin's theory to explain the origin and diversity of species on earth. This theory provides scientists with a way to make predictions about human evolution, biology, and behavior and to test their predictions against observations made in nature. These observations may involve laboratory experiments, field studies of our living primate relatives in remote rain forests, or excavations of fossils millions of years old. To give our readers an overall appreciation of human adaptation, anatomy, behavior, and evolution, this book integrates the advances that biological anthropologists have made in understanding human evolution and biology. We draw upon many different lines of evidence to demonstrate both the uniqueness of the human condition and those continuities that make humans part of nature.

biological anthropology– the study of human evolution, biology, variation, and adaptation (also known as physical anthropology).

Human beings evolved out of and are still today intimately connected with the natural world. Our ancestors lived as gatherers and hunters for the last several million years. We have been "civilized"—living in permanent structures packed into villages, towns, and cities, growing food plants, tending domesticated animals, and using metal tools—only for the last few thousand years. This period is less than one-half of one percent of our evolutionary history, which began approximately 2.5 million years ago when we became stone tool–using early humans. Our biology is still that of hunter-gatherers, quick-witted opportunists who can eat almost anything and who can survive under conditions of great hardship as well as prosperity.

ANTHROPOLOGY STUDIES HUMANKIND

Anthropology is the science that studies humans, their biology, adaptations, behavior, and variation within the context of a specialized adaptation of learned social behavior called **culture.** Anthropologists study such broad-ranging phenomena as physical and cultural differences among human groups, the structure of the many human languages, the adaptability of human groups to different environmental conditions, the patterns of growth, and the changing patterns of culture over time. This broad scientific agenda makes anthropology a discipline with many specialists and many subdisciplines. For this reason, anthropological research is frequently described as "multidisciplinary." One characteristic of all anthropologists is a commitment to understanding humanity in its entirety, as a functioning whole. For this reason anthropology is also termed "holistic."

Anthropology in the United States is made up of four fields: biological or physical anthropology, cultural anthropology or ethnology, archaeology, and linguistics. Biological anthropologists study the physical makeup, evolution, and variations of human populations, the relationships of humanity with the natural world, and the biological bases of human behavior. **Cultural anthropologists** study living societies of people, their customs, their myths, their kinship systems, their rituals, and all aspects of their social behavior within the uniquely human adaptation of culture. **Archaeologists** look at how human culture has adapted and evolved over time through the study of artifacts and sites. **Linguists** study language: its many varieties, the forces governing how languages change, the relationships between language and the brain, and the interactions between language and cultural concepts. The four disciplines are joined, sometimes loosely, by their shared focus on human adaptation within culture, that set of learned behaviors which, shared by each member of a society, mediates all social interactions.

Biological anthropology, the subject of this book, is closely related to the branch of biology known as **human biology.** Biological anthropologists strive to accurately describe human physical structure both in the present and in the past. They seek to understand how human structure functions in real life and how human individuals with that structure be-

anthropology–the study of humankind.

culture–learned aspects of behavior passed on from one generation to the next in human societies.

cultural anthropology–the anthropological study of human societies, their belief systems, their cultural adaptations, and their social behavior.

archaeology–the anthropological study of past cultures, their social adaptations, and their lifeways by use of preserved artifacts and features.

linguistics–the anthropological study of languages, their diversity and connections, and the interaction of language and culture in society.

human biology–the branch of biology that studies human physiology and adaptation; closely related to biological anthropological study of the same topics.

have. In addition, biological anthropologists investigate how function and behavior are integrated into the environment in which human beings live. Because they want to understand the origins of structures, biological anthropologists also explore human genetics, growth and development, and evolutionary history.

There are some strong connections between biological anthropology and other anthropological subdisciplines. Biological anthropologists may come into close contact with archaeologists in the cross-disciplinary area of **paleoanthropology,** the study of human evolution through fossils and artifacts (Figure 1–1). Archaeologists may find a fossilized human skull, but the job of describing and studying the specimen falls to the biological anthropologist. Or biological anthropologists may find it essential to put together their knowledge of skeletal biology with that of the cultural and living contexts that the archaeologist has discovered in order to better understand the adaptations of a past human population. Biological anthropologists who study the behavior of the nonhuman primates may have close intellectual ties to psychologists. Specialists in human growth and adaptation may feel particularly at home among a group of biologists who specialize in human biology. And biological anthropologists who investigate molecular biology and the genetics of human populations may work closely with geneticists and molecular biologists (Figure 1–2).

Figure 1–1 • Paleoanthropologist at work.

paleoanthropology–the study of the physical characteristics, evolution, and behavior of fossil humans and their relatives, incorporating parts of biological anthropology and archaeology.

Figure 1–2 • The four fields of anthropology and related fields that contribute to the knowledge of biological anthropology.

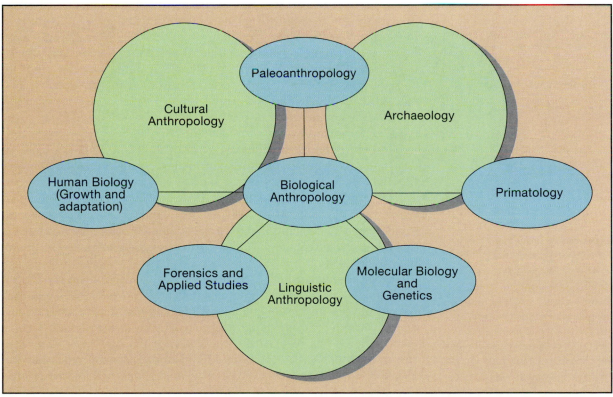

Many of the subject areas relevant to understanding human evolution and biology discussed in this book are taught not only in anthropology departments but within departments of biology, genetics, biochemistry, anatomy, geology, geography, environmental sciences, and psychology. Researchers in human evolution may call themselves biological anthropologists, biologists, geneticists, biochemists, geologists, anatomists, paleontologists, or psychologists, depending on their research specialty. We will use "biological anthropology" and "biological anthropologists" as the most inclusive terms to refer to this broad, interdisciplinary field and to those scientists studying human evolution.

The Scientific Method

Anthropology, biology, and other branches of science use a "hypothetico-deductive" scientific method that requires the framing of ideas in the form of **hypotheses.** A hypothesis is a preliminary explanation of observations phrased as a proposition: if X is true, then Y is true. The most significant characteristic of a hypothesis is that it must be *falsifiable;* that is, we must be able to disprove it. Testing and experimentation determine if a given hypothesis explains or conforms with what is observed. If it does not it is rejected or modified. A **theory** is a hypothesis or a series of hypotheses that has stood the test of time and has withstood numerous attempts at falsification. This methodology of hypothesis-testing distinguishes science from the humanities.

The most widely understood application of the scientific method is the experiment. Scientists formulate a question that they want to answer, devise a test in which the variables are all held constant except those being tested, run the experiment while varying the conditions of interest, and compare the results to a "control" in which all the variables are held constant. This is the standard mode of operation in experimental sciences such as physics and chemistry.

Biological anthropology also is an experimental science. Modern biological anthropologists must articulate the hypotheses they want to test before they set off on expeditions. It is not sufficient simply to write in to a funding organization expressing interest in observing monkeys in the wild, for example. A scientist must present a research plan. A researcher might propose testing the hypothesis that a male in a particular monkey species, when he displaces the dominant male in the social group, tends to kill infants that have been fathered by the previous male. This is a testable hypothesis. Either the males kill the infants most of the time or they do not.

Biological anthropology is also a historical science, concerned with reconstructing past events. Hypotheses relating to events that happened millions of years ago in the human evolutionary past may seem to be beyond the scope of "experiment" for the most part. But experiments have been designed that recreate the conditions of the past in order to test various hypotheses. Paleoanthropological studies, for example, may be designed to discover how and under what circumstances fossils or arti-

hypothesis—an explanation of a set of observations that can be disproved or falsified by additional observations or facts.

theory—usually a set of hypotheses that withstands attempts at disproof and continues to successfully explain observations as they are made, thus gaining scientific support over time.

facts were buried in sediments. In attempting to answer these questions, scientists conduct experiments to see what sorts of changes occur in bones in modern environments. They may observe hyenas at a kill, collect the bones after the hyenas are finished, and look at the bones under a microscope. They may examine the scratches on bone after trampling by a herd of cattle. Or they may cut meat off bones using stone tools and examine the cut marks made this way. These sorts of experiments may tell researchers whether a particular scratch pattern found in a fossil site was made by the teeth of predators, by trampling under hooves, or by the hands of ancient humans while obtaining meat for food.

In the natural sciences the concept of "experiment" has carried over to encompass comparative study of animals and plants in different habitats, environments, or time periods. In a real sense these natural scientists are doing "experiments," but instead of varying experimental conditions themselves, they allow nature to vary the conditions. For example, Charles Darwin undertook these sorts of studies in the Galápagos Islands off South America (see Chapter 2) when he compared the animal species to see how they had responded biologically to conditions on the various islands. In addition, for both ethical and practical reasons, biological anthropologists cannot perform controlled laboratory experiments on human beings for many of the questions that they want to answer. Here comparative study of human groups can be an "experiment" designed to test alternative hypotheses for human biological differences. For example, anthropologists interested in the causes of the unique physical attributes of people living high in the Andes Mountains (see Chapter 12) can compare the anatomy of members of the group who moved to the lowlands as children with those relatives who stayed at home. In this way, they can test whether environmental conditions or inheritance was the main cause of the mountain group's physical characteristics.

The Paradigms of Biological Anthropology

Like other fields of science, biological anthropology has a method of inquiry and an associated set of questions that serve as an organizing framework of inquiry, or **paradigm.** Observations that are made and tests or experiments that are undertaken are grounded in these paradigms. For example, if we observe that different peoples around the world have different colors of skin, we must explain how these differences are caused, how they originated in the past, and how they are affected by today's world. The paradigms of biological anthropology have changed significantly over the years.

Typology   In the early phases of biological anthropology, when scientific interest lay in putting the vast array of new information about human diversity in some sort of order, the paradigm of biological anthropology was **typology.** Typology is the designation of one individual drawn from a larger group as "typical" of that group. It is defined as the

paradigm–a framework for understanding and interpreting observations.

typology–"idealist" definition of an entire group by reference to a "type" that tends to ignore variation from that ideal.

Figure 1–3 • Johann Friedrich Blumenbach, the founder of biological anthropology.

"type." Typology was an attempt to define a clear set of criteria that could be used to characterize any given species and to classify individuals within those groups. For example, if a typologist was interested in studying dogs, he or she might choose a "type," say an individual German shepherd, to exemplify the concept of "dog" (species *Canis familiaris*). Although the researcher might be aware that there is quite a bit of variation in dogs, from Chihuahuas to Great Danes, typologists de-emphasize individual variation from the "type" because the goal is to classify the diversity of life. There is nothing wrong with typology, which is still the first step in biological investigations, because we must know and define the species with which we are working. But other paradigms have come into play that are important as well.

Typology was the first organized approach to studying the human species. The founder of biological anthropology, German scientist Johann Friedrich Blumenbach (1752–1840), whose interest lay in chronicling the worldwide diversity of modern human beings, used typology to define different human "races" or biological groups. He established "types" that were ideals of whole groups of people. Blumenbach divided the human species into five major divisions called "races" (Figure 1–3) based on physical characteristics and geography; this grouping became the accepted formulation for many years. Today's biological anthropologists have much more data on modern human biological variation than were available to Blumenbach, and few would now agree with his five-fold division of the human species. Yet Blumenbach's pioneering work was important in establishing the groundwork for the later development of biological anthropology.

Culture   *Culture,* the human adaptation of learned social behavior, became a second important paradigm in biological anthropology. In the early phases of the history of anthropology, all attributes of a human group were considered innate characteristics—that is, inherited and not affected by environment, much like the plumage and song patterns of bird species. Early anthropologists might describe a group of South Sea Islanders, previously unknown to Westerners, by the color of their skin, the color and curl of their hair, the clothes they wore, their marriage customs, the language spoken by the group, and even individuals' psychological attributes, all in the same context of innate characteristics. But as the European countries established colonies, and indigenous peoples began to migrate to Europe for a Western education, it became apparent that culture was not innate to a particular human group. A young Australian aborigine or a Masai from Kenya could be transplanted to England, attend Eton and Oxford, and end up speaking, acting, dressing, and thinking just like someone of similar educational background who was English. However, nothing changed the essential physical characteristics of the Australian or the Masai, even if he or she did speak with an "Oxbridge" accent. Clearly physical and cultural traits were under the control of different laws.

Cultural anthropologists, ethnologists, archaeologists, and linguists study how and why cultures differ one from another and how a particular culture meshes with its environment. A question that an anthropologist studying culture might ask, for example, is why a Polynesian tribe would have elaborate prayers, ceremonies, and gear for dangerous fishing on the open sea, and simple and few cultural attributes for relatively safe fishing in lagoons. One possible answer is that magic and religion, along with material culture, help humans cope with the environment. Culture, then, is one of the primary ways that humans adapt to their environment; and as such, biological anthropologists should be aware of its importance today and in the past.

Evolution by Natural Selection   The third paradigm of importance to biological anthropology is **evolution by natural selection.** Evolution by natural selection, the theory advanced by Charles Darwin, holds that nature will favor the fittest individuals, those that possess traits that allow them to survive and to have more offspring. The process of passing on these traits leads to biological differentiation over time, and eventually may result in the formation of new species (see Chapter 2). And it is this paradigm that biological anthropologists use for the most part as the basis for most modern research. Biological anthropologists study human biological variability. Some of this variability is associated with the geographic location of human groups. Other variability is due to biological and physical adaptation to particular environments. The evolutionary paradigm that biological anthropologists use helps to explain the biological variability seen in human groups, and it provides a means to make predictions and to test hypotheses. Chapters 2 and 3 deal at length with evolution by natural selection, and they provide the organizing framework for the succeeding chapters.

It is not quite accurate to say that the evolutionary paradigm has supplanted and totally replaced the earlier typological and cultural paradigms in modern biological anthropology. For example, the discovery and naming of a new species of lemur living in a remote forest in Madagascar (see Chapter 5), new genetic evidence supporting the separation of a third species of chimpanzee (see Chapter 7), or the naming of a new species of a presumed early human ancestor (see Chapter 8)—all basic typology—can still generate a lot of scientific interest. As for culture, studies of primate behavior that shed light on some of the basic social behaviors of humans (see Chapters 6 and 10); research revealing early human behavior, such as evidence of early human cannibalism as well as the florescence of art in late Stone Age peoples (see Chapters 9 and 10); and studies of the complex but important interactions of health and lifestyle in modern urban environments (see Chapter 13) are some of the most compelling in biological anthropology. All of these studies are now undertaken *within the context* of evolution, and herein lies its importance as a paradigm in the modern field of biological anthropology.

evolution by natural selection—Darwin's theory that inherited variability results in the differential survival of individuals and in their ability to contribute to offspring in succeeding generations.

SUBJECTS THAT BIOLOGICAL ANTHROPOLOGISTS STUDY

Biological anthropologists study how and why groups of people differ physically and genetically from one another, how they adapt biologically to their environments, how they grow and develop, and how the human species ultimately originated in the animal world. These questions can be framed broadly as questions relating to human evolution, that is, the laws that underlie human variation, adaptation, and patterns of physical change through space and time.

Human Differences

Biological anthropologists study human **variation** and ask questions that can be termed "human differences" questions. Two such issues are: "How and why do people around the world look different?" and "Are differences in human groups primarily the results of inheritance or of different environments?"

Human beings around the world look different partly because they are adapted to different environmental conditions and partly because each population has a different history of migrations and infusions of peoples from elsewhere. Untangling the causes of variation can be complex. Human beings have a remarkable ability as individuals to change their behavior and as social groups to change their culture, depending on the environment in which they find themselves. These changes can and do have biological effects. Humans have been able to adapt successfully to many different habitats in the world today. How and under what conditions adaptability is expressed in growth patterns, physiology, or anatomical traits is an area of ongoing research in biological anthropology.

How Human Populations Adapt

Biological change over time to accommodate environmental conditions is called **adaptation.** Adaptation within the existing physical or physiological capabilities of humans, which occurs within the lifetimes of the individuals involved, is known as **adaptability** (see Chapter 12). Such *short-term* reversible responses to immediate environmental challenges are part of the universal human biological heritage. Human adaptability includes biochemical, physiological, and behavioral responses to variable environments.

The *long-term* adaptation of humans and other populations of living organisms to the varied habitats into which they may have spread over time is a focus of evolutionary studies. This adaptation occurs by anatomical change and is little modified by environment during individuals' lifetimes. Much of this book deals in one way or another with evolutionary adaptations of humans.

variation–the range of differences in physical or genetic makeup across, within, and between populations of individuals of the same species.

adaptation–biological change effected by evolution to accommodate populations to different environmental conditions.

adaptability–the range of physiological and behavioral responses that an individual can make to adjust to environmental changes.

Origins

One of the most interesting and controversial issues that biological anthropologists have pursued, both today and in the past, is human origins. Such questions as "What living animals are most closely related to humans?" and "What was the ancestral form of the living relatives like?" are still issues today, as they have been for over a century in one form or another. The time of appearance of the unique human lineage has been the topic of lively debate, and estimates range a span of more than 30 million years. Paleontologist Bjorn Kurtén (1972), for example, suggested that the human lineage appeared very early, approximately 30 million years ago, while molecular anthropologists Vincent Sarich and Allan Wilson (1967) suggested that the human lineage separated from that leading to the African apes much later, not much more than 5 million years ago (Figure 1–4). The consensus is now for a "late" or "recent" divergence, that is, 5 to 10 million years ago. Many "tests" of the various hypotheses of human origins have been carried out over the last century. We will discuss them in Chapters 7 through 9.

Phylogeny, from the Greek word for "originating from branches," refers to the lineal relationships of fossil humans and other **primates**—"animals of the first rank"—including monkeys, apes, and prosimians.

phylogeny–the study of evolutionary relationships of organisms.

primates–the zoological order of mammals that includes living and extinct monkeys, apes, and humans, as well as more primitive taxa.

Figure 1–4 • Comparison of two widely varying hypotheses on the timing of the evolutionary divergences of the apes and hominids.

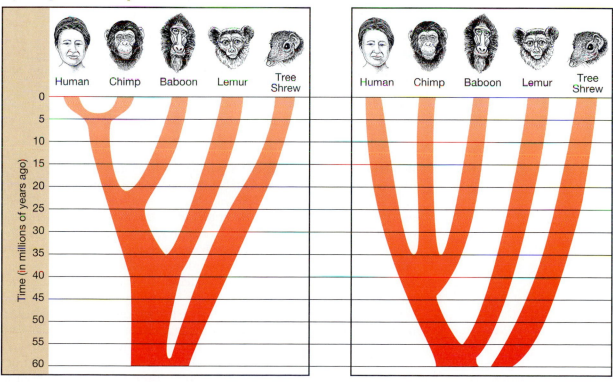

Sarich and Wilson (1967)   Kurtén (1972)

Figure 1–5 • Ernst Haeckel.

Determining these relationships has been a primary consideration of biological anthropologists since fossil specimens were first found and recognized. The German naturalist Ernst Haeckel (1834–1919) produced the first phylogenetic tree for the human species by making use of comparative anatomy (Figure 1–5), because almost no fossil humans were known at the time. Traditionally, phylogenetic studies have been "vertical" in their orientation because they extend back into history. In contrast, studies of the ecology and behavior of fossil species, now gaining much research attention, are more "horizontal" in design. Biological anthropologists are no longer satisfied with hypothesizing only evolutionary relationships between fossils. They want to know how early people and their primate ancestors adapted to their environments, to their diets, and to their social living arrangements and behavior.

Molecular Biology

A number of problems in human evolution are now addressed through the methods of molecular biology. Molecular evidence concerning the actual biological relationships of humans to the other primates is now rapidly accumulating. The data show that humans are most closely related to the African great apes, the chimpanzee and gorilla (see Chapter 7). In fact, human and chimpanzee are so close that they differ by only 1% to 2% of their DNA sequences. How humans and chimps can be so closely related genetically but so very different in their overall anatomy and behavior is a question that biological anthropologists are attempting to answer. Molecular data can serve also as a test of hypotheses based on the fossil record. For example, molecular data were used to disprove the hypothesis that a unique hominid lineage existed prior to 8 to 10 million years ago (see Chapter 7), and molecular data have played important roles in interpretations of the evolutionary history of modern *Homo sapiens* (see Chapter 9).

Behavior

Behavior—the patterning of animal activity over time—and how it relates to evolution and adaptation has become an important research focus in biological anthropology. Today's scientists want to know what animals did (not just what they were), what period of time they lived in, and what other animals they were related to. Contemporary human behavior is the evolutionary result of the behaviors in our ancestors that led to reproductive success—that is, successfully reproducing offspring in worlds long vanished and in ways of life quite different from today's. With a fuller knowledge of the behavior of our own closest living relatives, we can better understand how modern human behavior came to be. This comparative approach works because the early social and environmental situations to which the hominid lineage adapted in times past are similar to those of many nonhuman primates today. One of the keys, then, to understanding human evolution is a full appreciation of nonhuman primate social systems, and how and under what conditions they developed.

behavior–patterns of animal activity over time.

Biological anthropologists known as **primatologists** study primates, usually nonhuman primates. Primatologists often engage in studies of primate behavior in the wild. Such studies are called **naturalistic fieldwork.** Primatologists are interested in questions such as, "How and why do primate species behave differently from one another?" and "What can an understanding of this behavior tell us about the behavior of early humans?" These questions may be approached in a number of ways. For example, anatomical study can be used to deduce the movement capabilities of joints, or researchers may explore what sort of environment and animal–plant relationships may have existed. Archaeology can indicate what sort of cultural behavior took place; and the comparative study of behavior can assist in making deductions about humans in relation to other primates.

Figure 1–6 • Naturalistic field research in primate behavior.

Most of our knowledge of the behavior of the nonhuman primates is derived from recent fieldwork and new controlled laboratory experiments (Figure 1–6). These studies, especially long-term fieldwork, have clarified many misconceptions of how different primate species behave in the wild and what their true behavioral capabilities are. For example, Jane Goodall's 30-year field study among the chimpanzees at Gombe, Tanzania, has resulted in fundamental changes in how we view the human condition. We no longer think of ourselves as the only tool-using animals, since chimps have been observed regularly making and using simple tools. We no longer consider meat eating as uniquely human, because chimps have been observed catching and eating animal prey. Primatological studies now seek to understand nonhuman primates based on fact rather than folklore. As previously stated, living primates help anthropologists interpret the fossil remains of our ancestors, as well as providing case studies of evolution. These studies in turn help in our understanding of fossil bones and evolution when we consider the fact that these bones were once parts of living animals.

THE LANGUAGE OF BIOLOGICAL ANTHROPOLOGY

The language of biological anthropology is composed of the specialized jargons of a number of scientific disciplines, as well as some jargon unique to biological anthropology itself. Many of the basic descriptive terms in biological anthropology are anatomical. In our discussions of human evolutionary anatomy and fossil remains we will use a number of terms referring to the bones of the skeleton, the parts of the brain, and the teeth. Appendix 1 provides a synopsis of anatomical terms used.

A number of geological terms come into biological anthropology via the work of paleoanthropologists, who extract fossils from the ground and thus have much in common with earth scientists. The interaction of evolution with climate change, the drifting of continents over time, and the reconstruction of the ancient environments in which our ancestors lived keep this a lively area of research. Appendix 2 discusses basic geological terminology and illustrates the geological time scale.

primatology–science that studies primates, usually primate behavior and ecology.

naturalistic fieldwork–the study of primates in their natural environment.

A large component of the terms making up the biological anthropological lexicon comes from biology. The proliferating terms used in the rapidly developing fields of genetics and molecular biology make their way into biological anthropology, as do the terms used in ecology, evolutionary biology, zoology, and behavioral biology. Perhaps the largest source of new terms for the beginning student is the **taxonomy** or naming of all the different animals that are relevant to understanding human beings' place in nature. These organisms are largely unfamiliar to most people and they generally have long Greek or Latin names that are difficult to pronounce. We provide the English translations of the names when they are first mentioned, and they can also be looked up in the glossary. There is an order to the organization of these names, appropriately termed **systematics,** which is based on the closeness of relationship among the animals. Appendix 3 provides the taxonomy and systematics of the primates, that group of animals most closely related to human beings. The taxonomic classification of the human species is presented in Table 1–1.

In this book we discuss many different kinds of animals, and taxonomy gives us a clear-cut and unambiguous way to refer to them. Taxonomy begins with the **species,** originally a term that simply meant "kind" but now indicates a formal taxonomic unit basic to biological classification. A species is defined as a group or population of organisms, the individuals of which naturally interbreed and produce fertile offspring (see also Chapters 2 and 3). Species are designated scientifically by a system of *binomial* ("two-named") *nomenclature.* Our species designation is *Homo sapiens* (Latin for "human the wise"). When only the first part of the binomial name is used, it refers to the level above the species in the taxonomic hierarchy, the **genus.** A genus groups species that are similar in adaptation. We are classified in the genus *Homo.*

Genera (the plural of genus) are placed within **families.** Our zoological family, the **Hominidae,** is defined on the basis of our mode of movement or *locomotion.* Hominids walk on two legs. How two-legged walking, or bipedalism, evolved and what type of locomotion preceded it are among the oldest unsolved questions in biological anthropology (see Chapter 8). But bipedalism serves as a useful definition for all the known members of the hominid family.

taxonomy–the science of naming different organisms.

systematics–the science of classifying and organizing organisms.

species–an actually or potentially interbreeding group of organisms in nature.

genus–a taxonomic grouping of similar species.

family–a taxonomic grouping of similar genera.

Hominidae–the zoological family to which living humans and their bipedal relatives, all now extinct, belong.

Table 1–1 • Taxonomy of the Human Species
Kingdom Animalia
Phylum Chordata
Class Mammalia
Order Primates
Infraorder Anthropoidea
Superfamily Hominoidea
Family Hominidae
Genus *Homo*
Species *Homo sapiens*

Species

The concept of the biological species is important because we rely on it for purposes of constructing taxonomies and phylogenies. Ernst Mayr (1963) defined a species as "actually or potentially interbreeding populations which are reproductively isolated from other such populations." We will discuss the concept of "populations" in greater depth in Chapter 3, but now it is sufficient to realize that a **population** is a group of related individuals in one species that live together in one place. Only within a species are male and female animals able to mate and produce offspring who themselves are capable of reproducing. Sometimes animals in different species can mate and produce offspring, as in the case of a horse and donkey producing a mule, but the offspring will be infertile and incapable of having offspring themselves. We would say biologically that the horse and donkey species are "reproductively isolated" from one another.

Mayr's definition works well for living species, but it poses special problems for interpreting the fossil record. For example, we cannot determine whether animals that we know only from their bones and teeth could or did interbreed. Instead, we must use a concept of anatomical distance: how distant in physical form species are in the modern world. That is, we compare extinct and living species and extrapolate this into the past. Also, we can ascertain whether the anatomical differences between two fossils are about the same as, less than, or greater than, those between two known living species that can mate and produce fertile offspring. Because species possess their own unique adaptations, understanding the functional anatomy of fossils also helps to decide whether they were truly separate species in the past. Species determined from the fossil record are known as *paleospecies*.

Species, whether living or extinct, are defined in taxonomic usage by reference to a type. This may be a single specimen (a **holotype;** Figure 1–7) or a series of specimens (**paratypes**). **Morphology** is the study of form and structure in organisms. Morphological characteristics of the type are described and used to define an entire population of organisms, a

population—a geographically localized group of individuals in a species that more likely share a common gene pool among themselves than with other individuals in the species.

holotype—the single specimen on which a taxonomic name is based.

paratypes—a group of specimens on which a taxonomic name is based.

morphology—the study of the form and anatomy of physical structures in the bodies of living or once living organisms.

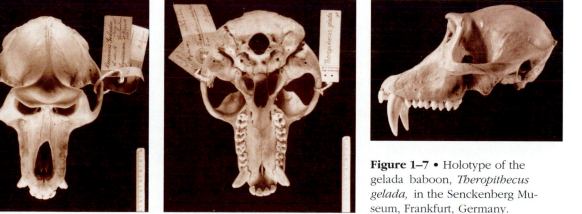

Figure 1–7 • Holotype of the gelada baboon, *Theropithecus gelada,* in the Senckenberg Museum, Frankfurt, Germany.

species. However, because individuals vary one from another in all biological populations, adequate allowance must be made for slight differences. Suppose we have a type specimen and an unknown specimen that may possibly be tagged with a new species designation. Before a species designation is made, this difference must be seen as greater than would be expected between any two individuals within a normal population. In the past, variation within populations was seldom recognized and, consequently, every new fossil discovery was given the name of a new species. Today, biological anthropologists study anatomical difference to discover at what point observed differences between two specimens are within the species limits or are large enough to place them in two different species.

Subspecies

Subspecies, also known as **races,** are populations within a species that are usually geographically distinct from one another, and may be distinguishable from other subspecies by external morphology and by genetic and behavioral differences. Members of subspecies may interbreed with one another and frequently do so at the fringes of their distribution. This pattern of interbreeding creates geographic gradients of physical or biological variations called **clines,** which sometimes make clear-cut distinctions between population centers in a species difficult to discern. Modern human beings may be one such species (see Chapter 11) but numerous species of African and Asian monkeys form well-defined subspecies over their geographic ranges. The gorilla is well known for its three subspecies: two lowland subspecies in central and West Africa, and the well-studied mountain gorilla in the east. In taxonomy a species name is a binomial, but a subspecies name is a trinomial. Thus, the mountain gorilla is termed formally *Gorilla gorilla beringei.* As we shall see later, geographically differentiated groups of a species form the bases of future species.

subspecies—a geographically defined population within a species, the individuals of which tend to share certain physical and genetic traits but who are nevertheless infertile with other members of the species; a **race.**

cline—a gradient of genotypes or phenotypes over a geographic range.

RECONSTRUCTING THE EVOLUTIONARY HISTORY OF SPECIES

Classification of any set of organisms should be based on an easily understood and reproducible set of criteria, so that scientists may communicate effectively about the organisms. In biological theory the ideal is that species classified together should be closely related to each other. Phylogenetic relationships are those that link species through their evolutionary history: a "family tree" through which species B is related to species C through an earlier common ancestor A (Figure 1–8). Classification schemes, then, should reflect our current knowledge of evolutionary history. This means that as further discoveries improve our knowledge of this history, they may change our classification schemes.

Higher levels of classification above the species (the levels of genus and family) should reflect true evolutionary groupings; in other words, there should be successive levels of more distantly related species as one goes up the hierarchy. However, this ideal is not always realized. A recent example of a taxonomic problem is the family of the great apes: the chimp, the gorilla, and the orangutan (Pongidae). In older classifications, the orangutan, chimpanzee, and gorilla were all classified in this family. Through both biomolecular and fossil discoveries (see Chapter 7) it became apparent that chimps and gorillas as a group were more closely related to humans, classified in the family Hominidae, than to orangutans. Pongidae therefore was recognized as a mixed classificatory term. In this book we use the family names of Panidae for the chimpanzee, Gorillidae for the gorilla, Pongidae for orangutans and their fossil antecedents, and Hominidae for humans and their fossil antecedents.

Some authors, such as Delson (1989), resolve this problem by including all the great apes and humans in the same family, which by the rule that the name first proposed has *priority,* is termed Hominidae. We feel that this approach has the disadvantage of understating the significant differences among these groups. Here we use Hominidae to refer only to bipedal, large-molared primates closely related to modern humans (see Chapter 8), a position also adopted by Fleagle (1988) and by most specialists working on this group (e.g., Johanson and White, 1979; Boaz, 1983; Hill and Ward, 1988).

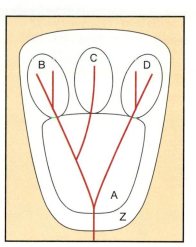

Figure 1–8 • A hypothetical phylogenetic tree with correlation between levels of taxonomic classification and taxonomy, based on single evolutionary origins (monophyly). A, B, C, and D represent species belonging to taxon Z. (From Schoch, 1986)

Phylogenetic Systematics

Before the discovery of molecular measures of genetic relatedness (and even afterwards), scientists were concerned with determining which morphological characteristics to use in classifying fossil species. For the purposes of classification, which were the important defining characteristics and which should be ignored? For example, if we wish to classify horses and cows, it hardly does any good to note that they both have four feet. Why? Because many other animals are also quadrupedal. Thus, the morphological characteristic of having four feet does not serve to distinguish horses and cows from each other.

The German biologist Willi Hennig instituted the field termed "phylogenetic systematics" during the 1950s, now more frequently termed **cladistics** (Greek for "splitting apart"). Cladistics is a way of analyzing relationships among animals in the fossil record by using only newly arisen or "derived" traits, or characteristics. It offers a clear method for determining which characteristics to use in classification. Characteristics that have been inherited from ancient, primitive ancestors are thrown out, and only the derived characteristics that are unique to the group , or *taxon,* are used for classification. These characteristics are termed **apomorphies** (Latin *apo*—"away from"; *morphy*—"body or form"), or "derived characteristics." In the example of horses and cows above, an apomorphy of cows might be taken to be the presence of horns, whereas four-footedness is discarded for purposes of this classification because it is a primitive character. Once derived characters are determined for a group of organisms, it is possible to draw a diagram of relatedness, or **cladogram.** The cladogram can then

cladistics—the common term for the study of the phylogenetic relationships among a group of related animals by reference to only derived traits shared in common.

apomorphy—in cladistic terminology, a newly arisen or derived trait used in systematics.

cladogram—branching diagram showing relative relationships among taxonomic groups of animals; not to be confused with a phylogenetic tree, which postulated ancestor–descendant relationships.

parallelism–the evolution of similar traits in two closely related species, such as elongated hind legs for jumping in two small rodent species.

convergence–the evolution of similar traits in two distantly related animals, such as similar streamlined body form for swimming in dolphins and sharks.

be used to construct a series of phylogenies, which hypothesize ancestor–descendant relationships (Figure 1–9), which must then be tested.

Scientists reconstruct the phylogenetic history of a species by using a basic principle of evolutionary biology: Descendants will resemble their ancestors because they are related genetically; that is, they share a large number of genes. A corollary to this principle is that descendants far removed in time from an ancestral population will be more dissimilar than populations not so distant in time from each other. The key assumption here is that anatomical similarity reflects closeness of relationship. The fact that virtually every anatomical structure of a human body can be matched in the chimpanzee body led Thomas Henry Huxley (1825–1895), for example, to hypothesize a close relationship between the African apes and humans (Figure 1–10). Sometimes, however, overall anatomical similarity may be misleading. Species that are unrelated or distantly related may adapt to similar environments and end up looking very similar (see Chapter 3). This phenomenon is known as **parallelism** or **convergence.** For example, the wings of a bird and those of a bat are formed by different bones, which indicates that they are evolved in parallel and not inherited from a common ancestral source.

Some species evolve very slowly, and a modern descendant species, a "living fossil," can closely resemble an ancestor. For this reason evolu-

Figure 1–9 • A cladogram and how it differs from a phylogeny. Any single cladogram can generate a number of different phylogenies. (From Schoch, 1986)

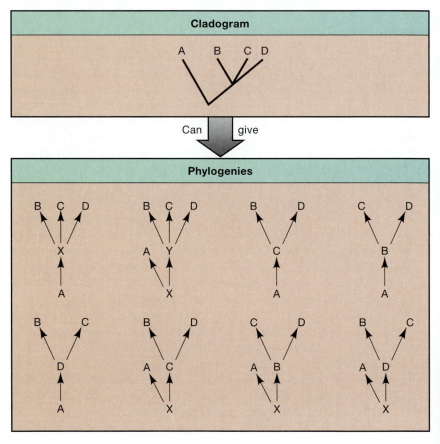

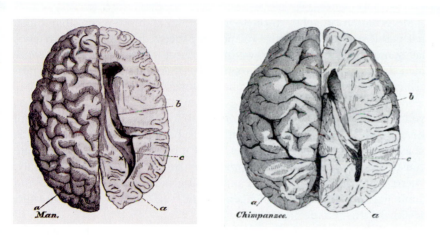

Figure 1–10 • T. H. Huxley's dissection of a human and a chimpanzee brain, showing the close anatomical similarity between the two: *(a)* posterior lobe, *(b)* lateral ventricle, and *(c)* posterior cornu.

tionists use the geological record to determine the age of fossils. Armed with data on anatomical similarity and geological age, they can then assemble a phylogenetic tree for the fossil forms under study.

Gene Lineages and Organismal Lineages

Molecular biologists have devised an alternative way to investigate the phylogenetic history of living forms. They reason that if the goal of evolutionary research is to discover the genetic relatedness of organisms in order to reconstruct their phylogenetic histories, why not measure genetics itself? By using techniques to determine the actual structure of the DNA molecule that makes up genes (Figure 1–11), they are able to assess the genetic relatedness of species directly.

Figure 1–11 • Chromosomes of human and chimpanzee compared. Within each pair, the human chromosome appears on the left, the chimpanzee chromosome on the right.

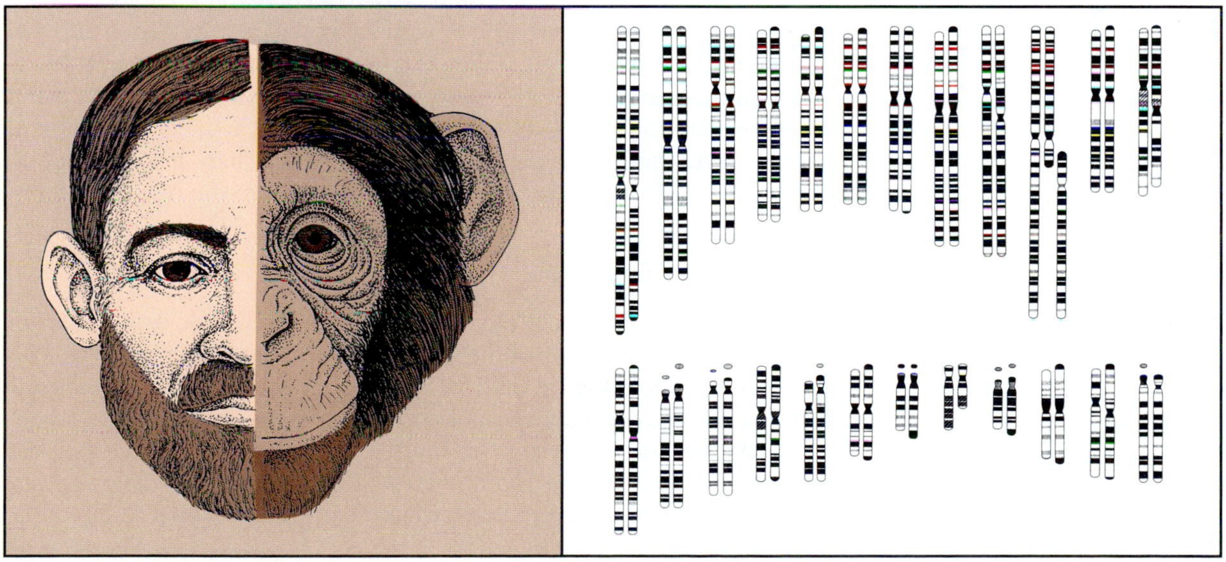

Molecular approaches to phylogeny are much more recent than those that use fossils only, and the relationship between the two approaches has sometimes been rocky. Two major areas of difference have separated the two disciplines. First, extracting DNA and other organic material from fossils has proven difficult. However, some recent progress has been made in isolating ancient DNA from fossilized human remains as well as from remains of other mammals up to 100,000 years old. Second, there is not necessarily a close relationship between genetic distances, as measured by molecular techniques, and morphological distance. Quite similar species of frogs, for example, may be very divergent genetically, whereas species very different morphologically, such as humans and chimpanzees, are quite similar genetically (see Chapter 3 for more discussion of this paradox).

Despite numerous recent debates between paleontologists, who use fossils to measure evolution, and molecular biologists, who use genes to measure evolution, their approaches attempt to measure the same phylogenetic history. They must, therefore, ultimately be compatible. As indicated, their data are not overlapping. Paleontologists have access to some species that have become extinct and have left no living descendants. Those species can contain clues about the twists and turns of phylogeny that cannot be discerned by molecular biologists who have no living descendant from which to work. Molecular biologists, on the other hand, have a superior method of determining true relatedness between species based on genetic similarity—a level of resolution that paleontologists can only approximate.

When molecular biologists reconstruct phylogeny, they are actually reconstructing gene lineages—ancestor–descendant lineages of specific sequences of DNA. When paleontologists reconstruct phylogeny, they are attempting to reconstruct population lineages of whole organisms (Figure 1–12). These two measures of phylogenetic change may not always coincide. Genes may evolve faster, more slowly, or stay the same, depending on selection, as organisms evolve within populations. But often the two measures will coincide. When they do not, the challenge will be to determine which of the many evolutionary forces have been at work to put the molecular and paleontological assessments at variance with one another. A better and more complete view of evolutionary history will ultimately emerge from a successful interaction between the two disciplines.

Ecology and Evolution

Ecology (from the Greek, meaning "study of habitation") is a field of study that integrates study of the habitat in which a population lives with its genetic, morphological, and behavioral adaptations. Each species is part of a complex ecosystem made up of a community of plants and animals. Within this ecosystem a species occupies its own **ecological niche,** a unique way of life to which it alone is adapted. A species' niche is defined by where it lives, what it eats, and how it goes about its daily life.

ecology—the science that studies the biological relationships between species and their environment.

ecological niche—the "ecological space" to which a species is adapted, including its habitat, diet, and behavior.

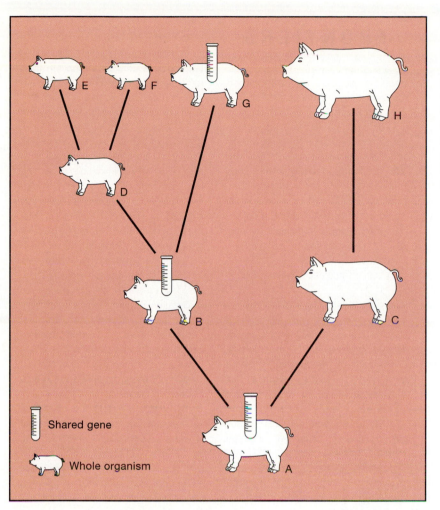

Figure 1–12 • Gene phylogeny versus organismal phylogeny. Species evolve through time both in body form and in molecular structure. The rates of both types of change can be remarkably constant, or they can vary significantly from one another. Biological anthropologists and other evolutionary biologists look at both types of evolutionary change.

Change in the environment in which a species lives is the driving force behind evolutionary change in populations. If the environment stays the same over eons, there is very little morphological change. But earth scientists have accumulated more and more evidence that shows that our planet has undergone many episodic and sometimes rapid climatic and environmental changes. A dynamic interplay has existed between ecology and evolution. Evolutionists are now looking at the geological record of climatic change, molecular phylogeny, and the paleontological record of species to piece together how the forces of evolution have formed the species that have existed on earth.

Evolution Versus Creationism

Early in the development of biological anthropology the subject of the evolution of the human species began to be considered. The earliest ideas on human origins were derived from studies of the anatomy of

FRONTIERS

Evolution and Creation: Current Controversies

By Eugenie C. Scott

"**C**reationism" in its broadest sense refers to the belief that God created, an idea foundational to Christianity, Judaism, and Islam. "Evolution," in the broadest sense, refers to the scientific idea that the universe has had a history: that the galaxies, solar system, planet Earth, and plants and animals exist today in a different form than they did in the past. *Organic* evolution describes the concept that living things share common ancestry and have, in Darwin's terms, "descended with modification" from ancestors who differed from them.

Creationism is therefore concerned with cause, specifically, Ultimate Cause. Evolution is concerned with what happened during the history of the universe, and, as a science, is incapable of saying anything about Ultimate Cause. *Whether* God created is thus truly not part of the creation/evolution controversy. Individuals who believe that God created the world using the process of evolution are known as "theistic evolutionists," and include Catholics and mainline Protestants (such as Episco-

palians, United Church of Christ, Presbyterians, etc.), as well as Reformed, Conservative, Reconstructionist, and most Orthodox Jews.

The term "creationist" has recently taken on a narrower meaning to refer to certain conservative Christians who attempt, through political and legal means, to insert into public school curricula a literal version of creation as found in the Book of Genesis. I will use this more narrow definition of "creationist" in this essay.

Creationist Opposition to Evolution

Antievolutionism has had a long history in the United States. Although the theory of evolution (change through time) was embraced by the scientific community by the beginning of the twentieth century, acceptance was slow to trickle down to the general public.

During the first decades of this century, a series of twelve pamphlets called "The Fundamentals" outlined a conservative Christian theology stressing biblical inerrancy and, for the most part, literal truth of the Scriptures.

Between 1915 and 1922, a number of states attempted to legally ban the teaching of evolution. John T. Scopes, the subject of the fictional *Inherit the Wind,* was brought to trial in 1915 for violating a Tennessee antievolution

law. He was convicted, and the laws remained on the books (although rarely enforced) until 1968, when they were declared unconstitutional by the U.S. Supreme Court.

Although textbook publishers had quietly reduced their coverage of evolution—virtually eliminating it by the mid 1930's—by the late 1960's, evolution had begun reappearing. The ready availability of evolution material in textbooks generated a new response from the antievolution forces.

Because the teaching of evolution could no longer be banned, creationists devised a new strategy to counter it. Creationists hypothesized that they could avoid problems with the first amendment if their version of the origin of matter could be presented as an alternate scientific theory, rather than as a Bible-based religious doctrine. Thus, "scientific" creationism was born.

In the late 1970's, model legislation was drawn up by creationists that would require "equal time" for the teaching of creation "science" and evolution. During 1980 and 1981, such legislation was proposed in twenty-two states. Because the "science" inherent in creation science was so sketchy, many physical anthropologists testified against such bills, and through their efforts and those of other scientists, the majority of these bills were defeated. Only Arkansas and

many different kinds of animals, compared with human anatomy. Human beings share many traits with apes, fewer traits with monkeys, fewer with cats, and fewer still with birds, reptiles, fish, and insects, respectively. The existence of fossil forms that bridged the gaps between the living animals was debated. Particular attention was focused on the human–ape common ancestor, which was given the popular nickname of the "missing link."

Two of the primary methods of modern biological anthropology in its investigations of human evolution involve (a) the use of **fossils,** usually

fossils—remains of animals and plants preserved in the ground.

Louisiana passed "equal time" bills, and legal challenges were immediately filed.

The trial resulting from the Arkansas challenge, billed as "Scopes II," resurrected some of the circus atmosphere of its predecessor. Creationists presented witnesses in support of the scientific validity of creation "science." They failed. Even the creationists' most highly-credentialed scientist, Chandra Wickramasinghe, stated under cross-examination that most of the law was "claptrap" and totally unscientific. Judge William Overton ruled in Arkansas Superior Court in January, 1982, that creation science did not meet the tenets of science, and that the Arkansas "equal time" law was unconstitutional.

The similar Louisiana case took several years to make its way to the U.S. Supreme Court. In *Edwards* v. *Aguillard*, the Court declared in 1987 that the teaching of creationism constituted religious advocacy. The strategy of "equal time" for creationism and evolution had met its final doom.

Current Events

Losing so thoroughly in the courts, creationists moved back to local school districts where they historically have been successful. Within a year of the 1987 Supreme Court decision, creationist leaders were promoting the avoidance of terms such as creation science and creationism, which involve the idea of a Creator. Instead, they began speaking in terms of "Abrupt Appearance Theory," "Intelligent Design Theory," and "arguments against evolution." The content of these new "sciences" is identical to the no-longer legal "scientific" creationism, but by using euphemisms, creationists hope to avoid entanglement with the First Amendment.

During the 1990's, it has still been possible to find the full range of antievolutionist activities, from attempts to ban the teaching of evolution (declared unconstitutional by *Epperson*), promotion of the "two model" approach (declared unconstitutional by *Edwards*), to use of the newer euphemisms, not yet tested in court. The next legal battlefield is likely to be at the school district level, over requirements that schools teach "arguments against evolution" or "weaknesses in evolutionary theory" wherever evolution is taught.

To this day, teachers pressed by parents (or administrators) to avoid the teaching of evolution frequently do so, not wanting to jeopardize either their jobs or community harmony. As a result, many students entering college have never been exposed to evolution, or they have only a fuzzy notion of what the term means ("Man evolved from monkeys?!"). This is a great shame, because as the famous geneticist Theodosius Dobzhansky said,

> Seen in the light of evolution, biology is, perhaps, intellectually the most satisfying and inspiring science. Without that light it becomes a pile of sundry facts—some of them interesting or curious but making no meaningful picture as a whole. . . . Nothing in biology makes sense except in the light of evolution.

The same holds true for physical anthropology. Students who are not taught evolution do not have the preparation that they need for further scientific study, or even to be educated citizens.

Eugenie C. Scott is Executive Director of the National Center for Science Education in Berkeley, California, and is a member of the Executive Committee of the American Association of Physical Anthropologists.

represented by bones that have maintained a resemblance to their original form and shape but have been mineralized over time, and (b) the analysis of molecules in the body. But early evidence for the great antiquity of human beings (and therefore premodern origins) came first in the form of stone tools discovered in France in the late 1700s. Later, fossilized bones of people were found associated with those of extinct animals. Actual evidence of a form of human so different that it would fit into no known living human group was not recognized until 1856, when the Neandertal "caveman" was discovered (see Chapter 8).

Even before scientists began to delve into human origins, religious scholars had questioned the status quo. As one of the founders of the scientific method, Sir Francis Bacon (1561–1626) had pronounced in the early seventeenth century that scholars should look to nature, not to books, for enlightenment. Theology was affected by Bacon's teachings as, during the next century—the age of enlightenment—a movement known as Biblical Criticism led to the acceptance of evolution within a theological framework. Internal evidence in the Bible, when read in the original Hebrew, began to reveal that the Old Testament had been written down over a number of years by many authors. For example, the book of *Genesis* has one account (*Genesis* 1) in which human beings are created last of all the creatures, and another one (*Genesis* 2) in which the first human being, a man (Adam), is created before the animals and names them as they are created. Woman (Eve) is created from one of Adam's ribs in this version. (Men and women actually have the same number of ribs—12 pairs or 24.) Both accounts cannot be literally true because they are contradictory.

A solution, for those who desire to seek one, is to accept that religious scripture, such as the Torah, Bible, or Koran, represents documents of spiritual and symbolic importance to many people throughout the world, whereas science deals with empirically testable hypotheses about the world. Because the two areas of endeavor do not purport to achieve the same ends, a dichotomy between them is unnecessary. Stokes (1988:16) makes this point in his restatement of the creation passages in *Genesis,* a version with which many scientists could agree:

> All known matter appeared in the simplest, elemental form through a single, unique event called the "big bang." With time, as things quieted down, heavier elements and compounds including watery mixtures of gas and dust appeared. The gathering, and compression of matter into galaxies produced light, nuclear reactions, and massive explosions (supernovas). Eventually all elements were produced and dispersed. From enriched mixtures of gas and dust came suns with attendant systems of planets. In one case, at least, a body (our earth) unusually rich in water was produced. A copious supply of water came from within and remained attached to its surface as liquid oceans and seas. Life as we know it emerged from water; and the oceans, as shown by fossils, were well populated by varied species before land life was in existence. On land, a great variety of bony vertebrate animals appeared and eventually occupied all continents and islands. Man was one of the last creatures to appear; his unique physical and mental attributes allow him to dominate all forms of life.

Evolutionary science, like all sciences, is neutral in one sense regarding theological beliefs. Supernatural events cannot be explained by science because science seeks the simplest possible *natural* explanations to understand observations. Religion, on the other hand, deals with the spiritual, symbolic, and moral spheres of human life. Science deals with falsifiable hypotheses, ideas that can be disproved, and gives precedence to material causality over supernatural causality; religion depends on faith, which is not subject to proof in a scientific sense.

In upholding the teaching of evolution in the public schools the American courts have reasserted the division between church and state. Yet science and religion can coexist, and both responsible scientists and theologians resist efforts to bring the two into unnecessary conflict. Most major Western religions accept evolution as part of the process of creation (Lieberman and Kirk, 1996). In the Anglican Church evolution has been formally accepted since the 1890s; the Roman Catholic Church has officially accepted evolution as "an open question" since the 1950s. More recently, Pope John Paul II announced he believed that "fresh knowledge leads to recognition of the theory of evolution as more than just a hypothesis." Other major denominations have followed suit.

THE PERSPECTIVE OF HUMAN EVOLUTION

The study of human evolution has much to contribute to a general understanding of human beings, their origins, adaptations, and way of life. The popular interest that surrounds biological anthropology is derived to a large extent from high-visibility discoveries of fossils. Initially, the fossils themselves were considered of paramount interest, but increasingly the *contexts* in which the fossils are found have become of equal, if not of more, importance. The context can tell how old the fossil is, what the climate was like when the species was alive, what other animals and plants were in the environment, what the species may have eaten, what other species may have eaten it, and many other aspects of its evolutionary history not discernible from its bones or teeth alone (Figure 1–13). In short, the total contexts of fossil discoveries have become important because we now want to understand how early humans lived and behaved, as well as how they are related to other life forms, including

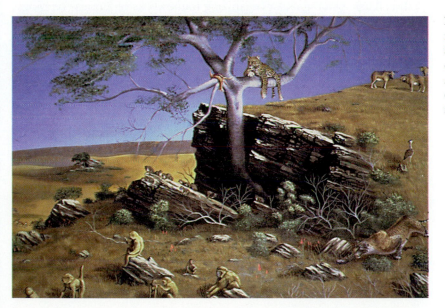

Figure 1–13 • Paleoecological reconstruction of Swartkranns, South Africa, showing the context of plants and animals from this site in their original surroundings. (From California Academy of Sciences, San Francisco)

today's humans. In this way, we seek to understand the natural history of our ancestors and of ourselves.

What an individual does during his or her lifetime affects the passing on of his or her hereditary characteristics. Behaviors that contribute to a longer childbearing or reproductive life and increase the number of offspring will tend to become more prevalent as evolution proceeds. Our behavior today is the result of millions of years and hundreds of thousands of generations of evolution. If we understand how our ancestors behaved and the conditions under which their behavior evolved, we will have a much better insight into our behavior today.

The increasingly well-documented human fossil record now demonstrates that for the longest part of our history we have evolved to social and technological conditions that no longer exist. Most of human evolution took place before even the advent of agriculture, some 10,000 years ago, when humans lived in small social groups. During this immense span of time, humans "evolved to feel strongly about a few people, short distances, and relatively brief intervals of time . . ." (Washburn and Harding, 1975:11). The final chapter in this book will discuss how a species with such an evolutionary heritage can cope with such issues as crowding and overpopulation, international conflict, pollution, health, and education.

 SUMMARY

1. The goal of this book is to provide a coherent integration of our knowledge of human evolution and biology. This synthetic approach focuses on the interrelatedness of biology, behavior, and evolution as well as the connections between humans and the natural world.

2. Anthropologists are scientists who study humans. They have used three basic paradigms, or organizing frameworks of inquiry: typology, culture, and evolution. Evolution is the paradigm that is most important for biological anthropology.

3. Evolutionary science does not address the issues of religious belief, although scientists do respond to attempts by creationists to insert untestable religious dogma into the scientific arena. Many theologians and scientists do, however, find a compatibility between religion and science.

4. Biological anthropologists pursue many questions about humans and use a wide range of techniques and methodologies, which include comparative anatomy, behavior studies of living animals both in the wild and in the laboratory, molecular biology, genetics, and population biology.

5. For biological anthropologists to communicate in the same scientific language, a system of naming and description must be uniformly followed. *Taxonomy,* a system of nomenclature or naming, is used to designate species. *Systematics* places the species within the hierarchy of more closely related and, then, increasingly distantly related, categories.

6. One goal of biological anthropology is the reconstruction of primate, especially human, evolutionary history. Phylogenetic questions ask how humans are related to other primates, other mammals, and other vertebrates. To answer these questions scientists rely on *cladistics*— the discovery of an overall framework of relatedness.

7. The perspective offered by this book on human evolution takes into account both cultural and ecological variables. The environments under which humans evolved for about 99% of the time that the species has existed on this planet were very different from those under which a majority of humans live today.

CRITICAL-THINKING QUESTIONS

1. Discuss the paradigm that biological anthropologists use to explain variability in human populations. How has this paradigm changed over time?
2. What role has molecular biology played in addressing human origins?
3. What is the biological definition of a species?
4. What is the difference between a species' phylogeny and its cladogram?
5. Why is it important to study extinct hominids?
6. What role has ecology played in our understanding of evolution?

SUGGESTED READINGS

Eaton, S. Boyd, M. Shostak, and M. Konner. 1989. *The Paleolithic Prescription: A Program of Diet and Exercise and a Design for Living.* New York: Harper and Row. A book on how human evolution holds many and varied lessons for modern medicine and health.

Eiseley, Loren. 1957. *The Immense Journey.* New York: Random House. Still one of the most readable accounts of a naturalist's approach to human evolution.

James, S., R. Martin, and D. Pilbeam. 1992. *The Cambridge Encyclopedia of Human Evolution.* Cambridge, England: Cambridge University Press. A source book for current ideas and data about human evolution, evolutionary theory, race, as well as other topics in biological anthropology.

Kingdon, Jonathan. 1993. *Self-Made Man: Human Evolution from Eden to Extinction?* New York: John Wiley. An original and engaging introduction to human evolution from the perspective of one of Africa's great zoologists.

Napier, J.R., and P.H. Napier. 1985. *The Natural History of Primates.* Cambridge, Mass.: MIT Press. A brief but excellent introduction to the living primates, their adaptations, and their behavior.

Steele, D. Gentry, and Claud A. Bramblett. 1988. *The Anatomy and Biology of the Human Skeleton.* College Station, Texas: Texas A & M University Press. A good general book on the study of human bones and their biological significance.

CHAPTER 2

Genetics and Evolution by Natural Selection

We human beings are literally part of the universe in which we live. The chemical elements, such as hydrogen, carbon, and iron, that make up our bodies are the same elements that make up the planets and stars: They differ only in proportions. These basic building blocks of physical matter on earth are constantly being recycled. Thus, our bodies may contain elements that were once parts of ancient sea algae, trees, dinosaurs, or mammoths. Each form of life has this basic bond to the earth and uses the elements found in nature to carry on its daily life functions and to reproduce more of its own kind.

The evolution of human beings, just as of any other species that has existed on earth, ultimately begins at the earliest appearance of life. The shared characteristic of all living things—the same basic chemicals used in the same ways for reproducing and carrying on life—is a monumental testimony to the shared ancestry of all life. We all go back to one primordial ancestor. Although it may stretch the imagination to realize that you and the salad that you ate for lunch have distant shared relatives, this is in fact the case.

Much of modern biology has become focused on the molecular level of organization. These exciting new advances in genetics and molecular biology are the focus of this chapter, which explores the common genetic and evolutionary heritage of all life on earth.

DNA: THE REPRODUCTIVE MACHINERY OF THE CELL

The origin of the reproductive machinery of the cell is difficult to reconstruct because there are no forms surviving that show the intermediate stages of reproductive development between the earliest and present life forms. We do know that all life today uses a variant of the same molecule, **DNA** (deoxyribonucleic acid), for reproduction, an indication that this adaptation is a very ancient one. DNA is a long, double-chain molecule conceptualized in the shape of a spiraling ladder and composed of alternating units of a five-carbon sugar called deoxyribose and a phosphate (Figure 2–1). The most important aspect of its structure is that to each of the sugar units is attached one of four chemical base units of two types: purines called adenine (*A*) and guanine (*G*); and pyrimidines called thymine (*T*) and cytosine (*C*).

The rungs of the ladder are hydrogen bonds attaching the appropriate bases on both sides. *A* pairs only with *T,* and *G* pairs only with *C* at their bonding points or ladder rungs. This characteristic ensures that, during DNA replication and cell division, the new cells receive exactly the same DNA components. Once a sequence of bases is constructed along one side of the DNA, the other side of the ladder may be precisely determined. The DNA bases on either strand are exactly *complementary* in sequence.

How DNA Replicates Itself

When DNA starts to replicate, or make copies of itself, as the cell begins to divide the two strands of the DNA unwind from each other. The cell machinery carries new bases, sugars and phosphates into the nucleus. They attach themselves in sequence so that a *T* attracts a new *A* to bond with it. On the opposite strand its former partner *A* attracts a new *T,* along with its sugar and phosphate. The new bases as they are added are linked by enzymes and a new chain is fashioned alongside the old chain. After replication there are two double strands, each composed of one entirely new strand and one entirely old strand. Because each half of the DNA directs a new complementary sequence to be formed, cell division results in each daughter cell receiving a faithful copy of the ancestral DNA.

DNA and Protein Synthesis

At some point in the evolutionary origin of life, the sequence of adjoined bases in the DNA molecule attracted to itself a sequence of amino acids. These amino acids linked up alongside the DNA in such a way as to

DNA—double-chain molecule, common to all organisms, that contains the genetic code.

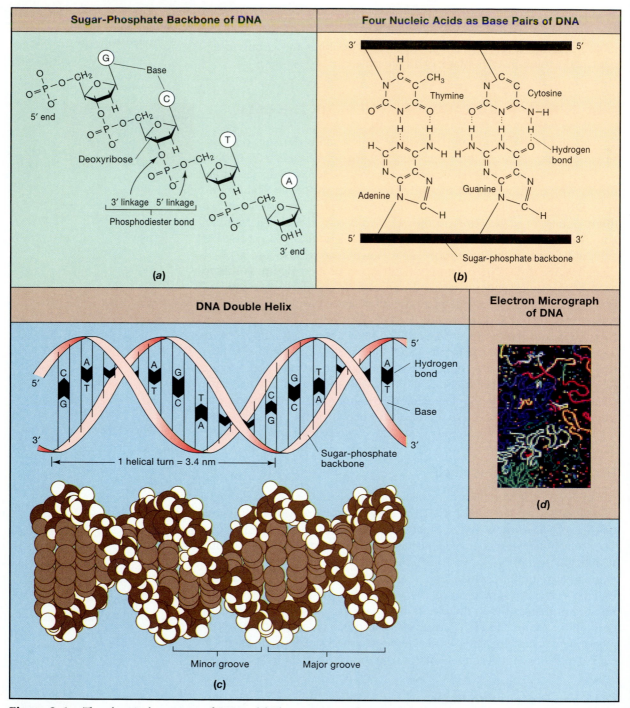

Figure 2–1 • The chemical structure of DNA. *(a)* The repetition of sugar and phosphate to form the backbone of the double helix. *(b)* The chemical construction of the four nucleic acids of the DNA code. *(c)* Diagrammatic representation of spiralled DNA molecule showing A-T, C-G bonds (top); molecular configuration of the molecules (bottom). *(d)* The actual DNA molecule, magnified by an electron microscope. (From Barrett et al., 1986)

form a protein molecule (Figure 2–2). Why? The probable reason that free-floating or "naked" DNA developed this function of attracting amino acids was to form a protective barrier around itself. Under special laboratory conditions simulating early earth environments, a mixture of proteins and nucleic acids (such as DNA) will form into droplets. These droplets enclose DNA within a protein envelope, as do the cells of all living organisms today. A protective envelope would have helped the DNA molecule to withstand turbulent water currents and helped concentrate chemicals useful for cell functions.

The exact structure of the protein molecules coded by the DNA may have been unimportant so long as the proteins served their function as the bounding membrane of the droplet. However, once this problem of maintaining the integrity of the droplet had been solved, distinct sequences of DNA bases began to code for specific proteins that would carry out unique functions within the "cell," extending its lifetime and thereby extending the lifetime of the DNA molecule enclosed within. One type of protein formed the cell wall, while others (the earliest enzymes) promoted or speeded up cellular reactions and became important in metabolism.

One hypothesis to explain the origin of cellular reproduction is that a chemical relative of DNA, the more simply constructed single-chain molecule called **RNA** (ribonucleic acid), was the first molecule to be able to replicate itself. As the parent cell divided into two, the original RNA and its copy, with whatever information they carried, were transferred to the next generation in each daughter cell. What exactly RNA did in the early cells is unknown. RNA survives today in the cell but it has less complex chemical tasks to perform than DNA, and its reproduction has to be aided by cellular enzymes. In some way, early RNA may have evolved into DNA, which is a more stable molecule and capable of producing copies of itself spontaneously without the help of enzymes.

RNA—ribonucleic acid, a molecule similar to DNA except that uracil (*U*) replaces thymine (*T*) as one of its four bases; the hereditary material in some viruses, but in most organisms a molecule that helps translate the structure of DNA into the structure of protein molecules.

Figure 2–2 • Diagrammatic view of amino acids being attracted to a free-floating DNA template. Specific polymerizing enzymes make the peptide bonds that link the amino acids and, in turn, assemble the protein. (From Watson, 1976)

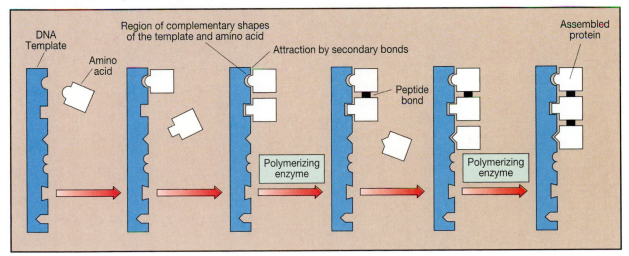

THE DNA MOLECULE EVOLVES

Besides reproducing itself, DNA has the function of producing proteins in the cell. The production of protein molecules on a consistent basis requires some kind of code. The DNA code consists of the bases *A* and *G* (adenine and guanine) or the bases *C* and *T* (cytosine and thymine) (Table 2–1). The bases are organized into groups of three known as

1st ↓ 2nd	T	C	A	G	↓ 3rd
Position →					Position
T	PHE	SER	TYR	CYS	T
	PHE	SER	TYR	CYS	C
	LEU	SER	STOP	STOP	A
	LEU	SER	STOP	TRP	G
C	LEU	PRO	HIS	ARG	T
	LEU	PRO	HIS	ARG	C
	LEU	PRO	GLN	ARG	A
	LEU	PRO	GLN	ARG	G
A	ILEU	THR	ASN	SER	T
	ILEU	THR	ASN	SER	C
	ILEU	THR	LYS	ARG	A
	MET	THR	LYS	ARG	G
G	VAL	ALA	ASP	GLY	T
	VAL	ALA	ASP	GLY	C
	VAL	ALA	GLU	GLY	A
	VAL	ALA	GLU	GLY	G

Table 2–1 • The Genetic Code Codon Sequences

The names of the 20 amino acids and their abbreviations are:

ALA	Alanine	LEU	Leucine
ARG	Arginine	LYS	Lysine
ASN	Asparagine	MET	Methionine
ASP	Aspartic acid	PHE	Phenylalanine
CYS	Cysteine	PRO	Proline
GLN	Glutamine	SER	Serine
GLU	Glutamic acid	THR	Threonine
GLY	Glycine	TRY	Tryptophan
HIS	Histidine	TYR	Tyrosine
ILEU	Isoleucine	VAL	Valine

The abbreviation STOP shows the three triplets which can terminate the polypeptide chain. U (uracil) is used instead of T in m-RNA.

codons, that are chemically recognized by a particular amino acid. Codons exist for all of the 20 amino acids that make up every protein manufactured by the cells.

All life forms on earth share the same DNA code. This deceptively simple system is able to code for the stunning amount of variety that we see in organisms. Species' body form, internal chemical makeup, and behavioral capabilities are all derived ultimately from sequences of DNA. In one way of looking at it, the only difference between a human being and a virus is simply a different sequence of the bases that make up their respective DNA's.

Because of the simplicity of the code, only two types of changes are important in the evolution of life. The first is an increase or decrease in the amount of DNA in the cell. The second is a change in the base sequence of the DNA. Before we consider these two types of changes, we will describe how the DNA molecule synthesizes proteins within living cells.

How Protein Synthesis Works

The genetic code specifies chains of amino acids that are combined to make up parts or all of a protein. Each amino acid consists of a basic chemical structure that is similar for all amino acids, and a unique side chain. One DNA sequence specifies the number, sequence, and types of amino acids in a linear fashion in what is correctly called a **polypeptide chain.** A protein is a *functioning* unit composed of one or more polypeptide chains that can have several genes controlling them. Some proteins such as *albumin,* a blood protein, are composed of and function with only one polypeptide chain. Other proteins, such as *hemoglobin,* a protein in the red blood cells that carries and releases oxygen, are composed of several polypeptide chains (Figure 2–3). Hemoglobin has four polypeptide chains and the molecule functions only when all are combined. Geneticists have now modified the "one-gene-one-protein" hypothesis to the more accurate "one-gene-one-polypeptide" hypothesis.

Most of an individual's DNA carries genetic information through a specific sequence of nucleotides or bases. A codon consists of three base positions in a row; at any one of those positions one of four bases can be inserted. Consequently, we have a potential of 4^3 or 64 different codons that, in turn, specify the 20 different amino acids used to construct a polypeptide (see Table 2–1 on page 30). Because there are more codon combinations than amino acids, more than one codon combination may specify the same amino acid. Proteins are molecules that can carry on many of the body's functions: for example, proteins are involved in making up the structure of the body, as in the case of *collagen,* which helps to form the hard substance in bones; other proteins have transport properties, such as a *transferrin,* which carries iron in the blood. Enzymes are proteins that speed up chemical reactions. An important enzyme is *carbonic anhydrase,* the protein that catalyzes the reaction in the lungs of $H_2O + CO_2$ to H_2CO_3 (bicarbonate), an important

codons—three-unit bases of DNA that code for one of 20 amino acids or that code for a stop on termination of translation of that particular segment of DNA.

polypeptide chain—a molecule consisting of a long chain of amino acids joined together by peptide bonds.

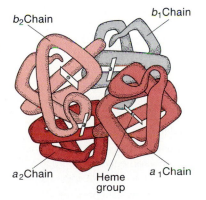

b_2Chain b_1Chain

a_2Chain   Heme group a_1Chain

Figure 2–3 • The molecular structure of hemoglobin.

acid/base buffer in the body. There are thousands of these different proteins in our bodies. Each protein has its origin in a certain sequence of DNA in the nucleus of the cells.

Other proteins in the body act as chemical messengers called **hormones** (Greek, meaning "to excite or set in motion"). Hormones can be released from the brain or other organs, travel through the bloodstream, and act on distinct target organs such as the breast, inducing it to produce milk, the testis to make sperm, or the kidney tubules to reabsorb water. Hormones have important functions in moderating behavior (see Chapter 10).

The foundation of molecular biology involves three substances—DNA, RNA, and proteins—and three processes—**replication, transcription,** and **translation** (Figure 2–4, Watson, 1970:331). The central dogma explains both how the genetic material passes on its inherited message and how it operates the cell, directing cell and tissue growth.

The DNA code is converted into a protein molecule by an involved sequence of interactions among DNA, enzymes, and RNA. In *transcription,* the DNA double helix molecule unwinds, the hydrogen bonds holding the molecular backbones together are broken, and the two sides fall apart. New bases are brought to the DNA and are combined until the end of the DNA message is read, much as in DNA replication. However, here only one side of the DNA is copied to make a coded message, called *messenger RNA* (or m-RNA). Codons are read from the DNA without overlapping (Figure 2–4). For example, bases *AAATTTGGG* are read in sequence: 123, 456, 789—not 123, 345, 567—which would result in codons *AAA, ATT, TTG.* Overlapping would obviously change the intended message. Within the protein-coding message in m-RNA, and unlike DNA itself, thymine (*T*) is replaced by a chemically similar base called uracil (*U*) that pairs with an adenine (*A*). The DNA message has been transcribed into RNA, and this molecule now carries the genetic information necessary to make the protein.

When the messenger RNA molecule has been completely transcribed, it slips off the DNA and exits from the nucleus. The m-RNA proceeds to the *ribosome,* where the proteins are actually assembled. On the surface of the ribosomes another type of RNA, called ribosomal or r-RNA, is found, to which the m-RNA binds. The m-RNA message is "read" as it travels along a ribosome, and the message is *translated* into a chain of amino acids. This translation of the message is the second step in protein synthesis.

Amino acids, found floating free in the cell cytoplasm, are attached to a molecule of a third type of RNA called transfer RNA (t-RNA). On t-RNA is a three-letter sequence of bases that recognizes a specific three-letter sequence on the m-RNA and binds to the m-RNA, carrying with it its specific amino acid. When the base sequence of the m-RNA is matched to the complementary base sequence of the t-RNA, the t-RNA's are aligned in order on the m-RNA and the genetic message is translated again down the chain. Because the amino acids are positioned on the m-RNA, they are linked together by enzymes that form the peptide

hormone–a chemical substance produced by an organ or structure of the body that acts on or affects another distinct organ or structure.

replication–a duplication process requiring copying from a template, in this case the DNA molecule.

transcription–transfer of genetic information encoded in a DNA sequence to an RNA message.

translation–synthesis of a polypeptide chain from an RNA genetic message.

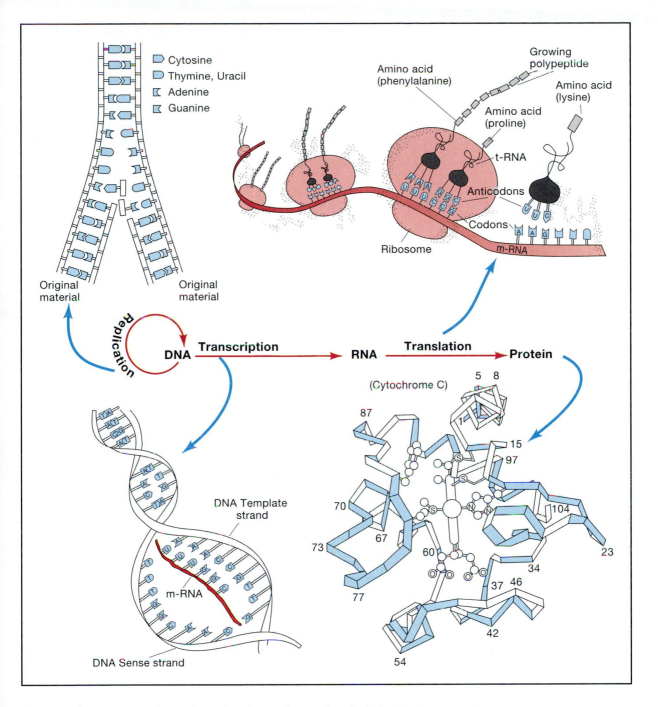

Figure 2–4 • Protein synthesis, the molecular mechanism by which the DNA message is translated into polypeptide chains. The two subunits of the ribosome become attached to the m-RNA during translation. The t-RNA carry their amino acids to the proper position in the polypeptide sequence, configuring their anticodon to the m-RNA codon. Polypeptide synthesis is accomplished when the amino acids join as the ribosome moves along the m-RNA strand.

bonds and create the polypeptides. If more polypeptides are needed, the m-RNA may be read again to make another copy, or it may be destroyed and its parts reused.

Gene Structure

Genes are composed of segments called **introns** and **exons.** Exons are parts of the gene that actually code for the amino acid sequence of the functioning protein. Introns are segments of DNA that are found between the exons, but their DNA sequences do not affect the amino acid chain in the protein. Introns are spliced or edited out of the genetic message during protein synthesis so that only the exons remain in the message.

Within the structure of the gene certain regions have been discovered that act as switches, turning on or off other functional parts of the gene. These are called *regulators*. In embryological and fetal development the process of regulating the genetic material programs the cells to different destinies. When it is necessary for cells to produce a protein, the regulator region turns on the protein specified by the gene or genes. Normally many genes are turned off. It is obviously an advantage to the cell to make these proteins when necessary and not have the whole protein-making machinery turned on all the time. Gene regulation is important in conceptualizing how two species that are genetically very similar, say, humans and chimpanzees, may differ so dramatically in their external or "phenotypic" appearance. Because gene regulation determines when and for how long certain genes are active, it thus has a major effect on resulting morphology and behavior.

The Increase in the Amount of DNA

The earliest cells had a relatively small amount of DNA, if we assume they had about the same amount of DNA possessed by living primitive organisms like bacteria. As early cells increased in size, perhaps from competition with other cells (a bigger cell is more difficult to attack and ingest), their DNA content increased. In living organisms cell and nuclear size increase with increased amount of DNA.

DNA content per cell over the history of life on earth has on average increased. However, the amount of DNA does not correspond closely to organismic complexity. Ferns and salamanders, for example, have much more DNA per cell than do human beings. Hinegardner (1978) has classified organisms into four classes based on their DNA content. Classes 1 (bacteria) and 2 (fungi) have relatively small amounts of DNA because of their simplicity. Class 3 includes most animals and some plants. This group is subdivided into 3a—those organisms in which DNA content does not differ greatly among species, and 3b—those organisms whose DNA content may differ within a group by as much as 100%. Finally, Class 4 is characterized by species with very high amounts of DNA. Human beings are in group 3a. How did this rather odd (to us) scatter of DNA patterns evolve in various organisms?

intron–noncoding sequence of DNA that is not transcribed by the m-RNA.

exon–the expressed segment of a gene, separated from other exons by introns.

Change and Loss of DNA in Evolution

Hinegardner explains the pattern by noting that for a set amount of DNA in an organism's cells, evolution over time will produce two changes. One, the base sequences will change, as the organism adapts to changing environmental conditions, and two, DNA may be lost. It may be lost, for example, through an adaptation that provides an animal with a longer, stickier tongue to eat ants, which makes the development of teeth and strong jaw musculature maladaptive. Consequently, the DNA that coded for these body parts is removed by evolution. For example, research on the DNA of fishes has shown that specialized species have less DNA per cell than more generalized species. Over a long period of time, a lineage of organisms can become very specialized and lose so much DNA that extinction results with even the slightest change in environmental conditions.

On the other hand, for unknown reasons, the DNA content of some species has increased at certain irregularly spaced intervals. We may presume that these increases conferred some advantage at each occurrence. New DNA can produce entirely new proteins that may have evolutionary significance to the species. Thus, DNA increase is quite important in the evolution of life because it provides a template of flexibility for future change.

prokaryotes–organisms like bacteria that lack a differentiated cell nucleus.

eukaryotes–organisms that have a nucleus containing DNA in their cells.

THE CELL NUCLEUS EVOLVES

The Earliest Organisms

The earliest organisms were only slightly more complex than the droplet precells scientists have synthesized in the laboratory. These organisms possessed a cell wall composed of proteins, with a double strand of DNA inside, and they reproduced by splitting in two. The earliest of these organisms metabolized anaerobically, but some later ones began to use oxygen as an energy source. These early organisms were either stationary, attached to the shallow sea bottom, or they moved around with a simple tail made up of protein. Called **prokaryotes,** they were the sole life on earth for some two billion years. Prokaryotes have a cell membrane, but the DNA inside the cell is floating about along with all the other chemicals in the cell. The DNA is in a chemical environment within the cell that necessitates that it direct all cell activities; it cannot be isolated from any of the subsidiary activities that the cell undertakes. This limits cell size and the diversity of tasks that prokaryote cells can perform.

The fossil record contains large fossilized cells dating between 1.5 and 1 billion years ago (Figure 2–5). These cells are called **eukaryotes** (Greek, for "true nucleus") because their DNA was separated by a membrane from the rest of the cell into what is called the nucleus. Scientists have deduced that these cells not only were capable of tolerating oxygen but used it to produce more energy than prokaryotes could. Consequently, eukaryotes were able to grow larger and move faster. The cells

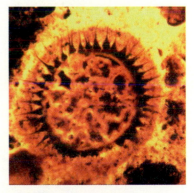

Figure 2–5 • One of the earliest eukaryotic cells, larger than its prokaryotic ancestors. The fossil cell comes from 590-million-year-old sediments in the Doushantuo formation, China. (Andrew H. Knoll, Harvard University)

mitochondria–organelles within the cell with their own DNA that carry on energy metabolism for the cell.

symbiosis–the theory that formerly free-living primitive organisms came together to form a single organism, capable of metabolism and reproduction as a unit.

mitochondrial DNA–the DNA within the mitochondria, abbreviated as mt-DNA; mt-DNA evolves approximately 10 times faster than the DNA in the cell nucleus.

in our bodies have nuclei, a characteristic that we inherited from the early eukaryotes.

The early eukaryotes were predatory. They could eat and digest large particles and even other cells. In contrast, prokaryotes can ingest only particles of molecular size that can diffuse through their cellular membranes. Eukaryotes also had a much more efficient energy utilization system. Each cell contained structures or organelles called the **mitochondria.** These structures provided the energy for cellular functions by extracting energy from the nutrients and oxygen that the cell absorbed. In addition, the chromosomes of the eukaryotes held much more genetic information than did those of the prokaryotes. The approximate date of divergence of prokaryotes and eukaryotes is about one to 1.5 billion years ago, based on both fossil and molecular evidence.

Symbiosis and the Origin of the Mitochondrion

Today no life forms intermediate between simple prokaryotic bacteria and complex eukaryotic organisms exist. This fact, and the relative rapidity of the appearance of eukaryotic multicellular organisms in the fossil record, have suggested to some microbiologists a new theory. This theory is called **symbiosis** (Greek, meaning "living together"), defined as "the merging of organisms into new collectives" (Margulis and Sagan, 1985:18). According to this view, the eukaryotic cell is a *chimera*—two primitive bacterial cells with disparate parts—that began to live as one unit. Each of the two subunits derived benefits from its association with the larger unit, and eventually both subunits co-evolved so that they could not survive without each other.

The evolution of mitochondria (Figure 2–6) is an example of symbiotic evolution. **Mitochondrial DNA** is separate from the DNA of the cell nucleus, and mitochondria reproduce by simple division like a bacterium. Early in the history of life a bacterium, ancestral to the mitochondrion of today, that could use oxygen combined with other microorganisms in a symbiotic relationship. The ancestral mitochondrion derived food and shelter from the new arrangement, while providing energy (ATP) from breathing oxygen, and removing waste (fermented food molecules) from this new combination of organisms that was to become the cell.

EVOLUTION OF DNA REPAIR AND SEXUAL REPRODUCTION

We are descended from ancient anaerobic photosynthesizing bacteria that moved out of the airless mud to the sunlit near-surface of the water. As atmospheric hydrogen was used up, these organisms took sunlight and hydrogen sulfide wastes from fermenting bacteria to derive hydrogen molecules. But in the early earth's atmosphere, no shielding layer of ozone existed to block out harmful ultraviolet radiation from the sun.

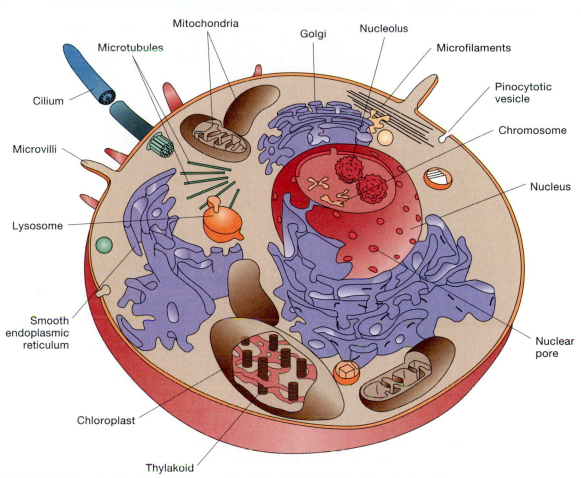

Figure 2–6 • View of cell subunits and organelles. Like the chloroplast, the mitochondrion was originally incorporated into the cell as a "parasite"; these subunits have their own DNA and have now evolved indispensable cell functions related to energy extraction in the cell. (From Barrett et al., 1986)

This radiation harms DNA by breaking the molecules apart and by creating *T–T* pairs (called thymine dimers) rather than normal *A–T* pairs, thereby rendering the bacterial DNA inactive and unable to function. DNA repair systems no doubt originally evolved to straighten out this ultraviolet light damage by creating **enzymes**—specialized proteins that promote chemical reactions in cells—to cut out a damaged part of the DNA. A new undamaged section of DNA was either borrowed from another bacterium or a virus and then re-inserted into the DNA by enzymes that can "cut and paste" sections of DNA.

Sexual reproduction is the production of new cells through the contribution of genetic material from two parents. Why this form of reproduction first evolved is not simple to understand. First and foremost, as organisms adapt to their environment, selection favors genes that tend to maximize the organisms' successful adaptation. That is, over time,

enzymes–polypeptides that catalyze or accelerate chemical reactions.

sexual reproduction–reproduction resulting from the exchange of genetic material between two parent organisms.

selection would favor genes that, in combination, would anatomically, physiologically, and behaviorally promote an individual's survival and favor its ability to reproduce. Under these circumstances it is logical to think that evolution would favor the situation wherein individuals that are well suited to their environment would pass on their genetic package with as little modification as possible. This would ensure that whatever successful adaptation was originally made would be maintained throughout later generations. Such a form of reproduction is asexual and is called *cloning*. Cloning exists today as a successful form of reproduction in many single-celled organisms, some plants, several insect species, and some fish, amphibians, and reptiles.

The idea for the origin of sexual reproduction through DNA repair is credited to Richard Michod of the University of Arizona, Tucson. In his view, gene exchange between individuals originated as a mechanism to repair damaged strands of DNA. The bacterium *Bacillus subtilis* uses a mechanism of DNA capture called **transformation**—independent bits of free-floating DNA from dead bacteria of the same species are captured and then used to repair damaged DNA in live bacteria. Experiments show that damaged bacteria incorporate more free-floating DNA than do undamaged bacteria. Undamaged bacteria also replicate more successfully than those damaged in laboratory situations by excessive ultraviolet light or excessive oxygen.

Transformation might be considered a form of proto-sex, a behavior which has obvious short-term individual benefits. But, according to Rosemary Redfield of the University of British Columbia, it is not the only possible explanation for the origin of sex. Redfield contends that hunger is the driving motivation behind DNA capture. She notes that the molecular spine of DNA is made up of alternating sugar and phosphate molecules and when DNA is broken down ("digested"), an organism can use the sugars and the attached base for energy. For example, when a bacterium runs out of internal sugars, it might find and capture external DNA as a new food source. Quite by accident undigested DNA, if it matches a bit of the organism's own DNA, might be incorporated into its host's genetic code. Thus, what started out as a unique feeding strategy may have been the origin of sexual reproduction and consequent genetic exchange.

EVOLUTION OF MITOSIS AND MEIOSIS

Mitosis

transformation—incorporation of another cell's DNA into a cell's own DNA structure.

When the first cells grew too large they spontaneously split apart. DNA, enzymes, and metabolic activity would then have been carried into two new daughter cells. But this process could be haphazard: If important parts of the DNA molecule and important cellular chemicals did not make it into a daughter cell, the cell would die. The process of cellular reproduction became more organized so that the same amount of DNA made it into the new cells as had been in the parent. This solution for efficient parceling out of the parent cell's DNA to offspring cells is accomplished by the process of **mitosis** (Greek, meaning "threading"). Mitosis takes place when DNA in a cell is replicated and then migrates to opposite poles of the cell as the cell divides into two new cells (Figure 2–7). The new cells can then carry on the same metabolic functions as the parent.

mitosis—the replication of the DNA during splitting of a cell and migration of each duplicated portion to a new cell.

chromosomes—structures composed of folded DNA found in the nuclei of the cells of eukaryotic organisms.

Meiosis

The cell and its functioning became more complex in the eukaryotes. The DNA in the nucleus was folded up into thicker threadlike structures known as **chromosomes** (Greek for "colored body" because of their

Figure 2–7 • The cellular processes of meiosis and mitosis. (From Barrett et al., 1986)

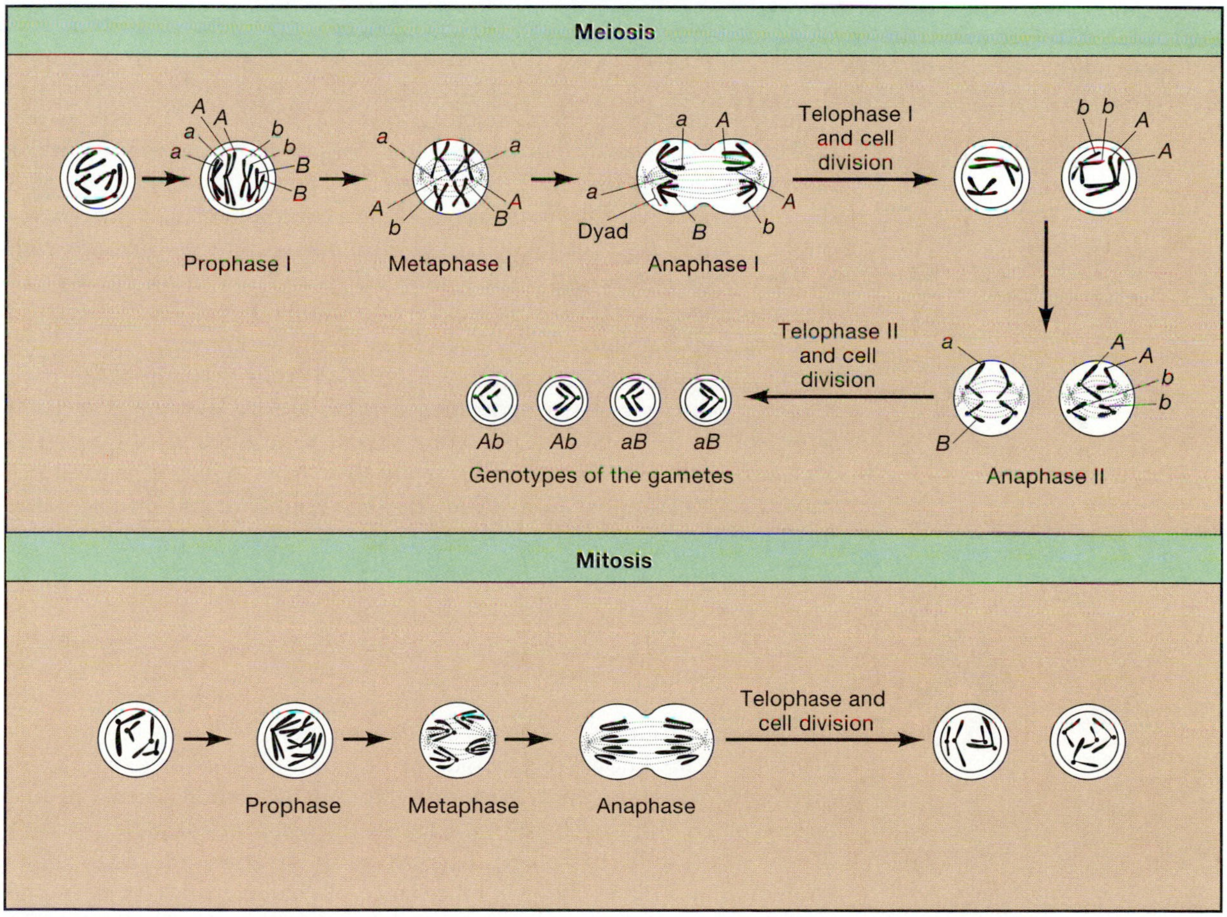

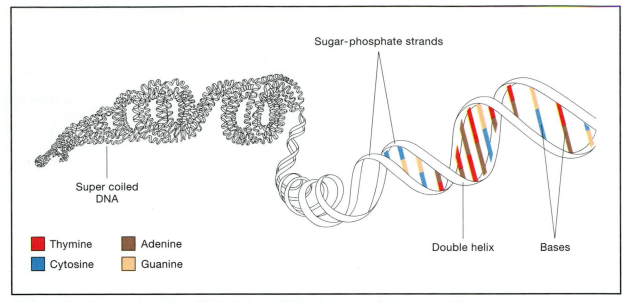

Figure 2–8 • Diagrammatic view of folded strings of DNA known as chromosomes. These structures are characteristic of eukaryotes.

appearance under the light microscope) (Figure 2–8). The eukaryotes possess sex cells, or cells with half the number of chromosomes as the body cells of each parent. Human egg and sperm cells are sex cells. As a sex cell divides, the chromosomes split into complementary halves without replicating. A sex cell with half its chromosomes then combines with another such sex cell to form a new cell with the normal number of chromosomes. This process is known as **meiosis** (Greek for "lessening," referring to the splitting in half of the pairs of chromosomes in the nucleus). The eukaryotes thus mix up the DNA from two parents in their offspring. One set of chromosomes is provided by the father and another set by the mother. Eukaryotic sexual reproduction originated at least 850 million years ago. This is the time from which fossilized eukaryotes with complex morphology become abundant and diverse in the fossil record.

DARWIN'S THEORY OF EVOLUTION BY NATURAL SELECTION

We turn now to a discussion of the development of the theory that explains the many known facts about the origins and diversity of species of organisms on earth: the theory of evolution by natural selection, first conceived of and developed by Charles Darwin (1809–1882). Darwin's theory successfully explained the observable diversity and adaptations of animals and plants, but not inheritance of characteristics, because the knowledge of genetic mechanisms and the genetic basis of variability escaped him. Next, we discuss the synthesis of the laws of genetic inheri-

meiosis—the process whereby eukaryote sex cells halve their DNA for combination with the sex cells of another individual.

tance, developed by Gregor Mendel (1822–1884), and Darwin's theory of natural selection, which together form the basis for the modern synthesis of evolutionary theory. Finally, we discuss the integration of modern cell biology and molecular genetics with the synthetic theory of evolution and how this integration has contributed to a more complete understanding of the intricate workings of the DNA molecule and the process of mutation.

Influences on Darwin

In 1830 the English astronomer Sir John Herschel (1792–1871) wrote that "[T]o ascend to the origin of things, and to speculate on the creation, is not the business of the natural philosopher" (Herschel, 1831:29). Yet one undergraduate at Cambridge University who read those words in 1831 was not dissuaded from a career that eventually led him to investigate the origin of biological species, "that mystery of mysteries" (Darwin, 1859:141). The student's name was Charles Darwin (Figure 2–9).

Darwin prided himself on his **inductive scientific method,** defined as the collection of data without preconceived notions or hypotheses (Hull, 1973:9–10). Nevertheless, the work of several influential scientists profoundly affected his later thoughts and views of his data, and they contributed to the **deductive** framework for his theory of evolution by natural selection.

Malthus's Theory of Populations In his *Essay on the Principles of Population* (1798), English economist Thomas Malthus (1766–1834) observed that human population numbers increase geometrically (multiplication by a constant factor) and food resources increase only arithmetically (addition by a constant factor). He put forward the idea that the world always tends to have more people in it than it has food to feed them. Population checks such as famine, disease, and war were to Malthus unavoidable facts of society. In 1838 the young Charles Darwin read Malthus's book "for amusement" (Darwin, 1859:1), anticipating a parallel between his observations on plants and animals and Malthus's "struggle for existence" theory about human beings. Instead, Darwin hit upon a crucial ingredient that he would later incorporate into his theory of natural selection:

> . . . it at once struck me that under these circumstances favorable variations would tend to be preserved, and unfavorable ones to be destroyed. The result of this would be the formation of a new species. Here, then, I had at last got a theory by which to work . . . (Darwin, 1859:1).

Lyell's Theory of Uniformitarianism During the latter nineteenth century, some earth scientists disagreed that small changes observable at work today could account for observed geological phenomena. They suspected that large-scale catastrophes, such as floods, earthquakes, or volcanic eruptions, were the primary forces that molded earth history.

Figure 2–9 • Charles Darwin.

inductive scientific method—inferring a generalized conclusion from particular instances.

deduction—inferring conclusions about particular instances from general or universal premises.

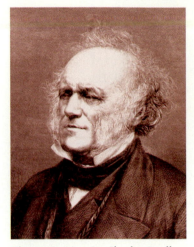

Figure 2–10 • Sir Charles Lyell.

The theory of **catastrophism,** which holds that earth history is explicable in terms of violent and sudden cataclysms that destroyed most living species, after which a new set of creations established new species, was popularized by the French naturalist Georges Cuvier. It accounted for change within a relatively short, and, at that time, generally accepted time frame. This presented a large obstacle for Darwin in that he could not reconcile the idea of a short geologic time scale with his idea of gradual morphological change in evolution.

Connected with catastrophism was **special creation,** an idea proposed by Cuvier and others to account for the repopulation of the flora and fauna after a catastrophe had wiped out previous species. Although both these explanations were of the miraculous type and, therefore, nonscientific, "special creation" was distinguished from the original "creation" because it had presumably occurred numerous times in earth history. Although this mechanism could explain a number of observations relating to the geological and paleontological changes seen in earth history, it was an assumption, and as such it was impossible to test directly.

Sir Charles Lyell (1797–1875; Figure 2–10), a Scot trained at Oxford as a lawyer, became one of the most influential geologists of the day. His landmark work, *The Principles of Geology* (1830–33), propounded the view that the earth's geological history could be explained entirely by heat and erosion, processes that we can observe at work today. Lyell appealed to a "principle of uniformity," and William Whewell, a reviewer of *The Principles,* coined the term **uniformitarianism** for Lyell's theory. Uniformitarianism is the principle that processes observable today can account for past events in geological history.

Charles Darwin first read Lyell's book on the round-the-world voyage of the British ship *H.M.S. Beagle* when he was employed as the ship's naturalist. In 1836 on his return to England, Darwin states in his *Autobiography* (1958:32–33) that he "saw a great deal of Lyell" and that "his advice and example had much influence on me." Uniformitarianism became one of the founding principles of modern geology, and, through Darwin, a major influence in biology. Lyell's uniformitarian theory provided the long time periods necessary for the slow and gradual change that Darwin envisioned.

Darwin Develops His Theory

Collecting Evidence for Evolution   Much of the data that Darwin used to construct his theory came from his experiences as ship's naturalist aboard the *H.M.S. Beagle,* which circumnavigated the globe in 1833–36 on a mission mapping the South American coast for British shipping interests. When Darwin sailed from England on the *H.M.S. Beagle,* he carried with him the idea of evolution advanced by French naturalist Jean Baptiste de Lamarck (1744–1829; Figure 2–11). Lamarck believed that species could evolve and did change over time. How these changes in anatomy and behavior occurred or whether the changes could produce a new species were still major questions. Lamarck's the-

catastrophism–theory that earth history is explicable in terms of violent and sudden cataclysms that destroyed most living species, after which a new set of creations established new species.

special creation–the nonevolutionary theory associated with catastrophism that held that totally new species, unrelated to prior species, were created after extinctions.

uniformitarianism–principle that processes observable today can account for past events in geological history.

ory proposed that changes or differences in the environment cause a "need" for organisms to change. This need causes biological change within the organism and makes it better suited to its new environment. Biological change, in turn, may be passed down to offspring. Lamarck proposed the idea of the inheritance of acquired characteristics (Figure 2–12) to explain the origin of variation among and between different species.

In South America Darwin found evidence of evolution, but his observations forced him to question Lamarck's idea of the inheritance of acquired characteristics. If Lamarck's explanation of the mechanism for evolution was correct, similar environments would produce similar species.

When Darwin arrived at the Galápagos Islands, off the northwest coast of South America, in September of 1835, he discovered some important facts. The Galápagos are volcanic and much more recent in origin than the neighboring mainland. Darwin immediately set to work collecting animal

Figure 2–11 • Jean Baptiste de Lamarck.

Figure 2–12 • Lamarckian evolution by the inheritance of acquired characteristics, in contrast to Darwinian evolution by natural selection.

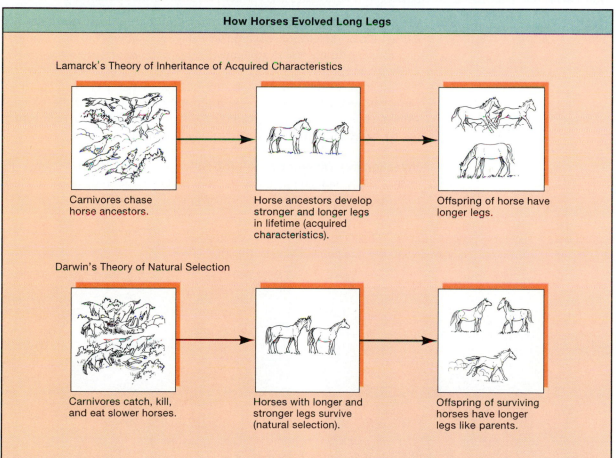

How Horses Evolved Long Legs

Lamarck's Theory of Inheritance of Acquired Characteristics

Carnivores chase horse ancestors.

Horse ancestors develop stronger and longer legs in lifetime (acquired characteristics).

Offspring of horse have longer legs.

Darwin's Theory of Natural Selection

Carnivores catch, kill, and eat slower horses.

Horses with longer and stronger legs survive (natural selection).

Offspring of surviving horses have longer legs like parents.

and plant specimens from the many closely spaced islands. In accordance with Lamarck's ideas, he expected the fauna and flora of the various islands to be quite similar to one another, because the islands were close together and shared the same climate. He found, in fact, quite a unique spectrum of species of birds, lizards, and tortoises on the islands. They were related, but also quite distinct from mainland South American forms.

As work progressed Darwin became aware of a strange and unexpected fact—the tortoises from each island differed from the tortoises of other islands. In fact, people could tell what island a tortoise came from by looking at the shell alone (Figure 2–13). How could this be so if species were adapted to the same environment?

Darwin began to think that because all the types of island tortoises were in most ways similar, they must have all descended from a common ancestral tortoise and had diverged over time by adapting to the various island environments. He concluded that geographic isolation was crucial to an understanding of evolution. Geographical variations were not separate "special creations" of species, but rather, they were local modifications of a single species.

Darwin found fossil evidence in South America that showed that evolution had occurred. He discovered in an ancient geological formation a fossil glyptodont, an extinct giant relative of the modern armadillo. An extinct llama skeleton discovered in Patagonia showed a clear connection to living South American llamas. In his *Journal of Researches* (1839), Darwin noted that "the most important result of this discovery is the confirmation of the law that existing animals have a close relation in form with extinct species." Darwin termed this "the law of the succession of types," an idea that formed the theoretical basis for connecting the fossil record with the diversity of living animals.

Investigating Differential Reproduction Darwin returned home in 1836 and devoted the remaining years of his life to the study of natural history. He began to study domesticated animals and to breed pigeons. He

Figure 2–13 • Natural selection in tortoises of the Galápagos Islands. A tortoise of the island of Santa Cruz (left) is compared with one found on Isla Isabella (right).

also wrote a number of classic studies on organisms like the barnacle and on the evolution of behavior (see Chapter 9). He observed that, through the process of artificial breeding, or *selection*, one could obtain populations or strains of animals that were quite different from each other and from the original parental form.

Almost all the pieces of the puzzle of evolution were in place: Individuals vary and forms could be artificially selected to breed so that change could come about; and these differences were heritable from generation to generation. What Darwin lacked was knowledge of how this inherited variability could be connected to his deduction that animals could change over time to adapt to their natural environments. Part of the answer, of course, came from Malthus's essay.

Malthus wrote in his essay that not all individuals born reached maturity. Many die from one cause or another before adulthood. A species does not continue to reproduce until it completely covers the earth with its offspring. Rather, there is some upper limit to population growth and populations maintain a stable number of individuals.

Darwin's argument started with the observation that individuals within a species vary one from another (Figure 2–14). A second observation was that this variability could be inherited. Because of variability, some individuals were better suited to survive in their environments than others. Invoking Malthus's ideas that species produce more offspring than can survive, Darwin reasoned that those individuals best adapted to their environment would survive longer and produce more offspring than those less well-adapted. He called the new theory **natural selection** to distinguish it from the artificial selection practiced on domestic animals by breeders.

natural selection—the process of differential reproduction whereby individuals well-adapted to their environment will be "favored," that is, they will pass on more of their heritable attributes to the next generation than other, less well-adapted individuals.

Figure 2–14 • Individuals vary one from another and variability is inherited.

In 1859, Darwin published the *Origin of Species by Means of Natural Selection.* He reasoned that differential survival occurred because individuals had different abilities *(fitnesses)* to cope with their environment. Differential reproduction would be the result of the survival of those individuals who were better adapted. Over the generations there would be selection among the various individuals in response to environmental conditions, with the better adapted individuals producing more offspring. Those individuals disfavored by selection might not reproduce at all or would have relatively fewer offspring than the more fit animals.

In the late 1850s, another English naturalist, Alfred Russel Wallace (1823–1913), developed similar ideas after he observed the different types of animals in Australia/New Guinea and those in Asia. The presence of similar-looking animals in both groups, despite the fact that they had evolved in isolation, led Wallace to formulate the general principles of natural selection. Wallace independently discovered from his work much of what Darwin had come to believe more than 20 years before. Darwin's first paper on his theory of evolution, along with Wallace's ideas on the subject, were together presented to the Linnaean Society in London in 1858, a year before Darwin's *Origin of Species.*

The Problem of Inherited Variation   Darwin had linked the concepts of excess reproductive capacity, differences in heritable adaptations, enhanced survival, and reproduction of the fittest. What the theory of evolution by natural selection did not explain was how variation had come into existence. The problem for Darwin was how to explain the origin of the variation that led to the differential success in reproduction and ultimately to the formation of new species.

How variation was maintained in populations was the second profound problem that Darwin considered. He believed that most traits, when combined in an offspring, were blends of the parental types. For example, the mating of a tall and a short individual would produce an offspring that was intermediate in height. Two intermediate-height individuals would produce an intermediate-height offspring. The consequence of this **blending inheritance,** however, is a loss of variation in the population. If inheritance by blending did occur, then after only nine generations one would have less than 0.1% of original variation left. This fact was noted by a Scottish engineer, Fleeming Jenkin, who published in 1867 an article that criticized Darwin's hypothesis of blending inheritance. How, he asked, could a single favorable change, a heritable **mutation** arising in one member of a population, ever come to predominate if at each successive reproduction its benefit was halved by blending with an individual lacking the trait? Jenkin's criticisms of blending inheritance left Darwin with a dilemma. If this model was incorrect, then there must be some other mechanism at work that could provide the enormous quantity of variation that Darwin observed. While Darwin, to no avail, pondered this question, unbeknownst to him the finishing touches to a new theory of inheritance were being applied by a Moravian monk who studied pea plants. To find such a mechanism, Darwin began amassing data from plant and animal breeders in England.

blending inheritance–the mixing in equal halves of the contributions of parents in their offspring.

mutation–any novel genetic change that may affect both genes and chromosomes. Such changes are spontaneous and random in occurrence. Mutations are the source of all variability in populations, and, if they occur in the sex cells usually during the formation of gametes, they hold the possibility of altering the phenotypes in succeeding generations.

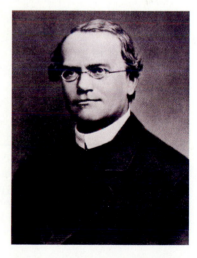

DEVELOPMENT OF A THEORY OF INHERITANCE

Experimentation did not support Darwin's hypothesis of blending inheritance. Sir Francis Galton transfused the blood of rabbits with different coat colors and then inbred the resulting strains, crossing offspring from the same parents. He found no mixing of coat colors. The German biologist August Weismann (1834–1914) hypothesized that all hereditary information resides in the reproductive cells, the "germ plasm," and that no changes in the body cells resulting from the environment could affect these germ cells. The nature of the units of heredity was still unknown, but Weismann's hypothesis formed one of the bases for modern **genetics,** the science that studies the mechanisms of heredity. The term "genetics" was coined by the English biologist William Bateson in 1900. In its rejecting the inheritance of acquired characteristics and embracing the modern concepts of genetics, Weismann's theory is also referred to as **Neo-Darwinism** (Grant, 1991:17).

In 1889 Sir Hugo De Vries developed a modified hypothesis called "intracellular pangenesis," which took recent discoveries about the cell into account. De Vries's experiments, along with those of two other workers, Correns and Tschermak, led to the rediscovery in 1900 of elementary principles of inheritance. Unknown at the time to these scientists, this research and conclusions similar to their own had been completed and published 34 years earlier.

genetics—the study of heredity and variation.

Neo-Darwinism—the combined theory of evolution by natural selection and modern genetics.

quantum theory of heredity—passing of traits as clear-cut quantifiable units not subject to subdivision; characteristic of Mendelian genetics.

genes—units of the material of inheritance, now known to be sequences of DNA.

The Laws of Heredity

Many scientists and historians have pondered the thought that, had Darwin but known of the work of the then-scientifically obscure monk Gregor Mendel (1822–1884; Figure 2–15), he would not have needed to make many of the compromises that he was forced into by criticism of the *Origin of Species*. Unfortunately, Mendel's work was either ignored by or unknown to the scientific world until 1900.

In 1856 Mendel began a series of breeding experiments involving crosses of individuals of the edible pea, *Pisum sativum*. His goal was to investigate the problem of why certain plant hybrids all looked alike in the first descendant generation (called first filial or F1 generation) but had a tendency to revert to their original states in the second generation (second filial or F2 generation).

Mendel's results are important because they established a **quantum theory of heredity,** distinguished from Darwin's blending theory of inheritance by having clearly defined units which remained discrete, generation after generation (Figure 2–16). A trait in *Pisum* was caused by two irreducible "factors," now known to be **genes.** Genes are discrete DNA sequences that code for amino acids, the constituents of proteins. The Danish biologist Wilhelm Johannsen proposed the term "gene" in 1909 to refer to Mendel's "factors."

Mendel found that in the garden pea one "factor" or gene was *dominant* to the other, which was *recessive*. Alternative versions of genes

Figure 2–15 • Gregor Mendel.

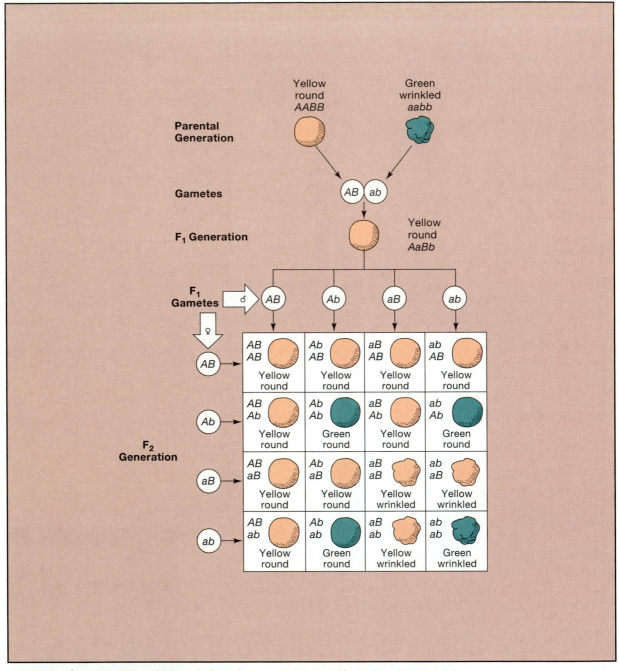

Figure 2–16 • The results of Mendel's breeding experiments with *Pisum sativum*. Two genes were responsible for each trait, they sorted out (segregated and assorted) independently, and the numbers of each type of plant resulting from the crosses were predictable. Alleles *A* and *a* code in combination for seed color. *A* allele is dominant over *a* allele. Alleles *B* and *b* code in combination for seed shape. *B* allele is dominant over *b* allele. (From Barrett et al., 1986)

occupying the same place on a chromosome, which may be termed *"A"* for a dominant gene and *"a"* for a recessive gene, are called **alleles.** Individuals who have the same alleles, as in the dominant alleles, *AA,* or in two recessive alleles, *aa,* are termed **homozygous** (Latin, for "similar yoking together"). Individuals who are *Aa* are termed **heterozygous** (Latin for "different yoking together"). The combination of genes, *AA, Aa,* or *aa,* is referred to as the **genotype.** Genes do not blend together in the heterozygote, but remain as two different alleles.

The Principle of Segregation

Mendel's experiments disproved blending inheritance once and for all. Mendel observed when crossing two purebred strains of his pea plants that the hybrids in the F1 generation exhibited only one form of the parents' traits. For example, if plants that produced only green seed pods were crossed with plants that produced only yellow seed pods, invariably the F1 offspring produced green seed pods. If later crossed together, F1 plants would give rise to offspring whose seed pods typically appeared in a ratio of 3 green-seed-pod-producing plants to 1 yellow-seed-pod-producing plant, regardless of the number of plants involved. These results clearly did not support the idea of mixing or blending of equal parts of the parents' inheritance in their offspring.

Mendel discovered that the alleles, *A* and *a,* which in different combinations were responsible for seed pod color, split apart independently during the production of sex cells. This important principle is termed **segregation,** sometimes also called Mendel's First Law. Mendel determined that a "true-breeding" plant produces only one type of allele, either *A* or *a*. *A* in this case is dominant to *a,* so when the two come together in a fertilized plant, *A* is expressed and *a* is not. Only in *aa* plants is the trait *a* expressed. Thus, Mendel's hypothesis could explain why all the first generation plants look the same (all are *Aa*) and why the second generation plants show traits that had apparently disappeared (¼ are *aa*). The old mystery of "reversions" was solved.

The Principle of Independent Assortment

Mendel studied seven traits of *Pisum sativum,* and he found that all seven traits were randomly combined with one another in their offspring. Wrinkled seeds, for example, separated independently from yellow pods, as did the other five traits. It is now known that Mendel's seven traits are all coded for by genes that exist on separate chromosomes of *Pisum.* Thus, while alleles, which are situated at comparable places on a paired set of chromosomes, are said to segregate, chromosomes and the genes they carry are said to **assort** independently. This conclusion means that during sex cell formation the genes on the different chromosomes are split up and combine randomly. Thus, whether a pea plant inherited a pair of alleles for a wrinkled or smooth seed was irrelevant to the combination of the other six traits that Mendel examined.

allele—alternate form of a gene.

homozygous—bearing two identical alleles at a genetic locus.

heterozygous—bearing two different alleles at a genetic locus.

genotype—the genetic composition of an organism, as compared to phenotype, the manifestation of its genes.

segregation—the separation of recessive and dominant alleles during reproduction, allowing maintenance of their separate identities and later full expression of their traits; sometimes referred to as Mendel's First Law of Segregation.

assort—the independent separation of pairs of genes on one chromosome from pairs of genes on other chromosomes; also known as Mendel's Second Law of Independent Assortment.

They were all scrambled up each generation in an independent way. The principle of independent assortment is also termed Mendel's Second Law.

Mendel's dramatic results were to some extent fortuitous, for two reasons. First, the seven traits he studied were situated on one of each of seven chromosomes of *Pisum*. Had they not been, they would not have assorted independently, as Mendel found, because if two traits were on the same chromosome pair they would have been transmitted to the next generation together. Second, the traits that Mendel chose to study also showed clear dominance and recessiveness. Mendel could have studied many other traits that have a much less straightforward heritability.

Later the Swedish botanist Herman Nilsson-Ehle proved that traits could be carried on the same chromosome pair when he crossed red-kernel and white-kernel wheat strains and did not find segregation in a clear-cut dominant–recessive allelic system. Instead of white and red kernels segregating in a 3 to 1 ratio as expected in the F2 generation, he found five color classes grading from red to yellow-white. It was clear from these results that one externally observable phenotype—the external appearance caused by the genetic complement, the genotype—could be under the control of more than one set of genes. These genes could be located at more than one place, or **locus,** on the chromosome, or on different chromosomes (Figure 2–17). Furthermore, these genes, when combined in offspring, did not necessarily follow a dominant–recessive relationship. The cases described above are examples of **polygenic** inheritance that may result in a gradational or quantitative set of phenotypes. **Epistasis** is a term used to describe the dominance of one gene on one chromosome over that of another on a different chromosome. In cases where genes are clearly dominant or recessive, as in human eye color, ratios of phenotypes can be calculated. On the other hand, in most cases where genes are co-dominant, that is where they are both expressed to some degree, or in which there are many genes determining a trait, such as height or skin color, Mendelian ratios do not appear.

Chromosomal Theory of Heredity

In 1903 two researchers, Sutton and Boveri, independently hypothesized that Mendelian factors behaved very much like chromosomes. It is now known that humans have 23 pairs of chromosomes. Our closest relatives, the African apes, chimpanzees, and gorillas, have 24 pairs of chromosomes. Human females have 23 identical pairs of chromosomes that include the sex chromosomes (two *X* chromosomes). Human males have 22 pairs of identical chromosomes (called **autosomes**), and one pair that is different: the sex chromosomes, one *X* chromosome inherited from the mother, and one *Y* chromosome inherited from the father. The 23 pairs of chromosomes are called the full **diploid** (*diplo* meaning two) set. During meiosis, the diploid set of these chromosome pairs splits, with only one chromosome of each pair going to a sex cell or gamete. The 23 chromosomes contained in each gamete constitute the **haploid** (*haplo* meaning single) set. When gametes unite during the

locus–a "place" on a chromosome or segment of DNA where a gene is located.

polygenic–a trait controlled by interaction of genes at more than one locus.

epistasis–gene masking the effect of another gene.

autosomes–referring to chromosomes other than the sex (*X* and *Y*) chromosomes.

diploid–having two sets of chromosomes, as normally found in the somatic cells of higher organisms.

haploid–having a single set of chromosomes, as found in the sex cells or gametes of higher organisms.

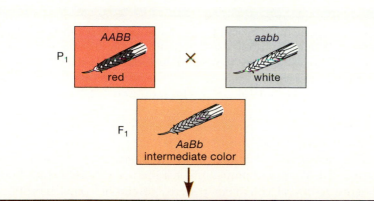

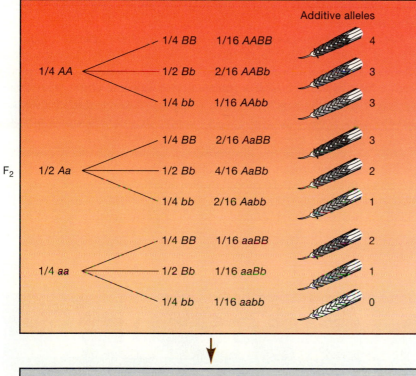

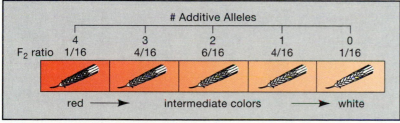

Figure 2–17 • Phenotypic traits can be determined by several genes, sometimes on different chromosomes as shown initially by the work of Nilsson-Ehle on wheat. This polygenic inheritance could explain the observations of Darwin and others that had been used in support of "blending inheritance" and helped to reconcile "Darwinism" and "Mendelism."

process of fertilization to form a new individual, the diploid number of chromosomes is reestablished.

Chromosomes are now known to consist of very long strands of DNA, complexly folded and twisted (see Figure 2–8, p. 40). Genes, as we have seen, are sequences of the DNA found at particular loci on the

karyotype–identified and numbered arrangement of chromosomes.

chromosomes. In human beings a chromosome is composed of about 1 meter of DNA coiled upon itself many times. Because each human cell contains 23 pairs of chromosomes, it has about 46 meters of DNA (Margulis and Sagan, 1986b:279).

Traditionally, the human set of chromosomes is labeled 1 to 22, by size, with number 1 being the largest, and the sex cells, *X* and *Y,* constituting the 23rd pair. A picture of chromosomes arranged in order is known as a **karyotype.** Advances in staining chromosomes known as "banding techniques" allow us to see more structure in chromosomes (Figure 2–18). These techniques involve the use of enzymes or fluorescent stains to reveal consistent patterns of chromosomal morphology. Geneticists are able to identify each human chromosome by its different band morphology.

Chromosome number by itself tells us little about genetic organization, as some mammals may have as few as 6 or 8 chromosomes, whereas flies have 4 or 6 and some plants have hundreds of chromosomes. Even within the higher primates, chromosome counts vary from 8 to numbers in the seventies. What is important is that each individual has a full set. Without a complete or full set, the individual may not develop properly and may have anatomical abnormalities.

Prior to cell division the chromosomes of dividing cells are usually visible as coils wound up in the nucleus of the cell. During *interphase,* the phase between cell division, chromosomes duplicate and carry out their specific activities. At some point, varying with the tissue, cells divide into two new daughter cells with a complete complement of all of the organelles, chromosomes, membranes, and enzymes necessary for cell function.

Figure 2–18 • The human karyotype. Banding techniques show the intricate structure of the human chromosomes.

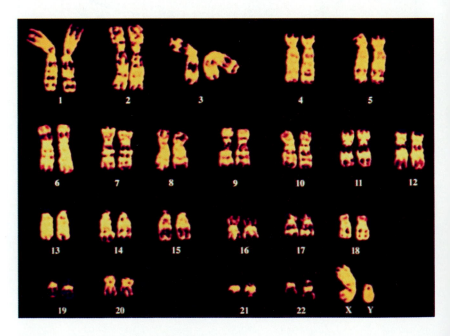

Gene Linkage and Crossing Over

As they studied the inheritance of more traits caused by single genes, researchers found that some genes do not follow Mendel's law of independent assortment. Remember that Mendel's Second Law, which holds that genes assort independently, is only true if the genes are located on separate chromosomes. Groups of specific genes found on closely associated loci on the same chromosome are usually passed on together and, thus, they are termed **linked.** In humans one example of linkage is that between two blood group genes called Rh and Duffy, both located on chromosome 1.

Linkage of genes was found to vary from nearly complete to about 50%. Or, in up to 50% of the cases, linked genes on chromosomes were *not* passed on together. This observation was explained by a hypothesis of the Belgian biologist Janssens. He suggested that paired duplicate homologous chromosomes would become tangled up during meiosis, and, as they were pulled apart by the spindles, they would break. Because they were lined up, the homologous sections of the paired chromosomes would get traded by hooking on to the broken ends of the other chromosomes. The process is called **crossing over** (Figure 2–19). Genes that were close together on the chromosome very rarely had a

linkage–the tendency of genes to be inherited together because of their location and proximity to one another on one chromosome.

crossing over–the exchange of genes between paired chromosomes during cell duplication.

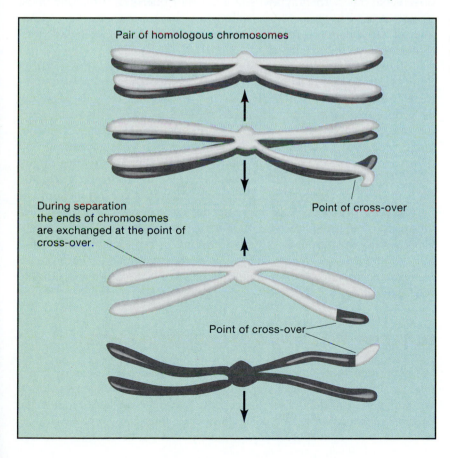

Pair of homologous chromosomes

Point of cross-over

During separation the ends of chromosomes are exchanged at the point of cross-over.

Point of cross-over

Figure 2–19 • The mechanism of crossing over in chromosomes that is the basis for constructing gene maps.

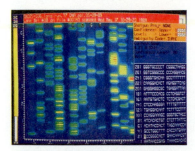

Figure 2–20 • The human gene map. Most of the traits found on genes relate to biochemical activity and specific diseases. (From McKusick, 1989)

break occur between them. They were thus closely linked, that is, near 100%. Genes more distant on the chromosome had a higher probability of intervening breaks or crossing over, hooking up with another chromosome, and thus being distantly linked.

T. H. Morgan of Columbia University used Janssens' hypothesis to "map" genes. The more often two traits caused by single genes were inherited together, the closer they were on the chromosome. By quantifying all known genes in fruit flies *(Drosophila)* Morgan was able to discover on which chromosomes and in what sequence genes occurred. Using largely the same techniques, human geneticists have constructed maps of all 23 pairs of human chromosomes (Figure 2–20). Discovering the entire DNA sequence of the human genome is the goal of the Human Genome Project, currently a major genetic research effort in the United States.

Mendelian Genetics and Molecular Genetics

With the discovery of DNA as the genetic material by Watson and Crick in 1953, the era of molecular genetics began. Although the relationship between segments of DNA and genes, together with their relationship to observable traits (phenotypes) still is a major question in biology, most geneticists and historians of science agree that the principles and findings of Mendelian genetics are now translatable into molecular terms (Sober, 1984).

Today it is estimated that there are some one hundred thousand billion (10^{14} or 100,000,000,000,000) cells in the human body. Almost all of these, except for the red blood cells and the mature sex cells, carry exactly the same kind and amount of DNA. All of these cells result from the one-cell embryo at fertilization. During development these cells become progressively different depending on which genes are turned on or off and at what time. Cells proliferate into the different tissues of gut, brain, kidney, and eye. Although nerve cells, for example, carry the same DNA as skin cells or as kidney cells, they all differ in function.

The DNA, or more strictly the segments that we speak of as the genes, are responsible for (1) carrying the instructions necessary for the organism's development from its origin at fertilization to maturity; (2) the cell's ability to metabolize (utilize energy) or catabolize (break down products of metabolism); and (3) carrying the essential genetic information for the next generation.

MUTATION: THE SOURCE OF GENETIC VARIATION

We have seen how Darwin's theory of natural selection required "inherited variability" in organisms as the raw material with which evolution worked, and how Mendel's findings provided a mechanism for transmittal of genetic material from one generation to another. Darwin had called attention to what animal breeders termed "sports"—novel forms of animals, such as short-legged sheep or tailless cats. Sometimes breeders could trace the lineage of such a breed to a single animal. To Darwin such heritable changes could be of great importance if natural selection were to produce new species. But what was the real nature of these heritable changes?

Hugo De Vries, in his attempt to answer this question, believed that if Mendel's system worked perfectly, no new genes would ever be produced. Parents' genes would simply be passed on to offspring, shuffled up a bit, but still basically the same. De Vries then focused attention on the evidence for heritable genetic changes, changes that he termed *mutations,* as the source of genetic novelty.

Mutation is a sudden change in the characteristics of an organism that can be inherited by an offspring and, thus, increases the genetic variation in a group of organisms. All the differences at the genetic level we see today in human beings result from mutations in a sperm or egg somewhere in our evolutionary history. The altered sequence of DNA is called a *mutant*. Probably the most important cause of gene mutation may be mistakes in DNA replication in which the wrong base is substituted. Changes can also occur on a larger scale and may affect the number or structure of chromosomes. We shall discuss both of these types of mutations in this section (Figure 2–21).

Mutations are important to evolution only if they can be inherited. **Genetic mutations** occur in the sex cell lineage and can be passed on. **Somatic mutations** occur in non–sex-cell tissue, such as skin or neurons. These cannot be inherited. Because we have many thousands of genes, each of us has a high likelihood of carrying a new mutation in our genes.

New genetic input into a population via a mutation can be beneficial or detrimental to the organism that possesses it. The mutation may help the individual adapt better to its surroundings. For example, a new gene can make an enzyme work faster, or at a different temperature, or on a different molecule. This may result in an organism that can better respond to the varying demands of the environment.

On the other hand, and much more frequently, a new mutation may result in a defective enzyme or even no enzyme at all. A mutation might lead to infertility, even if life itself were not compromised. Such an outcome is called a *genetic death*.

Mutations can be caused by many agents, ranging from X-rays to ultraviolet light to chemicals such as caffeine commonly found in coffee and teas. Some food additives have been shown to cause mutations in bacteria. Some chemicals in our environment from cigarettes, air pollution, and chemical waste may cause mutations in genes. When altered, specific genes, called *oncogenes,* may be responsible for the unregulated cell growth that characterizes cancer.

Mutations can run the gamut from lethal to beneficial. A vast majority of them may be neither, but may be "neutral" in evolutionary terms. **Neutral mutations** at the biochemical level have no effect on the function of a protein. It may not matter if a codon substitution in the DNA results in a different amino acid substitution at a certain position in a polypeptide chain.

genetic mutation–a heritable change in the genetic material, located in the sex cells, that brings about a change in phenotype.

somatic mutation–a nonheritable change in the genetic material of the cells of the body.

neutral mutations–mutations that are not acted upon by selection, ones that do not affect the fitness of an organism in a particular environment. Neutral mutations accumulate at a more or less constant rate over time.

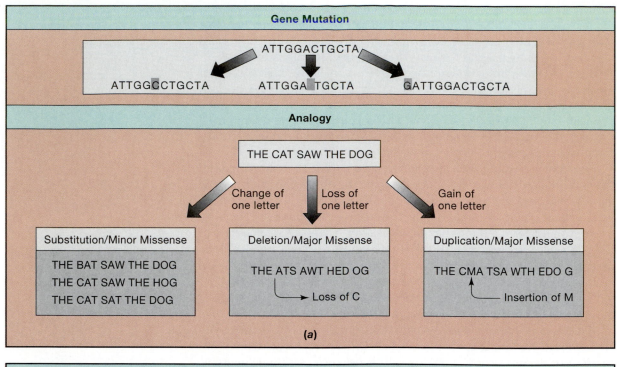

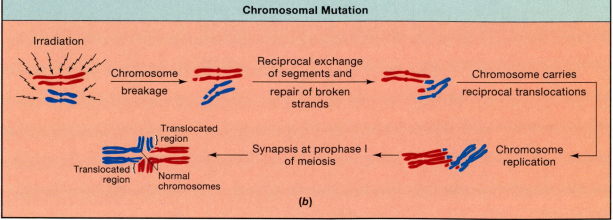

Figure 2–21 • Examples of mutation: (*a*) gene mutation, in which a single base is changed (from Barrett et al., 1986), and (*b*) large-scale chromosomal mutation (from Klug and Cummings, 1994).

Mutations are constantly recurring phenomena in biological populations, and they create genetic diversity that can be used by natural selection. For example, some bacteria are evolving in response to the challenges that antibiotic medicines present to them. Certain mutational changes in a bacterium called *Gonococcus,* responsible for a type of venereal disease, now make it difficult for the antibiotic penicillin to work. A newly evolved bacterial enzyme called penicillinase can now break up penicillin, allowing the bacterium to continue to survive and replicate.

Chance, not necessity, dictates the occurrence of new mutations. Exposure to a new drug to inhibit bacterial growth does not cause a new mutation. Instead, the changed conditions allow those individual bacteria with a pre-existing mutation to survive, whereas "old type" bacteria would be killed. Mutations, even though they are random, occur at a rate consistently high enough to allow evolution to work with the new genetic variability introduced into the population, as we shall see in Chapter 3.

THE SUCCESS OF SEXUAL REPRODUCTION

Sex and its overwhelming success as a form of reproduction in the vast majority of living organisms remains to be explained. Darwin viewed sexual reproduction as critical to the maintenance of genetic variability in populations. This variability was the grist upon which natural selection operated to produce individuals better adapted to a slowly changing environment. However, to John Maynard Smith (1978) along with Lynn Margulis and Dorian Sagan (1986b), sex was a mechanism that did nothing more than scramble up a perfectly good existing combination of genes, and that undid every good recombination it had created in the previous generation. To these authors, the logical evolutionary outcome for reproduction should be a mechanism that reverts from sex to cloning once a successfully adapted gene combination has been produced so that the combination remains intact generation after generation. The question these authors ask is why sex became the predominant form of reproduction.

Sexually reproducing organisms may have an advantage over clones if both were to live side by side in stable environments where competition between many different forms of life is intense. For example, results of a two-year study of sweet vernal grass by Steven Kelley of Washington State University suggests that sexually reproducing variants of these plants out-reproduced the clone variant by about 1.5 times. Kelley believes that the sexually reproducing grass variants flourished because they were less prone to attack by pathogens that could cause disease, and, perhaps, early death. The idea that all living organisms must evolve mechanisms to protect themselves from pathogens that generally reproduce and mutate more rapidly than themselves may well explain the success of sexual reproduction. Through sexual reproduction, organisms stand a chance of survival in the face of disease by creating genetic barriers to pathogen attack through a continual reshuffling of their genotypes. We will pursue this idea further in Chapter 12.

 ## SUMMARY

1. The DNA molecule, which has the chemical ability to attract free-floating amino acids, was the important ingredient in the production of proteins needed for cellular life and cellular reproduction.

2. All organisms have been adapted by evolution in ways that enhance reproduction, metabolism, locomotion, and ways of finding food.

3. Sexual reproduction originated as part of the process for repairing DNA, a process that transfers DNA from one organism to another. Mitosis and meiosis are mechanisms that evolved in early animals for sexual reproduction.

4. Early influences on Darwin's development of the theory of evolution were Charles Lyell's work in geology and Thomas Malthus's work on population growth. Darwin's voyage on the ship *Beagle* provided him with the raw data on which to build his theory.

5. Darwin realized that animals were variable, that much of this variability was inherited, and that limited food supplies meant that not all offspring could survive and reproduce. He reasoned that those individuals best suited to the environmental conditions would have more offspring and pass on their characteristics to future generations.

6. Darwin failed to discover the mechanism by which variability could be passed on to offspring. Much of the solution to this problem lay in the undiscovered work of Gregor Mendel, which furnished the foundation for modern genetics.

7. The chromosomal theory further explained how genes could operate under Mendel's laws. Changes in genes, called mutations, provide the raw material on which natural selection acts.

8. Molecular genetics and the discovery of DNA provided the bases for understanding how genetic information was passed from cell to cell and how proteins necessary for cellular life were produced. Molecular biology explains the structure of the gene, how mutations arise, and the kinds of structural changes that result from mutations.

 **CRITICAL-THINKING QUESTIONS**

1. Name the oldest microscopic fossils found. What characteristics did they possess that allowed scientists to classify them as a life form?
2. Describe the difference between prokaryotic and eukaryotic cells.
3. Briefly describe the evolution and function of mitochondria.
4. What is the selective advantage of sexual reproduction over cloning?
5. How did Darwin and Wallace independently come up with the theory of natural selection? Briefly explain the theory of natural selection.
6. What contributions did Malthus and Lyell make to Darwin's theories?
7. What are genetic mutations? Explain the role that natural selection plays in maintaining mutations in the gene pool.

 **SUGGESTED READINGS**

Dawkins, Richard. 1989. *The Selfish Gene*. New York: Oxford University Press. A seminal work, originally published in 1976, that restates Darwin's theory in light of modern knowledge of genetics.

Gould, Stephen Jay. 1989. *Wonderful Life: The Burgess Shale and the Nature of History*. New York: W. W. Norton. The story of the Cambrian-Age Burgess shale of Canada and the near-surrealistic animals that populated the earth's early seas.

Margulis, L., and D. Sagan. 1986. *Microcosmos: Four Billion Years of Evolution from Our Microbial Ancestors*. New York: Summit. A good general book on the intimate biological interconnections between our everyday macroscopic world and the teeming microorganisms that share it with us.

Mayr, E. 1991. *One Long Argument: Charles Darwin and the Genesis of Modern Evolutionary Thought*. Cambridge, Mass.: Harvard University Press. A historical account of Darwin's formulation of the theory of natural selection, written by a major evolutionary biologist.

Price, P. 1996. *Biological Evolution*. New York: Saunders. A concise review of evolutionary theory, focusing on macro- and microevolutionary themes.

Stanley, Stephen. 1991. *Earth and Life through Time*. New York: W. H. Freeman. An overview of geology and paleontology during earth history.

Williams, G. C. 1992. *Natural Selection: Domains, Levels, and Challenges*. New York: Oxford University Press. A review of how natural selection works in evolution.

CHAPTER 3

Populations, Species, and Evolution

Major steps in the history of life were taken when simple replicating molecules first organized into cells and eventually into free-moving animals, and when natural selection began acting on these organisms to change their genetics, anatomy, and behavior (see Chapter 2). This chapter deals with how animals, by exchanging genetic information, have become organized into groups of interacting individuals called *populations*. Through sexual reproduction, genes are reshuffled in the resulting offspring. From the gene's

standpoint it finds itself first enclosed within a cell, then within an individual organism, and finally within a **gene pool,** the total genetic makeup that is shared by all members of the species. How evolutionary forces affect genes at the species level, and how genes affect the physical and behavioral traits that we see today, are the subjects of this chapter.

POPULATIONS

In Chapter 1, a species was defined as a "genetically distinct population." These genetically distinct, or isolated, species are incapable of producing offspring with members of another species. However, one troubling concern continues to plague this definition. Some so-called species, such as lions and tigers, can interbreed and produce viable hybrid offspring (in this case, the offspring are called *ligers*). Other species, such as chimpanzees and gorillas, cannot interbreed. There is a time dimension to the definition of the term *species:* Closely related species, while morphologically distinct, may be able to interbreed, while more distantly related species may not.

gene pool—the shared genetic makeup of a population.

60

The fact that some species can interbreed complicates a simple definition of genetic populations or gene pools. There is no easy resolution to this problem of definition. We do know, however, that over time, barriers to reproduction increase. These barriers, or **reproductive isolating mechanisms,** may be of different kinds, from genetic (two species may have different numbers of chromosomes) to behavioral (two species may have different mating rituals).

For purposes of defining the genetic limits of a population, some species, like humans, have such extensive geographic ranges that they should be viewed as having many geographical subdivisions that define *local* populations, or demes. A **deme** is a local population within which gene flow is common among members and outside of which gene flow is limited. The precise definition of a population, therefore, depends upon the genetic cohesiveness of its members and may or may not be synonymous with the term *species*. Because a population is a group of interbreeding individuals that is located in a definable space, each population has a specific genetic profile described by noting percentages or frequencies of alleles.

reproductive isolating mechanisms—genetic separation of populations by geography, ecology, behavior, physiology, or anatomy.

deme—a population within which there is a high degree of gene exchange.

mean—the statistical average of a measurement of a population.

HOW INDIVIDUALS WITHIN POPULATIONS VARY

Individuals within a population vary for any trait or characteristic (Figure 3–1). This variation may be described by using the concept of the **mean:** a statistical measure of the average for any trait in the population. But no single individual in the population will exhibit the mean for all traits. Individual "A" may be average for height, but his hair and eye color may be lighter than the mean. Individual "B" may be average for eye color

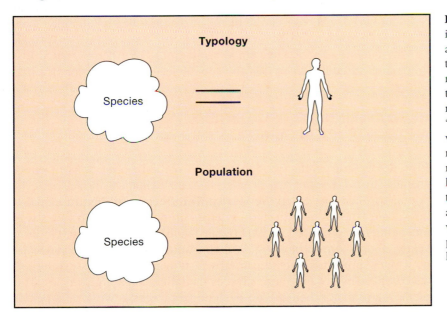

Figure 3–1 • Two ways of looking at species: the "typological" approach (top), which results in the choice of an ideal type to represent the species, and tends to underestimate or ignore normal population variation; and the "population" approach (bottom), which recognizes a statistical range of variability around a mean for any trait within a population. Modern biologists and anthropologists use the latter approach because it conforms with our current understanding of population genetics and morphological variation within species.

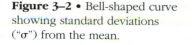

Figure 3–2 • Bell-shaped curve showing standard deviations ("σ") from the mean.

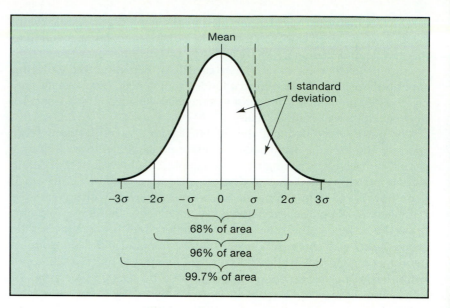

standard deviation–in statistics, a measure of variance about the mean within any population; defined as the square root of the average of the squares of the deviations from the mean.

Hardy-Weinberg equilibrium– a hypothetical condition in which there is no selection or other forces of evolution acting on a population and in which gene and genotype frequencies stay the same from one generation to the next. For two alleles at one locus, alleles p + alleles q = 100%.

but taller and with darker hair than the mean. Perhaps even more important than the average is the amount and range of variation within each characteristic. Range is the limit to which a characteristic can be expressed. For example, average human height is about 5.75 feet, but the range in height for normal adults is from about 4.5 feet to more than 7 feet. To quantify the amount of variation for a single characteristic or trait, the **standard deviation** is used, defined as the extent of the observations found on either side of the mean. In a normal, bell-shaped curve (Figure 3–2), 68% of the individuals measured for a trait will lie within one standard deviation from the mean, and almost 95% of all individuals will lie within two standard deviations.

New genetic methodologies and techniques have demonstrated just how much variability there is at the genetic level in natural populations.

HARDY-WEINBERG EQUILIBRIUM AND POPULATION GENETICS

How do the forces of evolution work in natural populations to effect changes in the frequencies of alleles? A mathematical model basic to population genetics called the **Hardy-Weinberg equilibrium** explains how alleles should be expected to behave in populations. This idea was independently proposed in 1908 by an English mathematician, Godfrey Hardy, and a German biologist, Wilhelm Weinberg. The model shows us how to test predictions about natural selection and how to assess the relative importance of the various forces that affect allele frequencies. The model states that if there are no evolutionary forces at work on a particular gene under study, the frequency of the alleles of that gene will remain the same, generation after generation. By definition, a population in Hardy-Weinberg equilibrium is not evolving. Therefore, any observed changes in allele frequencies are clues that one or more evolutionary force is responsible. Determination of evolutionary change is based on the comparison of expected allele frequencies in Hardy-Weinberg equilibrium to what is actually observed and measured in nature.

The Hardy-Weinberg model is based on several assumptions about the evolutionary forces that might affect equilibrium. The first assumption is that individuals in the population must mate randomly for any particular characteristic. This is true, for example, in the case of blood types, because most people are unaware of what blood type (A, B, or O) their prospective mate might have. It is not true, however, for all characteristics. For example, height is one trait that individuals might use as a criterion in choosing a mate; that is, taller individuals might favor taller mates.

The second assumption concerns the size of the population. This assumption can be stated as follows: The smaller the population, the greater the probability that chance factors or **sampling error** will occur. Because sampling error in small populations can cause results that deviate from what is expected under the Hardy-Weinberg equilibrium, this factor must be taken into consideration.

The third assumption concerns mutations. If the rate of a mutation from *A* to *a* is recurrent and continuous, eventually all the *A* alleles will mutate to *a*. Because all mutations are chance events, it is just as likely that the same allele *a* could show a reverse mutation to *A*. Under these circumstances an equilibrium will be reached if the losses of *A* by mutation to *a* are balanced by the gains from *a* to *A*. When such an equilibrium is reached for any single gene, the frequency of mutation does not affect the Hardy-Weinberg model. In actuality, the frequency of mutation is usually so low that, even without equilibrium, Hardy-Weinberg frequencies are not affected.

The fourth assumption relates to a shift in population numbers caused by immigration or emigration. These movements of individuals may result in a shift in allele frequencies. If a population is large, the effect of shifts in its membership may not affect Hardy-Weinberg frequencies. However, small populations can certainly be affected.

The following example will demonstrate how the Hardy-Weinberg model can be used to show that evolutionary change is occurring. By examining a small population of individuals who live in a village in Kenya we might discover that a number of individuals show symptoms of a disease called sickle-cell anemia. Sickle-cell anemia is a malformation of the red blood cells that, as a heterozygous trait (*AS*), protects individuals against endemic malaria, but that, as a homozygous recessive (*SS*), can result in death (Figure 3–3). Sickle-cell anemia results from a single base substitution in one codon on the DNA molecule affecting the beta chain of hemoglobin. This base substitution changes the amino acid

sampling error—the degree that a sample of a population misrepresents or is not reflective of the composition in some trait of a larger population because of chance.

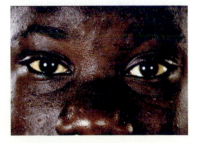

Figure 3–3 • An individual with sickle-cell anemia.

at position number 6 (from glutamic acid to valine), which in turn, produces a defective hemoglobin *S* (Figure 3–4).

In examining the hemoglobin type of 100 individuals of this African sample, exactly four individuals have sickle-cell disease; 64 individuals have normal hemoglobin, and 32 individuals are found to have both hemoglobin alleles, *A* and *S*. In this example, observed genotype frequencies are calculated to be 64% *AA,* 32% *AS,* and 4% *SS*. The sum of these is 100% or 1.0.

The frequencies of the genotypes in the population have been determined by directly counting the individuals. To calculate the allele frequencies in the population, first count the number of alleles in the various genotypes and total the *A* alleles and the *S* alleles. Totaling all the hemoglobin alleles for 100 people, there will be 200 alleles (as each person has two alleles). By calculation, four *SS* individuals have 8 *S* (4 × 2) alleles; 32 *AS* individuals have 32 *A* and 32 *S* alleles; and 64 *AA* homozygotes have 128 *A* (64 × 2) alleles. In total there are 40 *S* alleles (8 + 32) and 160 *A* alleles (128 + 32). The frequencies of the 200 total alleles are *A* = (160/200) 0.8 or 80% and *S* = (40/200) 0.2 or 20%.

Given these actual allele frequencies, the expected genotype frequencies can be calculated based on Hardy-Weinberg expectations, to see if this Kenyan population is undergoing evolution. The following equation for Hardy-Weinberg equilibrium is used: $p^2 + 2pq + q^2 = 1$, in which p equals the frequency of allele *A* and q equals the frequency of allele *S*,

$$p^2 = (.8)^2 = .64 \text{ (frequency of } AA \text{ genotype)}$$
$$2pq = 2(.2)(.8) = .32 \text{ (frequency of } AS \text{ genotype)}$$
$$\text{and } q^2 = (.2)^2 = .04 \text{ (frequency of } SS \text{ sickle-cell genotype)},$$

which again totals 1.0. In this example, the expected genotype frequencies are exactly the frequencies originally observed and counted in the population. The assumptions of Hardy-Weinberg have been met, the population is in equilibrium, and thus, no evolutionary change is occurring.

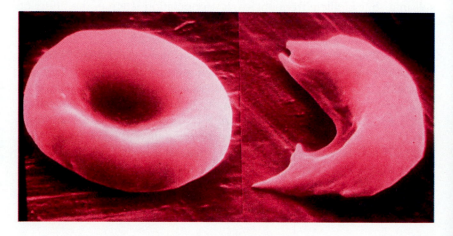

Figure 3–4 • Normal (left) and sickle-cell (right) red blood cells.

If the expected genotype frequencies do not come out the same as those originally observed, one of the assumptions of the Hardy-Weinberg model has been violated. Under such circumstances an investigation is needed to determine, for example, whether or not matings in the population were really random. The fact that a small population was sampled might also affect the calculations. Or, perhaps, natural selection may have been acting to remove unfit genotypes from this population. It is just such a deviation from expectation that allows us to pinpoint evolution in action. These forces that affect Hardy-Weinberg equilibrium will now be examined in greater detail.

Mutation

When considered gene by gene, mutations are rare in human populations. It is estimated that new mutations occur in 1 in 10,000 (1×10^{-4}) to 1 in 1,000,000 (1×10^{-6}) per allele per generation. In the entire population between 1% to 2% of new births may show genetic abnormalities. Table 3–1 lists some common human diseases caused by mutations and their estimated mutation rates. Today some 2,000 different genetic diseases have been catalogued. Given the number of human genes, many of us probably are born with new mutations, all of which contribute to population genetic variability.

Table 3–1 • Mutant Traits Caused by Single Gene Mutations

Mutant Trait	Appears Once in Each	Mutation Frequency per Million
Dominant		
Pelger anomaly (abnormal white blood cells; reduces resistance to disease)	12,500 gametes	80
Chondrodystrophic dwarfism (shortened and deformed legs and arms)	23,000 gametes	42
Retinoblastoma (tumors on retina of eye)	43,500 gametes	23
Anirida (absence of iris)	200,000 gametes	5
Epiloia (red lesions on face; later tumors in brain, kidney, heart, etc.)	83,000 gametes	12
Recessive Autosomal		
Albinism (melanin does not form in skin, hair, and iris)	37,700 gametes	28
Amaurotic idiocy (Infantile) (deterioration of mental ability during first months of life)	90,900 gametes	11
Total colorblindness	35,700 gametes	28
Recessive X-linked		
Hemophilia	31,250 gametes	32

From Winchester (1972).

Gene mutations, as opposed to chromosomal mutations, are changes in the DNA base sequence. If a mutation is lethal before the age of reproduction, then it never increases in frequency in the population, causing the death of its carrier before it has a chance of being passed on. However, not all mutations are lethal. They run the gamut from lethal to detrimental to neutral to, in rare cases, beneficial. Mutations as a force in evolution are the ultimate source of new genetic material, and they alter the Hardy-Weinberg equilibrium by automatically changing gene frequencies with the input of new alleles.

Mutations that are "invisible" to selection are known as *neutral mutations*. New neutral mutations can, over time, replace original alleles simply by chance, although this occurs at a much slower rate than if selection had affected replacement. The rate at which a mutant substitution occurs, and the rate of fixation of that mutant allele, determine whether and how rapidly a mutation will become fixed in a population.

The rate of substitution of neutral mutations within a population appears to be fairly uniform. This rate, termed K, is defined as the long-term average of mutants that are substituted in a population per locus per unit time. For the hemoglobin molecule the observed rate of amino acid substitution is close to 10^9 amino acid sites per year. K is independent of the size of the population involved. It is simply a function of the rate of occurrence of the mutation.

This rate is different from the rate at which a single mutation increases its frequency in a population or the amount of time that it actually takes for one mutation to fix itself by chance. Having more than one mutation present in a population will raise the odds that this particular mutation will ultimately become fixed. The time it will take for fixation by chance is dependent only on population size. The equation $K = 4N_e$ describes this situation. In a population of 10,000 (N_e), it will take 40,000 generations to fix a neutral mutation. On the other hand, if the rate of mutant substitution is the result of natural selection, then fixing a mutation with a selective advantage may be expressed by $K = 4(\mu)(S)(N_e)$, where μ is the mutation rate and S is the selective advantage. For the same population of 10,000 individuals, a mutation rate of 10^{-7} exists and a selective advantage of 0.2, $K = 0.8 \times 10^{-3}$ substitutions per generation. In this case the mutation would be fixed in only about 1,000 generations (Figure 3–5).

Inbreeding

inbreeding–the increased incidence of mating within a deme or population that results in an increase in homozygosity within the population.

Mating between individuals who are genetically related is called **inbreeding.** In humans, culture and social customs, such as incest rules or taboos, place restrictions on inbreeding. Some human groups have sanctioned inbreeding as a method of maintaining the "purity" of a particular lineage. For example, in dynastic Egypt, inbreeding in the royal family, even between brother and sister, was encouraged in an attempt to preserve "pure" bloodlines. The important result of inbreeding is an increase

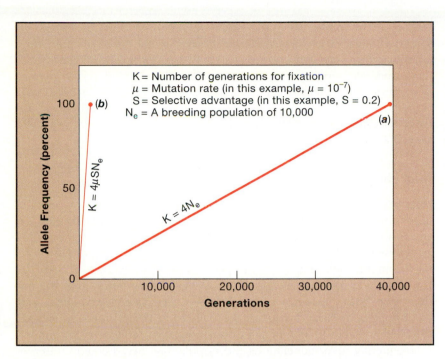

K = Number of generations for fixation
μ = Mutation rate (in this example, $\mu = 10^{-7}$)
S = Selective advantage (in this example, S = 0.2)
N_e = A breeding population of 10,000

(b)

$K = 4\mu SN_e$

$K = 4N_e$

(a)

Allele Frequency (percent)

Generations

Figure 3–5 • (*a*) Fixation of a neutral mutation by chance depends only on effective population number, in this case 10,000 breeding individuals. (*b*) Fixation by natural selection depends on the selective advantage of the mutant allele and the rate of mutation, as well as the effective population number.

in the level of homozygosity in the population. Because inbreeding is a form of nonrandom mating, it alters genotype frequency, which affects the Hardy-Weinberg equilibrium.

Inbreeding affects a population in other ways besides increasing homozygosity. For example, if a recessive deleterious allele is present in both mates, their offspring have a one in four chance of having a disease caused by the homozygous condition. In a randomly mating population, however, the chance of incurring a recessive homozygous condition of this sort is probably no more than one in 10,000.

The consequences of inbreeding in a population can be shown by the following example. Initially, let two alleles be present in equal frequency (*A* and *a* both = .50). At Hardy-Weinberg equilibrium, one expects 0.25 *AA*, 0.5 *Aa*, and 0.25 *aa*. After one generation of inbreeding (*AA* × *AA*, *Aa* × *Aa*, and *aa* × *aa*), the frequency of genotypes becomes 0.375 *AA*, 0.25 *Aa*, and 0.375 *aa*, a decrease of 50% in the heterozygotes. In the second generation the frequency of heterozygotes decreases to 0.125, one-half of the previous generation. For each succeeding generation inbreeding lowers the frequency of the heterozygotes by one-half. Allele frequencies have not changed, however, remaining at 0.5 for both *A* and *a* alleles.

The rate of human inbreeding varies from one population to another, but is generally very low. The effects of inbreeding are noticeable in populations that are usually geographically remote or are isolates within a surrounding large population due to religious or cultural practices. For example, the Dunkers of Pennsylvania, a religious isolate descended from German immigrants in the nineteenth century, marry almost exclusively within their own community. Consequently, average inbreeding coefficients are high. In contrast, Arctic Eskimo populations, though remote and with small population sizes, have maintained a low level of population inbreeding because of cultural practices that prohibit marriage between closely related individuals. Population numbers of our early ancestors were probably quite small; inbreeding may well have played an important role in human evolution.

Migration

Migration is the movement of people, hence their genes, from one area to another. There are two extremes in migration. The first is an outward expansion of a population in which individuals reach an area that may be sparsely inhabited or perhaps even unoccupied. Although migrations may continue over time, at some point gene flow diminishes between the migrant and its parent population. As gene flow diminishes, the migrant population becomes increasingly distinct genetically from the parent population. New mutations occur in each population and natural selection operates to adapt each population to its separate environment. Consequently, over generations the populations may become different not only in terms of gene frequencies but also in terms of morphological characteristics (such as height, weight, and hair color). In all probability, such situations have taken place many times in human evolution. For example, the Neandertals in Europe were likely the result of populations that were partially isolated by the geography of Ice Age Europe.

The second extreme is when two populations come into contact. In this case, the result is eventual homogenization. Let us suppose that two populations originally differ in terms of allele frequencies. As one migrates into the geographical range of the other and mating takes place between them, the gene pools of each population become less different as genes are shared by both groups. When mating becomes completely random the populations eventually fuse into one group.

An example of homogenization in progress can be seen in the United States between Americans of European ancestry and Americans of African ancestry. Mainly between the years 1619 and 1808, Africans, primarily from West Africa, were brought to America as indentured servants and slaves. The genetic composition of the present African-American population is different from that of the ancestral population, the result of admixture with European-Americans over some 350 years. The presence of European alleles in African-Americans indicates gene flow. For example, today the frequency of sickle-cell anemia among African-Americans is about 10%, compared with about 22% estimated to be the frequency among individuals of the founder African population brought to this country. This reduction in the frequency of this trait can be partly accounted for by gene exchange with other groups of Americans. In addition, natural selection has worked to eliminate this gene in America, a nonmalarial environment, through selection against the *SS* homozygote.

migration—the movement of a reproductively active individual into a population from a distant population, thus bringing new genes into that population.

Chance Sampling

Sometimes change in the frequency of alleles occurs by chance. How rapidly such changes occur depends on the size of the population. The chance that an allele becomes fixed in a population rather than lost through the process of genetic drift is related to how frequent that allele is in the population. The rarer the allele, the more likely that it will become lost. Given an original population with two alleles in equal frequency, the chance that one will replace the other is 50%. If the original frequencies of the alleles are not equal, their chances of becoming fixed in the population are the same as their frequencies. For example, if A is at 90% and a is at 10%, then A has a 90% chance of becoming fixed in the population and a has a 10% chance. Change by chance is called **genetic drift.** Genetic drift is not consistent from generation to generation as is the case with natural selection, since the rate can fluctuate, producing higher frequencies in one generation and lower frequencies in a succeeding one. Change, in other words, is erratic.

One special case of genetic drift is called the **founder effect.** In this situation, colonization of an isolated area by a small number of individuals determines the genetic characteristics of a new population. Small founding populations usually possess allele frequencies that are quite different from those of the parent population. The causes of this difference are twofold. First, imagine a small group setting out to inhabit an isolated South Pacific atoll or an isolated African valley (Figure 3–6). The small group of founders of perhaps 25 individuals would not by chance exactly represent the genetic complement of the larger population to which they belonged. They would not have the same frequencies of alleles, and even whole alleles might be absent. The 25 individuals, thus, represent only a sampling of the larger group.

genetic drift—gene frequency changes due to chance effects, not affected by selection; most common in small population sizes.

founder effect—a type of genetic drift caused by sampling a small amount of genetic variation from the original population in a group of individuals colonizing a new area.

Figure 3–6 • An example of the founder effect: syndactyly, the genetically inherited "lobster claw" deformity frequently found in this isolated African population near the Mozambique–Zimbabwe border, traceable to one group of immigrant ancestors.

Deleterious mutations can become common in small populations by inbreeding, or by selection favoring their position in heterozygote combinations, as in the case of the sickle-cell anemia example. The following two cases are found in different human populations, apparently introduced by a small group or a single founder and increased to unexpectedly high frequencies.

The first example concerns a rare dominant trait associated with the degeneration of the central nervous system called *Huntington's chorea*. This allele has been located on a specific chromosome, allowing for early detection in individuals who may carry it. Previously the only way to detect the gene was to observe the onset of symptoms, which usually occurred in individuals at about 30 years of age. The first appearance of chorea, or dancelike jerking motions of the limbs, usually meant death for those individuals who displayed it, yet unfortunately at the age where the disease could be detected many individuals had already passed it on to their offspring. In many populations around the world the frequency of the heterozygote through which the dominant allele expresses itself is about 1/10,000. However, in Tasmania, a state of 350,000 people, there are 120 cases of this disease, or about 1/3,000. The spread and higher frequency of this condition is no doubt part of an effect of inbreeding within a small population. Researchers have determined that the dominant allele for Huntington's chorea was brought to Tasmania by one woman who immigrated there in 1848.

The second example concerns a disorder called *phenylketonuria* (PKU). Recessive alleles in the homozygous state result in a deficiency of an enzyme, phenylalanine hydroxylase. As a consequence, the amino acid phenylalanine accumulates in the bloodstream and ultimately causes mental retardation. A diet low in phenylalanine, however, can alleviate the symptoms.

The incidence of PKU varies among different populations. The Japanese reportedly have the lowest rate (1 in every 60,000 newborns), whereas Caucasians are affected on the order of 1 in 15,000. The highest incidence of PKU, about 1 in 5,000, occurs in Ireland and western Scotland and among Jews of Yemenite origin living in Israel. Although researchers have identified about 20 different mutations that can cause PKU, suspicion was that only one mutation was responsible for the cases involving the Yemenite Jews because their population of only 250,000 was so small. By retracing Jewish history, genealogist Yosef Shiloh of Tel Aviv University was able to determine that all of the present carriers of the allele descended from individuals who had lived in a single village, San'a in Yemen, until at least the late seventeenth century. This mutation must have arisen in a single individual sometime before that time and was later spread in other parts of Yemen and finally to Israel (Figure 3–7). The high frequency of this allele is a curious genetic anomaly and suggests a selectively advantageous situation for the heterozygote carriers. There is some evidence to suggest that a different mutation for PKU in Irish and Scottish women may result in lower rates of spontaneous abortion (Wright, 1990).

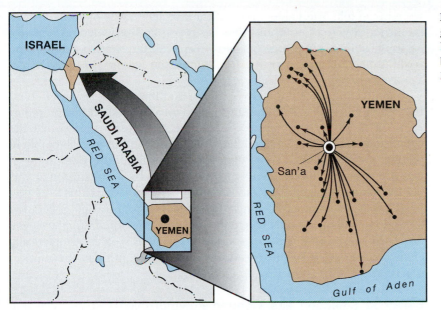

Figure 3–7 • The spread by migration of PKU from Yemen to Israel. (Adapted from an illustration by Ian Warpole, © 1990 *Discover* Magazine.)

HOW EVOLUTION CHANGES POPULATION ALLELE FREQUENCIES

Selection

Natural selection is the mechanism by which a population becomes better adapted to its environment over time. For natural selection to work, the adaptations must be at the genetic level so that they can be passed on to offspring. Those individuals who are more "fit" leave more offspring on average than do less "fit" individuals. **Fitness** is defined as the percentage of offspring a genotype has, relative to the number of offspring of the maximally fit genotype in the population. Fitness values for a population relate to a specific point in time for a specified environment. Fitness of specific genotypes may change over time as a result of changes in the environment.

fitness–the extent to which the genes of an individual survive in its descendants.

directional selection–selection that acts to move the mean of a population in one particular direction.

Directional Selection   **Directional selection** provides a typical example of natural selection in which a given genotype is favored among individuals, eventually becoming homozygous for the favored allele. One of the best examples of directional selection was witnessed in a population of the English peppered moth, *Biston betularia* (Figure 3–8). All of the individuals in the population were colored in a light gray variegated pattern. However, suddenly in 1848 a very dark-colored form of the moth appeared, over the years gradually increased in frequency to greater than 90%, and spread throughout England. The biologist H. Kettlewell studied this phenomenally rapid change in the moth population. He noted that the first dark-colored moths occurred at about the same time that major environmental effects of the British industrial revolution

Figure 3–8 • The English peppered moth (*Biston betularia*) shown in light and dark gray variants.

were being felt. The lighter color of the original moths blended in with the lichen-covered tree trunks they rested on and provided an effective camouflage from bird predators. However, with the sooty pollution from coal-burning factories covering tree trunks, the lighter moths stood out against the darker background.

Experimenting with this hypothesis, Kettlewell released different-colored moths in polluted and unpolluted areas, and then recaptured as many of them as possible at a later time. He demonstrated that the lighter gray moths in sooty polluted conditions were more vulnerable to predation by birds than were dark moths. Further work demonstrated that the new dark moth phenotype was caused by a mutation that was dominant to the "gray color" allele, and under the conditions of a polluted, sooty environment it quickly became favored. In one generation of random mating, a rapid change in gene and genotype frequencies will occur. In only a few generations, the gray allele would be practically eliminated. Because of decreased levels of pollution today the proportion of gray moths is once again increasing.

Balanced Selection and Genetic Polymorphism   When selection acts to favor alleles only when they occur in certain combinations, genetic diversity is maintained in the population. This balancing of selection both for and against certain alleles is termed **genetic polymorphism.** In the example of sickle-cell anemia, *AS* individuals may be less prone to disease in an environment where malaria is prevalent. If individuals move away from this environment or if the environment is changed through the eradication of mosquitoes that carry the malarial parasite, *AS* individuals lose their selective advantage. They suffer from the effects of the sickle-cell allele itself, whereas *AA* individuals do not.

In Figure 3–9 we show how the sickle-cell allele is maintained over time in a malarial environment. If we start out with an initial structured population of 100 people with 80% having genotypes *AA* and 20% having genotypes *AS,* the allele frequencies are *A* = 0.9 and *S* = 0.1. Given random mating by the parental population, after only one generation of selection 10% of the *AA* population die of malaria, leaving only 73 new *AA* individuals. Eighteen people who have the *AS* genotype are protected. However, we lose one individual (a lethal *SS*) who was produced from the mating between *AS* people. We now have 91 survivors, but the allele frequencies have not changed from the original population and remain 0.9 and 0.1 for *A* and *S,* respectively. What *has* happened is that, whereas some people die of malaria, more of the sickle-cell disease people live than would be expected, because of the effects of the *S* gene in the population. Everything else being equal, allele frequencies would not change from generation to generation. What has changed is the total number of people in the population. With malaria, 91 survive when the *S* gene is in the population. If the population existed in a malarial environment and *S* alleles were not present, only 90 people would survive, because the fitness of the *AA* individual is still equal to 0.9. So the population is better off with the sickle-cell gene than without it, even though

genetic polymorphism—the existence of two or more genetic variants within a population; can be a balanced polymorphism when selection favors the heterozygotes, as in sickle-cell anemia.

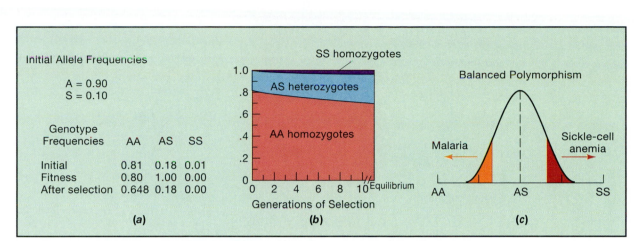

Figure 3–9 • Diagrammatic representation of how selection acts in relation to the sickle-cell trait on a population living in a malarial environment: (*a*) calculation of allele frequencies *A* and *S* after one generation of selection, (*b*) graph of allele frequencies *A* and *S* carried to 10 generations (equilibrium), and (*c*) graph showing proportions of the population (shaded areas) who do not survive because of malaria or sickle-cell anemia.

the *SS* genotype is lethal. The net result of this system is to keep both alleles present in the population so long as conditions do not change.

Average Population Fitness   Because natural selection operates for or against a specific genotype in a population, the net outcome is the removal of unfavorable alleles. If this process continues long enough and the environment does not change, homozygosity in the population increases, to the point that all individuals become homozygous for the loci favored by selection. However, unfavored alleles are never completely eliminated from a population. The average fitness of the population increases as the number of unfavored alleles decreases (Figure 3–10).

In some cases, such as with balanced polymorphisms, selection acts to maintain heterozygosity. Although the effect of this heterozygosity may be to lower the overall fitness of the population, it also serves to increase the genetic variability of the population. This variation may be very important to the future of any population when environmental conditions change and new selection comes into play on the population. A population with little genetic variation to call upon faces the possibility of extinction.

How Microevolution Leads to Macroevolution

Evolution is defined as genetic change in a population over time. **Microevolution** describes small-scale genetic changes, ones that occur over a few generations. Microevolutionary change occurs within the confines of a single species, resulting in a shift in percentages of alleles and of morphological characters. The change in coloration of the English peppered moth is an example of microevolutionary change. Microevolutionary change begins the process by which populations diverge from

microevolution—small-scale change in gene frequencies or other biological traits in a population or species over a relatively brief period of time.

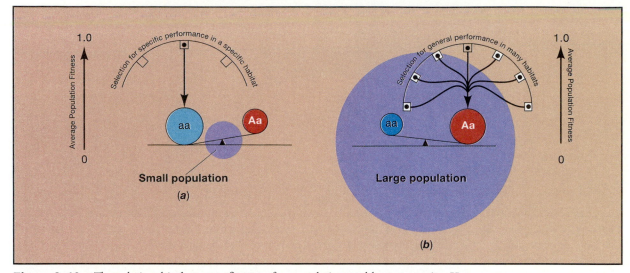

Figure 3–10 • The relationship between fitness of a population and homozygosity. Heterozygosity decreases average population fitness but increases the population's variability and consequent future ability to respond to new selection pressures. In small marginal populations (*a*), selection favors the homozygote and leads to the fixation of specific adaptive features. In large populations (*b*), the scale usually tips in favor of the heterozygote but suffers from decreased average population fitness because homozygotes, which are less fit than the heterozygotes, are continually produced.

one another, which can ultimately lead to the formation of new species. **Macroevolution** is long-term, producing changes that result in new species over time.

HOW NEW SPECIES ARE FORMED

Macroevolutionary change results in *speciation,* the process by which new biological species form. There are essentially two competing theories of speciation. First, Darwin clearly believed that macroevolution is essentially microevolution extended over long periods of geologic time. Small changes over time gradually accumulate to constitute the large changes that ultimately distinguish new species from older ones. This process, known as **phyletic gradualism,** was criticized by scientists who saw what they considered too many "gaps" in the fossil record.

The concept of sudden "jumps" or "leaps" in evolution spawned the second theory, which was outlined by the geneticist Richard Goldschmidt in an attempt to reconcile the sporadic fossil record with modern genetic theory. He suggested that large-scale mutation could cause such jumps in evolution. Paleontologist George Gaylord Simpson (1944) argued that gaps at the level of the species could probably be accounted for as byproducts of incomplete or poor fossil preservation. Yet he was concerned about the gaps that existed between the higher taxa. As a

macroevolution–large-scale change in gene frequencies or other biological traits in a species or higher level taxonomic grouping, generally over a relatively long period of time.

phyletic gradualism–term coined by Stephen J. Gould to characterize Darwin's idea of evolutionary rate; slow, gradual change over long periods of time.

consequence, he developed the concept of **quantum evolution** that could explain how some populations rapidly shifted in their adaptations. In terms of geologic time, such leaps could be so rapid that the chance of finding an intermediate fossil form that reflected these shifts would be quite slim.

Though the predominant viewpoint concerning the rate of evolutionary change leaned towards the gradualistic model, the idea of rapid leaps continued. Stephen J. Gould and Niles Eldredge (1993) promoted the idea that short bursts of change might periodically occur. This they labeled **punctuated equilibrium.** They argued that most species exhibit little or no change throughout most of their evolutionary history (stasis), and that adaptive change (punctuation) is a relatively rare, rapid event, rather than a gradual process. Such change would only occur during speciation.

EVOLUTION OF BEHAVIOR

In the first part of this chapter we have investigated the relationship between genetics and morphological and physiological variation as observed among different individuals in a population. In this final section we want to explore what effects genetics can play on behavior. Behavior is a major component of individual fitness. For example, an animal that uses its cunning skills is just as likely (perhaps more so) to acquire a mate than an animal whose large size is its only advantage. Adaptive behaviors have a positive selective value and, thus, are likely to have a genetic component that enables these behaviors to be passed on to new generations. As different behaviors emerge as important facets of a species adaptation, they become an integral part of a species biology, closely bound to its genetic endowment. Although Darwin is most remembered for observing physical characteristics in his formulation of natural selection, he is also responsible for placing animal behavior in an evolutionary context. In his book *The Expression of the Emotions in Man and Animals* (1872:12), Darwin showed that there were continuities between animal and human behavior, implying a common inherited basis. He concluded that behavioral traits as well as physical traits were subject to evolution.

Behavior can be defined as patterns of activity through time. This definition allows scientists to measure and compare behavior between individuals in different species. Understanding how animals interact in social groups is also an important aspect of the study of behavior, because humans and most other primates are highly social species.

Sexual Selection

Charles Darwin in his second major book, *The Descent of Man and Selection with Respect to Sex* (1871), elaborated on the concept of **sexual selection.** Sexual selection is based on two levels of selection. The first

quantum evolution—stepwise evolutionary change.

punctuated equilibrium—term coined by Stephen J. Gould and Niles Eldredge to characterize evolution typified by long periods of little or no change (stasis) interrupted by bursts of rapid change (punctuational events).

sexual selection—selection within a species based on mate choice or competition within the species, usually between males.

sexual dimorphism–presence of two distinctly different forms of male and female individuals in a species.

is competition for mates, occurring among adult members of each sex—in other words, male versus male and female versus female. The second is based on mate choice. In most vertebrates it is generally the female who is more selective, choosing whomever she considers the best available male.

Darwin noted that sexual selection can result in the evolution of two sexes, the adults, who can differ from one another substantially in their external morphology, a condition known as **sexual dimorphism** (Latin, meaning "two-bodied") (Figure 3–11). Sexually dimorphic secondary sex characteristics may be simultaneously threatening to rivals and attractive to potential mates. Darwin also noted the paradoxical situation in which characteristics that are advantageous in competition with one's rival may be very disadvantageous when it comes to the basic issues of survival. For example, male–male aggression, which occurs during the mating season in many species of prosimian primates, such as lemurs (Figure 3–12), often results in the severe wounding of both contestants. But because the chance, however small, of a male's mating with a receptive female is overpowering, virtually all of the males engage in this sort of combat. Larger body size and elaborate coloration of the pelage usually differentiate male from female morphologies in primates as well as in many other kinds of animals, because much of male–male competition depends upon aggressive display.

As Helena Cronin (1992:286) describes the situation:

> If you were asked to invent an irksome challenge to Darwinian theory, you could get a long way with a peacock's tail. And if you were asked to think up a solution to the challenge that would disconcert Darwinians, you would need to go no further than Charles Darwin's own theory of sexual selection . . . (Natural selection) should abhor the peacock's tail—gaudy, ornamental, a burden to its bearer. Darwin took the view that natural selection would indeed frown upon such flamboyance. It had been concocted, he decided, by female preference.

Thus, the "good taste" theory of female choice was born; females choose their mates on aesthetic grounds; male ornamentation developed to

Figure 3–11 • Sexual dimorphism in mandrills and in human beings.

Figure 3–12 • Ring-tailed lemur males fighting during the mating season.

charm the females and "for no other purpose" (Darwin, 1871:92). Reactions to this idea developed into two different viewpoints. First was the idea that sexual selection was, in reality, unimportant and that gaudy ornamentation could be explained in terms of natural selection, having significance in warning, territorial or threat display.

The second viewpoint announced the arrival of "good sense" female choice. In this case females choose their mates on the basis of male vigor, good health, and territory size; in other words, these were sensible choices to make. The fact that one embellishment is chosen over another is arbitrary. The characteristic, itself, is unimportant. What is important is that at one time a preference for some characteristic was made and it became reinforced and elaborated in a positive feedback loop. Once preference for, let us say, gaudy-colored tails was established, then it was "good sense" for females to continue to make choices for mates on that basis, as all other females would be doing the same.

Sexual selection can lead both to the evolution of behavioral responses, or strategies, and to physical traits. The female reproductive strategy has the primary goal of protecting her offspring, and may include prolonging the period of sexual receptivity, aggression against competitors, which may involve the harassment and killing of the offspring of others, and the suppression of sexual receptivity in subordinate females. Females may also compete directly for resources necessary for producing and nurturing their offspring, and for attracting the highest ranking males that they can.

Males, on the other hand, may compete through a variety of behaviors that include guarding of territory, dominating other animals, and guarding of females. Other responses, such as "nuptial feeding," or bringing food to sexually receptive females, may be part of a reproductive strategy important in the evolution of our own lineage (Parker, 1987).

ethology–naturalistic study of animal behavior and its evolution.

Trivers (1972) has argued that differences in male and female reproductive strategies may be accounted for by the investment each parent makes in their offspring. Females usually invest more of their time and energy in a smaller number of offspring and are more selective in their choice of mates. Males, conversely, increase their reproductive success by producing more offspring by mating with as many females as they can.

Ethology

Scientists have realized that behavior evolves to allow a species to adapt effectively to a particular ecological niche. To study behavioral adaptations of a particular species, the animal should be studied in its natural habitat. **Ethology** is the biological study of animal behavior that deals with species-specific or genetically linked behavior (Lorenz, 1965). Ethologists recognize the value of observing behavior in its entirety within an environmental context, because only under these circumstances can the evolution of behavior patterns be fully comprehended (Eibl-Eibesfeldt, 1989).

A species' characteristic physical features develop within certain limits, through an interaction of the genotype with the environment. In a similar manner, a species' behavior—how individuals acquire food, how they interact with other members of the species, how they avoid danger, how they reproduce, and how they raise their young—is also a result of genetic development within a range of appropriate environments. As the ethologist Konrad Lorenz (1965b:xii; Figure 3–13) has noted, "behavior patterns are just as conservatively and reliably characters of species as are the forms of bones, teeth, or any other bodily structures." However, the scientific study of behavior and its evolution is a relatively new field, and many of the interactions of behavior, genetics, and environment are yet to be investigated.

Ethology as a field began with Darwin, who first treated behavior in the same evolutionary context as anatomical structure and physiology. He stated (1872:350), "that the chief expressive actions, exhibited by man and the lower animals, are now innate or inherited,—that is, have not been learnt by the individual,—is admitted by every one." Although this tenet may have been generally accepted during Darwin's time, the rise of experimental psychology and ethology with their emphases on learned behavior did not allow ethology to progress until well into the twentieth century.

Much of human ethology deals with the nonverbal, nonlearned, and noncultural behavior we share with other animals. Anthropologist Sherwood Washburn once suggested that human ethology might be defined as the science that pretends humans cannot speak. Although he intended it as a critique, because much of human behavior *is* mediated, expressed, and even caused by linguistic cues, it is an apt description of a science that intends to study human behavior within an evolutionary context. To understand the roots of human behavior, one must look at the nonverbal behavioral commonalities that humans share with the animal world.

Figure 3–13 • Konrad Lorenz and his geese.

Ethologists seek to establish a behavioral profile or **ethogram** of a species—a catalogue of all the behavior patterns of an animal. In practice this is difficult. What is a "behavior pattern"? What are the basic units of behavior to be catalogued? If ethology is indeed a comparative science, what behaviors could be compared from one species to another? The first answer to these queries is behavior that is closely tied to genetics.

ethogram—the behavioral repertoire characteristic of a species.

fixed action pattern—inborn, genetically programmed behavior that is always released by the same stimuli and always shows the same sequence of actions.

Fixed Action Patterns

The ethologists Konrad Lorenz and Niko Tinbergen discovered in 1938 that animal species have what they termed "inherited coordination." In more recent literature, **fixed action pattern** (FAP) has replaced the earlier term. Fixed action patterns are behaviors that (1) are *form-constant*—each instance that they are expressed, the same muscles contract and the animal moves in the same sequence; (2) appear spontaneously during development, requiring no learning; (3) are characteristic of all members of the species; (4) cannot be unlearned; and (5) are released or caused by a particular stimulus, external environmental condition or internal physiological environment of the animal. Numerous cases of FAPs are now known from observations of insects, birds, fish, and other vertebrates (Figure 3–14).

A curious attribute of the FAP is that, once started, an FAP must complete execution, in computer-like fashion, regardless of any further environmental information. A greylag goose mother, for example, once she has seen a loose egg away from the nest and has gone to retrieve it, will always make the same beak movements to roll the egg back to the nest even if an ethologist surreptitiously takes the egg away before the goose gets to it! Because an egg almost never disappears from under the nose of a goose under normal circumstances, natural selection has produced this FAP in the species and it functions quite successfully. The ontogenic development of an FAP may, however, be affected by environmental conditions. For example, a rat mother seemingly is endowed with an FAP to groom and care for her pup, for she will do so even when she

Figure 3–14 • Fixed action patterns can be observed in a chameleon's unerring tongue capture of a flying insect; in a mother wren's placing of food in the open mouths of her nestlings; and in the vocal alarm calls of a ring-tailed lemur group, elicited by aerial movement of a bird of prey.

has been raised in isolation. If the mother is reared in isolation under the additional condition of wearing a collar that prevents her from grooming herself, then she will neglect and even abuse her offspring.

The disadvantage to FAP for solving behavioral problems is that they lack flexibility. An FAP may be ineffective as a behavioral strategy when a species is confronted with changing environmental conditions. Undoubtedly, this is one of the strong selective reasons for behavioral evolution leading to a preponderance of learned behavioral responses in mammals. Human fixed action patterns are discussed in Chapter 10.

 **SUMMARY**

1. Species are genetically distinct populations reproductively isolated from other species. By definition, viable offspring cannot be produced from matings between individuals of two species.
2. Species can be geographically subdivided into smaller breeding units called demes. Differences in allele frequencies between populations may be the result of a number of evolutionary processes such as selective mating practices, random genetic drift, and migrations, as well as natural selection.
3. Changes in allele frequencies in a single population over time can be determined from the Hardy-Weinberg equation. This equation states that if none of the evolutionary processes are operating on any given chromosomal locus, then whatever the allele frequencies are at that locus at that moment, they will remain the same until affected by some process later on. The assumptions for population equilibrium are: random mating practices are in effect, new mutations do not exceed the loss of existing ones, no population movements have occurred, and the population number is large enough to discount accidental or chance factors from playing a role in allele frequency shifts. Finally natural selection must be ruled out in that no single genotype is preferred over any other.
4. Neutral mutations are those that pass through the selective filter that deleterious or advantageous mutations must face. As neutral mutations may exist at any locus there is a chance that they can become the predominant allele and, subsequently, fixed in a population. Fixation by chance is always a slower process than fixation by natural selection. Inbreeding and genetic drift both act to increase homozygosity, which decreases variability in the gene pool.
5. Natural selection is a process by which a population over time becomes better adapted to its environment. Natural selection is based on individual fitness, which is a measure of reproductive success in a specified environment. Directional selection is selection favoring a particular genotype. Balanced selection favors the heterozygote genotype.
6. Microevolution is genetic change over time that occurs within a single species. Macroevolutionary change is change over longer periods of

time and involves the formation of new species from ancestral ones. New species arise from macroevolutionary change either by phyletic gradualism or by punctuated equilibrium.

7. Specific behaviors as well as specific morphologies can be favored by natural selection. The model of sexual selection accounts for certain kinds of sexually dimorphic behavioral as well as morphological patterns.

8. Ethology is the study of animal behavior that is programmed genetically. The fixed action pattern is the simplest kind of genetically programmed behavior that appears usually without much modification or flexibility as a result of specific stimuli perceived by the animal.

 ## CRITICAL-THINKING QUESTIONS

1. What are reproductive isolating mechanisms?
2. What are the assumptions of the Hardy-Weinberg equilibrium model?
3. Pick one example of the Hardy-Weinberg equilibrium that has been covered in this chapter and explain it.
4. Define macroevolution and microevolution; how do they affect speciation?
5. How has sexual selection affected individual morphology?
6. Describe the five criteria that are used in determining fixed action patterns.

 ## SUGGESTED READINGS

Dobzhansky, T. 1971. *Genetics of the Evolutionary Process*. New York: Columbia University Press. A review of the forces of natural selection by a pioneering geneticist.

Eibl-Eibesfeldt, I. 1989. *Human Ethology*. New York: Aldine De Gruyter. A text on the evolutionary aspects of human behavior.

Mayr, Ernst, and W. B. Provine (eds.). 1980. *The Evolutionary Synthesis: Perspectives on the Unification of Biology*. Cambridge, Mass.: Harvard University Press. Essays on the synthesis of genetics and organismal biology.

Provine, William B. 1986. *Evolution: Selected Papers by Sewall Wright*. Chicago: University of Chicago Press. A compendium of articles and reviews by one of the major contributors to the new evolutionary synthesis.

Simpson, George Gaylord. 1953. *The Major Features of Evolution*. New York: Columbia University Press. Still a classic presentation of the forces of evolution and how paleontology relates to evolutionary science.

Smith, John Maynard. 1978. *The Evolution of Sex*. Cambridge, England: Cambridge University Press. A general discussion of the evolution of sexual reproduction.

———. 1993. *The Theory of Evolution*. Cambridge, England: Cambridge University Press. A recent overview of current evolutionary thought by one of the major living evolutionists.

CHAPTER 4

Stages of Vertebrate Evolution

Humans are animals, just one of many species that inhabit the planet. We humans are intimately linked to the natural world by a network of ecological relationships with our environment and with species that are alive today, as well as with a unique and unbroken series of ancestors extending back to the primordial seas, to the beginnings of life itself (Figure 4–1). The very early stages of human evolution, when human ancestors could be called fish, amphibians, reptiles, and primitive mammals, constitute the subject of this chapter. How do we trace this ancestry?

HOMOLOGOUS STRUCTURES

There are no tombstones marking the graves of our long-lost mammal-like reptile forebears and no family genealogies of ancestral amphibians with which we can piece together our early family tree. Instead, we compare anatomical characteristics of living and fossil animals to discover ancestor–descendant relationships. Studies of molecular evolution also provide important data on relationships between animal species and their common ancestors, but only comparative anatomy and paleontology can fill in what the actual ancestral species may have looked like.

All anatomical traits that scientists use for studying the comparative evolutionary relationships of animals must be based on a common

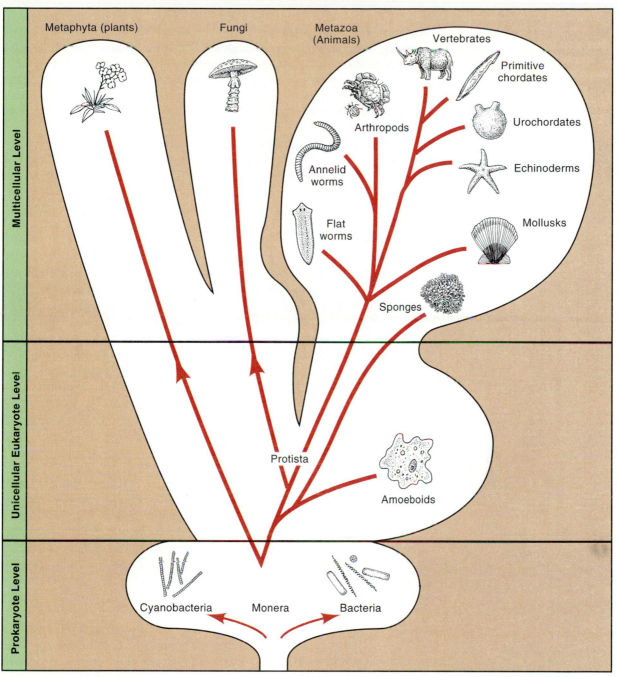

Figure 4–1 • Phylogeny of the animal kingdom.

genetic groundplan. In other words, they must be **homologous.** Evolutionary scientists determine whether structures are homologous by tracing their origins, both through the fossil record and through the embryological history of structures in modern species. Our third finger and fingernail, for example, are homologous to the foreleg and hoof of the modern horse. Horses have a documented loss of the side toes through evolution, whereas humans have retained the more primitive five-fingered hand. Some similar morphological features are not, however, homologous. The wings of birds and bats, for example, are not homologous. Bird wings developed from and are supported by the first finger of the hand skeleton, whereas bat wings are supported by the fourth finger. Birds and bats evolved independently from flightless wingless ancestors. Nonhomologous structures that are similar in external appearance but have evolved from different sources, like bird and bat wings, are called **analogous** structures.

Anatomical structures, such as limbs or eyes, are formed by the proliferation of cells that have become specialized by evolution to perform certain functions in the body. As we saw in the preceding chapters, individual cells of all eukaryotic organisms function and reproduce in the same way; that is, all eukaryotic organisms are alike on a cellular level. As we narrow our focus successively on the taxonomic groups to which the human species belongs, we see more and more commonalities in higher levels of cellular organization, in how the cells come together to form structures and perform functions.

CLUES FROM MORPHOLOGY, EMBRYOLOGY, AND PALEONTOLOGY

When cells of similar type proliferate they form **tissues,** groupings of cells of the same type, such as bone or muscle, that we can see with the naked eye. The morphology of tissues provides one of the most important, and traditionally the only, basis for taxonomic classification and evolutionary study of animal species. Although it is difficult to exactly reconstruct what an animal looked like while it was alive from its bony remains, a great deal can be determined by comparing bones of unknown origin to bones that are known to belong to specific animals. Through such comparisons, morphological patterns can be deduced by studying the origin and insertion (the attachment areas) of muscles and the shape of the bone itself, which may reflect the kind of locomotor behavior that particular animals exhibit. Long gracile (slender) limb bones, for example, in primates reflect a fast, leaping arboreal form of locomotion. In modern classification, genetics and behavioral characteristics can also be used. Fossils provide paleontological evidence of change through time. With fossils the evolutionary history of animals can be reconstructed by studying and interpreting the changes in homologous structures. In this

homologous—similar because of common descent or common inheritance.

analogous—similar because of adaptation for similar functions.

tissue—literally meaning "woven"; in anatomy referring to an aggregate of cells of the same type, which form a structural unit of the body.

chapter we will discuss the morphological basis for understanding human evolution.

Although biological anthropology focuses on primates generally and hominids specifically, there is little in the paleontological record to support an *anthropocentric* (Greek, meaning "human-centered") view of evolution. Many animal groups now extinct, like the dinosaurs, were larger, fleeter, more numerous, and ecologically dominant for much longer periods of time than hominids have been in existence. More often than not, ancestral hominids were far from the dominant members of the faunas of which they formed a part. The mistaken view that evolution has been a steady progression leading to our own species is termed **orthogenesis** (Greek, meaning "straight beginning"). To the contrary, a long and frequently tortuous chain of evolutionary events has led to our being here now.

THE CHORDATES

To understand our own anatomy, we must understand the anatomy of our earliest vertebrate ancestors. The first actively moving organisms—animals—appeared in the earth's seas sometime before 700 million years ago. Because these animals' bodies were soft, their remains were easily destroyed before they could become fossilized. The indications of animal life from this time consist of burrow trails left in the mud of shallow sea floors. Among the animals that made these tracks were the common ancestors of all other living and extinct animals. The first **chordates** must have evolved in the late Archean Era, about 580 million years ago, but the fossil record of this very ancient time is of little help in deciphering chordate beginnings.

Chordates are animals with a stiffened rod of **cartilage,** the *notochord* (Greek, meaning "back string") running down the middle of their backs. They also have nearby a *dorsal nerve cord* and a series of *branchial arches* ("gill" arches or the walls of tissue that separate gill clefts or slits). These characteristics are not necessarily found in adult chordates, but they do occur at some stage of an individual's development. We are chordates, and our most basic patterns of morphological organization have come down to us from our ancient chordate ancestors.

However, in the late Archean Era the dominant animal groups were nonchordates that had evolved the first skeletal elements. These were body coverings with a protective function, probably for defense against attack by predators or worms. Hard parts external to the body cavity, known as the **exoskeleton** (Latin, meaning "outside bony framework"), served as an anchor for muscles as well. Although an exoskeleton is an efficient adaptation for powerful movement, which we can observe today in such living arthropods as insects and crabs, it limits the size of a species. As the animal grows it must "molt," split out of its old exoskeleton and

orthogenesis—mistaken view of evolutionary change always proceeding in a "straight-line," directed course.

chordates—animals with a notochord and a dorsal nerve cord.

cartilage—a supporting tissue more elastic and flexible than bone; e.g., the "gristle" in meat.

exoskeleton—a hard and inflexible outer covering of the body of invertebrate animals such as insects and crustaceans.

grow another one. If an arthropod is greater in size than a lobster or a large crab, its body cannot retain its integrity during the molting period when there is no support for internal structures.

Other groups, including the ancestors of chordates, did not evolve hard outside coverings. Instead, these prechordates were dome-shaped, soft-bodied animals living attached to the bottom of shallow seas (Figure 4–2). They fed on microorganisms, which they filtered out of the water. Embryological and life-cycle studies of the living sea squirt, which in many ways is similar to these early prechordates, has suggested how our phylum arose.

Although the adult sea squirt is an immobile species that stays attached to the shallow seabed, its immature form is an active swimmer. In the swimming stage, the sea squirt has clearly defined head and tail regions, and the tail has a notochord running through it, like chordates and unlike the adult sea squirt. A nerve cord on the dorsal (back) side of the notochord transmits impulses that activate muscles. All these immature sea squirt traits are found in adult chordates.

As chordates, we share at some phase of our development all of the following characteristics with other members of the phylum:

- a solid notochord
- a dorsal nerve chord
- one or more pairs of branchial or pharyngeal clefts

We share other characteristics with other chordates and with some non-chordates: *bilateral symmetry*—similar right and left sides of the body; *cephalization*—specialization of a head region; a tail at some stage of development; a true *endoskeleton*—a bony or cartilaginous framework overlain by muscle in the body; *segmentation of the body*—similar structural units throughout part or all of the body; and a three-layered structure of *ectoderm, mesoderm,* and *endoderm* (Latin, meaning "outside," "middle," and "inside skin") during development.

Figure 4–2 • The adult sea squirt (right) is a sedentary animal living attached to the sea floor. Its larval stage (left), however, is free-swimming and possesses the defining traits of the phylum Chordata. Evolutionary differentiation of the chordates likely took place when larval prechordate forms like the sea squirt became able to reproduce (pedogenesis).

Humans have now lost the solid notochord, but its remnants persist as the semiliquid *nucleus pulposus* (Latin, meaning "pulpy center") of the intervertebral discs of our backbones. When we have a "slipped disc," it is this evolutionarily ancient structure that oozes out to press against a spinal nerve and cause pain. The early chordate dorsal nerve cord, greatly enlarged and specialized, has become our spinal cord. Branchial clefts, homologous to gill slits in fish, are present in the developing human embryo, but they become substantially modified in the mature fetal condition. For example, the auditory ("eustachian") tube (running between the throat and the middle ear) and the ear canal (running between the middle ear and the outside of the head) form the remnants of the cleft between our first and second branchial arches, the tissue divisions between the clefts. That is why we "pop our ears" when undergoing changes in altitude, and hear through a canal originally evolved by our ancient ancestors to filter microorganisms out of sea water.

We retain the bilateral symmetry that separates us from the *radially symmetrical* (able to be cut up into equal-sized parts from a central point fanning outward) starfish group (the coelenterates) and the differentiation of head region and the internal skeleton of our early chordate ancestors. Much of body segmentation has been lost, but our vertebrae, ribs, sensory nerve distribution, and patterns of certain muscles, such as the *rectus abdominis,* show this heritage. Furthermore, we have a tail until the eighth week of embryonic development.

THE FIRST VERTEBRATES: OUR FISH HERITAGE

When environmental conditions change so significantly that major ecological niches open up, evolution rapidly fills those niches. "Fanning out" of species in *adaptive radiations,* resulting in occupation of new niches and the formation of new species (see Chapter 1), has occurred numerous times throughout the history of life. These radiations seem to follow periods of significant environmental change and large-scale extinctions. Adaptive radiations may also be related to new adaptations that appear in a species. This chapter will describe several adaptive radiations that are relevant to human evolution.

Near the beginning of the Paleozoic Era, the so-named "Age of Fish" (some 570 million years ago), there was a major adaptive radiation of animals. This explosion of new forms may have been the result of increasingly high levels of oxygen in the environment. Gill-feeding, gill-breathing, free-swimming chordates appeared at this time, about 550 million years ago. They were the ancestors of the vertebrates.

The first **vertebrates** (animals that have "vertebrae" or backbone segments) in the fossil record are very primitive, jawless, small fish. Collectively often referred to as the *ostracoderms* (bony skins), they had a large muscular pharynx that allowed them to rapidly suck up and process large quantities of food-laden water. Vertebrates are chordate animals that share the following characteristics (Smith, 1960; Figure 4–3):

vertebrates—animals with backbones and segmented body plans.

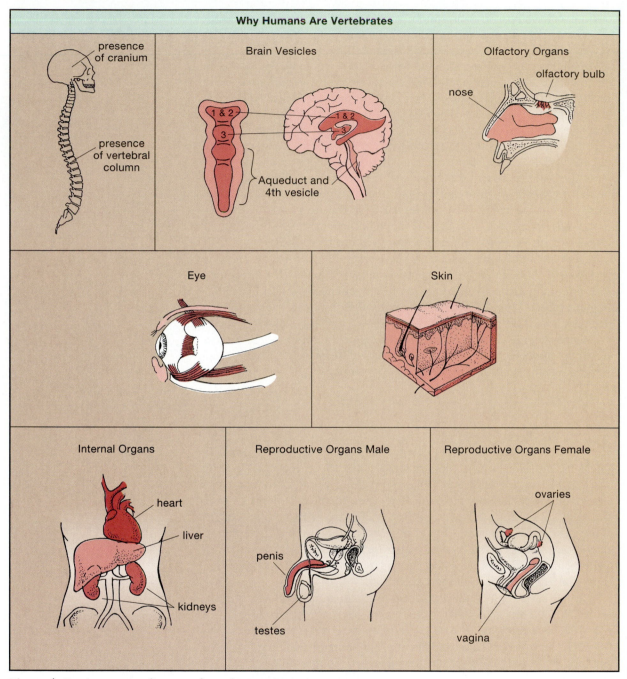

Figure 4–3 • A summary diagram of vertebrate traits.

- a bony vertebral column
- a cranium (skull)
- a brain of three primary parts, or vesicles
- olfactory organs, for sense of smell
- true eyes
- a true skin of dermis and epidermis
- details of internal organs (heart, kidney, liver, pancreas, ear, and pharynx)
- details of reproduction

The co-occurrence of these features is found first among small ostracoderm fish of the Silurian Period (430 to 390 million years ago). The morphology of these earliest vertebrates forms the ground plan for the evolutionary modifications that characterize the many different groups of backboned animals.

The Evolution of a Bony Skeleton

Why did ostracoderms evolve skeletons of bone and cartilage? One likely explanation is that a rigid backbone provided a frame firmer than the primitive notochord for swimming movements. Skeletal support also allowed the attainment of large body size, which was advantageous in avoiding predation: the larger an animal, the fewer the predators that can eat it.

The bones in our bodies are divisible into two categories: **cartilage bone** and **membrane bone,** depending on how they *ossify,* or turn into bone. We have inherited both types from our ostracoderm ancestors. Vertebrae and most other *postcranial* (Latin, meaning "behind the head") bones are cartilage bones because they develop from a cartilage base, with bone cells replacing the cartilage cells during bone formation. Growth of cartilage bones takes place at lines of growth called *epiphyses.* In this way vertebrates increase in size as they grow while the skeleton continues to support the body. Membrane bone, on the other hand, lacks epiphyses and instead develops within a netlike membrane. Membrane bone forms from gradual replacement by bone cells within this sheet of mesodermal tissue.

Membrane bones first evolved in the ostracoderms as head armor, most likely to protect them from attacks by predators. Their enemies were likely giant, six-foot, fresh-water scorpions with pincers almost a foot long. By contrast, our ancestors during the Silurian were a mere six inches in length. Membrane bones in the head provide the foundation for the top part of the cranium in all vertebrates. The bones forming the part of our skull that surrounds the brain, the **neurocranium** (Latin, meaning "brain skull") are membrane bones (see Chapter 2).

The ostracoderms possessed an improved sensory apparatus compared with their chordate ancestors. They had brains that, though tiny by comparison with those of modern fish, had three separate parts, or *vesicles,* a structure that is common to all more complex vertebrate

cartilage bone—bone formed by development from cartilage and growth at epiphyses, characteristic of vertebrate limb bones.

membrane bone—bone formed by development from a connective tissue membrane, characteristic of vertebrate skull bones.

neurocranium—that part of the skull holding the brain.

brains. They had true eyes, not only sensitive to light but able to discern form and movement. They also had a sense of smell. This increased efficiency in sensing environmental stimuli and processing this information probably aided them in obtaining food and avoiding predators.

The Evolution of Biting Jaws

Fish with biting jaws, called **placoderms** (Latin, meaning "plate-skinned"), first appeared in the Devonian Period (390–340 million years ago). How and why did their jaws evolve?

The upper and lower jaws of placoderms evolved from the first two **branchial arches.** Our skull is a welding together of the neurocranium and the part derived from the branchial arches, the **splanchnocranium.** Strangely, our teeth do not come from the branchial arches. Embryology shows that they are derived from ectodermal tissue instead, that is, from the hardened parts of the skin surrounding the mouth. The evolution of biting jaws and sharp teeth signals that placoderms had become predatory, feeding on other fish and invertebrates. Predation allows a species to take advantage of "prepackaged" food of higher quality (other animals) but in smaller quantities, rather than eating widely scattered, lower quality but usually more abundant food (such as plant food) in larger quantities. It also creates changes in body shape. For example, to prevent placoderms from turning in the water, pairs of laterally placed fins evolved from flaps of skin and muscle from the body wall. Two pairs of fins, one in front and one behind, constituted the preadaptation that later fish were to employ to conquer the land. These fins evolved into limbs.

The Evolution of Limbs and Lungs

During the Devonian Period, the first modern fish evolved. They are called the lobe-finned fish, the **sarcopterygians** (Greek, meaning "fleshy appendage"). They had thick and fleshy lateral fins, which were an effective and important part of their adaptation to a fresh-water environment. Some lived in ponds and streams subjected to periodic drought, a situation common in semiarid parts of the tropics today. Their stout fins allowed them to support their bodies on land and to slither from a drying pond to one with more water. The bones of the front and back fins of lobe-fins became heavier structures. The anatomy of these types of fish form the basic plan on which all later land vertebrate limbs evolved.

As part of the adaptation to periodic drought, lobe-finned fish evolved an *air bladder,* an outpocketing of the pharynx into which air was gulped. The air bladder extracted oxygen from the air and allowed the fish to make the overland trek necessary for it to reach its normal environment, water. With relatively little modification in basic plan, the lobe-fin lung became the air-breathing lung of the land vertebrates.

placoderms–early fish with biting jaws.

branchial arches–the tissue in between the gill slits in the embryos of vertebrates.

splanchnocranium–that part of the skull holding the mouth and jaws.

sarcopterygians–lobe-finned fish capable of some support of the body on land.

FIRST FORAYS ONTO DRY LAND: THE AMPHIBIANS

The class **Amphibia** (Greek, meaning "dual life") comprises vertebrates that are essentially land-living fish, inexorably tied to water because of their mode of reproduction. Amphibians lay eggs in water, and their larvae are swimming, gill-breathing forms that die if exposed to air. Modern-day amphibians, such as frogs and salamanders, show this type of reproduction. Only in the adult stage do stout limbs develop that are capable of supporting the animal's body on land.

The best known of these early amphibians are the **labyrinthodonts** (Latin, meaning "labyrinthine [very complex] tooth"), animals superficially similar to crocodiles but much more primitive.

The limbs of the labyrinthodonts show the greatest departure from the structure of their fish ancestors. The proximal elements (bones nearer the body) of both front and back limbs are single (the humerus and femur, respectively), and the distal elements (bones farther from the body) are paired (the radius and ulna, and tibia and fibula, respectively; see Figure 4–4 and Appendix 1). There are small blocky bones making up the hand and foot skeletons, and five digits on each. We share this primitive skeletal arrangement and associated musculature with the labyrinthodonts and with all land vertebrates.

By the end of the Carboniferous Period (340–270 million years ago), the large amphibians had decreased in numbers. By the Triassic Period, only small species related to frogs and salamanders survived. Coincident with the demise of the early amphibians was the ascendency of the reptiles, a group much better adapted to full terrestrial life.

Amphibia–class of vertebrates that includes frogs, salamanders, and extinct species living much of their lives on land but whose reproduction remains tied to water.

labyrinthodonts–extinct, predatory amphibians of the Carboniferous Period some of whom were ancestral to the first reptiles.

Figure 4–4 • Comparison of forelimb bones to show homologies from lobe-fins through amphibians and reptiles to mammals (modern humans).

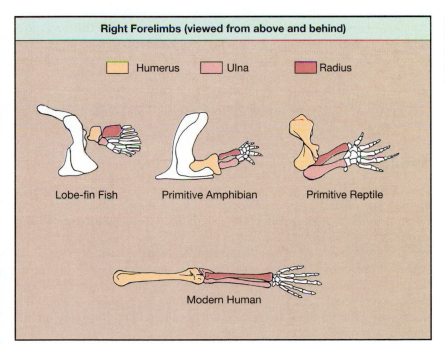

Right Forelimbs (viewed from above and behind)

Humerus   Ulna   Radius

Lobe-fin Fish   Primitive Amphibian   Primitive Reptile

Modern Human

REPTILES CONQUER THE LAND

Why did land life evolve? As we have seen, the process was initiated by the need of water-living animals to move overland from a drying body of water to one that could sustain them. But what selective forces would have acted to create the reptiles, which for the most part are fully terrestrial? The answer lies in the paleoecology of the Paleozoic Era (570–220 million years ago).

At the onset of the reptiles, in the Carboniferous Period, the waters were teeming with life while the land was relatively unpopulated. Amphibian eggs and larvae became subjected to new difficulties in their aqueous environment, because as living forms diversified and grew in numbers, more and more species preyed on defenseless eggs and larvae. As we have seen, the Paleozoic Era was a time of marked seasonal droughts, when ponds and streams could dry up completely, killing all the eggs and larvae living in them.

These problems were solved for reptiles with the evolution of the **amniote egg,** which was laid and hatched on land. Reptile offspring thus had a much higher chance of survival and were favored by natural selection. Although the earliest reptiles still lived close to water and preyed on water-living species, the land-laid egg led to the adaptive radiation of land vertebrates.

The amniote egg takes its name from an inside membrane, the *amnion,* that surrounds and protects the developing embryo (Figure 4–5). In amphibians, the developing embryo receives oxygen and food, and releases wastes, through the egg wall, in direct connection with the surrounding water. The water also protects the embryo from mechanical injury. Because reptilian eggs are laid outside water, four additional structures have evolved to carry out these functions: (1) the *shell* provides the interface between the dry air and the wet ancestral amphibian environment, as well as protecting the egg from breakage; (2) the *chorion* is a membrane just inside the shell that takes in oxygen and gives off carbon dioxide through the shell; (3) the *allantois* forms a sac into which body wastes are deposited; and, (4) the *yolk sac* provides nourishment to the embryo.

Adaptive Radiation

From the earliest reptiles evolved the wide diversity of more advanced reptiles that characterized the Mesozoic Era (220–70 million years ago), referred to as "the Age of Reptiles": sharklike ichthyosaurs, lizards and snakes, marine plesiosaurs, mammal-like reptiles, dinosaurs, and eventually birds (Figure 4–6). The **mammal-like reptiles (therapsids)**, described by paleontologist Alfred Romer as appearing to be "an odd cross between a lizard and a dog," lived between the late Carboniferous and the Triassic Periods (290–190 million years ago). They signal some of the major and most fundamental changes in skull and jaw form, teeth, and limbs that separate reptile from mammal.

amniote egg–an egg characteristic of the reptiles that could be laid and developed out of water.

mammal-like reptiles (therapsids)–reptiles with a skull opening behind the eye (subclass Synapsida) and with differentiated teeth.

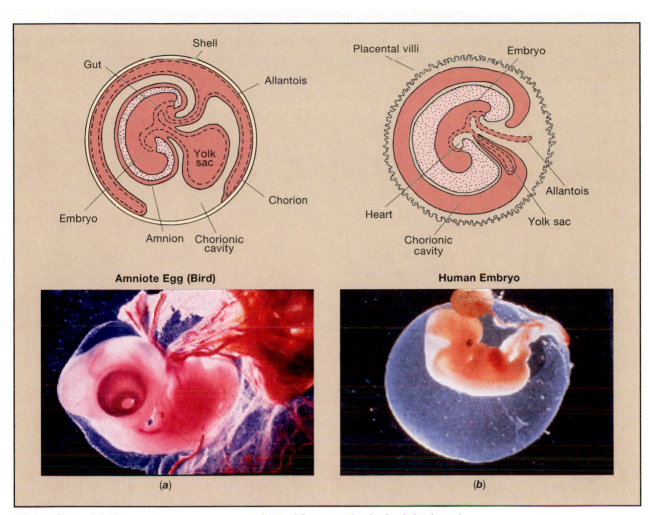

Amniote Egg (Bird)   Human Embryo

(a)   (b)

Figure 4–5 • (*a*) The amniote egg structure, inherited from reptiles by both birds and mammals; (*b*) the human embryo with homologous parts labeled.

The Evolution of Skull, Teeth, and Limbs

Skull form in the mammal-like reptiles is the key to understanding their ancestral relationship to the mammals. The jaws and teeth of the mammal-like reptiles show progressive features. All the bones of the jaw except the tooth-bearing part, the dentary, were reduced. This is the only bone forming the jaw in mammals. Unlike the more primitive reptiles, which had simple conelike teeth, therapsids had teeth of different form and function in different parts of the mouth. They had front *incisors* for cutting and nipping, single *canines* for puncturing, and back teeth for chewing. This condition is a clear precursor to the **heterodonty** ("different teeth") characteristic of mammals.

heterodonty–the condition of possessing teeth differentiated for different functions; contrasted with the homodont dentition of many reptiles, such as living crocodiles.

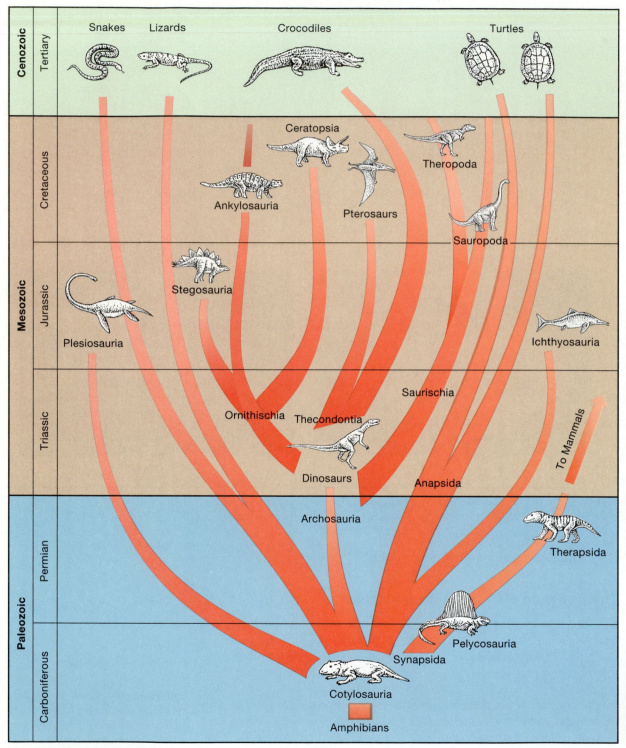

Figure 4–6 • Reptile phylogeny.

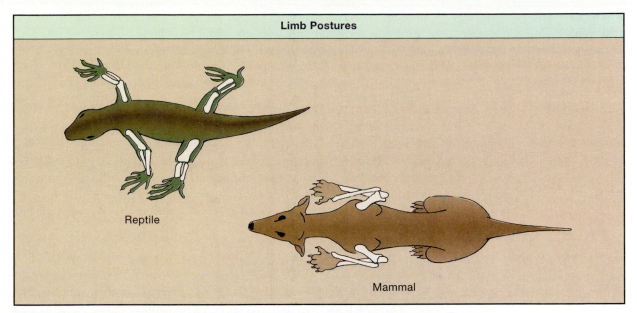

Limb Postures

Reptile

Mammal

Figure 4–7 • Compared with quadrupedal reptiles, early mammals showed more efficient locomotor adaptations. In mammals, the limbs moved to a position underneath the body and closer to the median plane, resulting in an increase in speed. At the same time, the side-to-side bending motion of reptiles was reduced.

Limb structure and the mode of walking (**locomotion**) in the therapsids showed marked advances over those of their ancestors. The limbs grew longer and moved from positions at the side of the body to underneath it. The vertically aligned skeleton of the limb (Figure 4–7) supported the body above the ground, rather than having the body supported by muscular contraction of the limbs alone. This development allowed the therapsids to become relatively fleet terrestrial predators, the first ancestors in our lineage not entirely dependent on aquatic sources of food.

The mammal-like reptiles were a successful group and speciated into many different niches—herbivorous and carnivorous, large and small. During the Triassic Period, however, they largely died out, probably in ecological competition with the very successful dinosaurs. Only a few small and insignificant species survived, scurrying about in the shadows of their ponderous contemporaries. These evolved into the first mammals.

locomotion–the means of moving about.

MAMMALS EVOLVE AND RADIATE

We live today in a world replete with many varieties of warm-blooded, large-brained, haired animals that nurse their young: members of the class Mammalia. Such is the diversity of advanced mammals that it is at

marsupials—pouched mammals.

placentals—evolved mammals with a very efficient reproductive system, which includes a placenta, a structure that provides the developing embryo with well-oxygenated blood.

first difficult to believe that they are all descended from common ancestral populations that radiated only at the beginning of the Cenozoic Era, "the Age of Mammals," some 70 million years ago.

During much of early mammalian evolution, reptiles were the ecologically dominant life form on earth. During much of this long period, the mammalian ancestors of humans were small, rat-sized insect-eaters that lived primarily in trees and hunted at night (Figure 4–8).

The first mammals are identified by their teeth, which, unlike those of the earlier reptiles, possessed a heterodontic pattern (Figure 4–9). The molars have a triangular outline with three well-defined cusps. The ridges between the cusps on upper and lower molars slice past each other as the mouth is closed, affording an effective mechanism for cutting up and chewing food. From this basic design all other mammalian chewing teeth have evolved.

New Reproductive Strategies

The earliest mammals may have been egg-laying, like their reptilian ancestors. In fact, the two most primitive living mammals, the platypus and the spiny anteater, which live in Australia, bear their young in this way. Because the general history of mammalian reproduction is one of greater protection of progeny, in the Mesozoic Era a new type of reproduction evolved in which young were born alive. Mammal mothers retained the reptile-type egg internally in special structures in their bodies where the embryo developed. The result was that the egg was better protected, and thus, mammalian offspring survived at higher rates. Because the rate of predation on newborn and immature mammals was still high, selection favored offspring that were protected by an adult until they were capable of making their own way.

During the Cretaceous Period the **marsupials** (Latin, meaning "pouch" [*marsupium*]) and the **placentals** (referring to the membranous structure in the uterus, the *placenta*, that provides prenatal nourishment to the developing embryo and fetus), the two dominant forms of mammals, appeared. Marsupials were the more common of the mammals during the Cretaceous (125–70 million years ago), when the dinosaurs

Figure 4–8 • Reconstructed view of an early mammal (*Megazostrodon*) from the late Jurassic of North America.

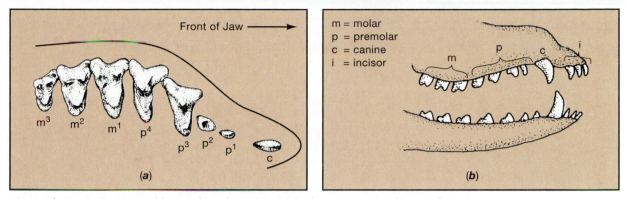

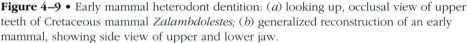

Figure 4–9 • Early mammal heterodont dentition: (*a*) looking up, occlusal view of upper teeth of Cretaceous mammal *Zalambdolestes;* (*b*) generalized reconstruction of an early mammal, showing side view of upper and lower jaw.

still reigned. The marsupials are pouched mammals, two living examples of which are the opossum and the kangaroo. They bear their young in a very immature state of development after a brief period of gestation. The baby then climbs tenuously along the mother's abdomen into the pouch and clasps onto a teat (*mamma,* from which the name of the class derives), where it nurses until fully developed.

Although the marsupials' reproductive adaptation did little more than internalize the reptilian egg and nurture the young externally, the more advanced placental mammals internalized both processes and improved on the method of nurturance of the embryo. The *chorion,* a membrane that surrounds the embryo, became fused with the wall of the mother's uterus, forming the placenta, richly supplied with blood vessels. The placenta attaches to the embryo via the *umbilical cord,* carrying oxygen and nutrients to the embryo and carrying wastes away. That the placental form of gestation proved ultimately more successful is evidenced by the placental species' having generally replaced marsupials when they have come face-to-face in ecological competition.

Homeothermy

The Mesozoic mammals physiologically were probably capable of maintaining their internal body temperature at a more constant level than their reptilian ancestors had been able to do. This ability is termed **homeothermy** (Latin, meaning "same heat"), more commonly "warm-blooded," and it allowed mammals to be active during relatively cool periods, such as at night. Similar-sized (small) reptiles today are quiescent when they are cold, and must raise their body temperature behaviorally through activities such as sunning themselves. Homeotherms use muscular contraction (in movements and shivering), constriction and dilation of surface blood vessels, sweating, panting, and insulation by hair to maintain body temperature.

homeothermy—the maintenance of constant body temperature; "warm-blooded."

Warm-bloodedness allowed a greater range of activities, particularly in hunting and escape from predators, and especially at night and in cooler seasons of the year in temperate regions. Two other nonmammalian groups independently evolved homeothermy—the birds and at least some of the dinosaurs.

As part of their more active physiology, mammals evolved a heart and circulatory system that kept oxygenated and deoxygenated bloodstreams separated and created greater blood pressure. Because more oxygen and more blood could be delivered to the tissues per unit of time, a higher **metabolic rate** (oxygen consumption and energy production) was possible. The ancestral fish circulation was a simple pumping mechanism, with the *ventricle* pushing blood through two systems of capillaries: first to the gills to pick up oxygen and then to the body to nourish the tissues and pick up waste carbon dioxide. With the advent of the air-breathing lung, a three-chambered heart evolved. The right and left *atria* received blood from the body (deoxygenated blood) and lungs (oxygenated blood), respectively. Blood from the two atria then emptied into the single ventricle, which in turn pumped the blood to both the body and the lungs. In mammals, as well as in some advanced reptiles and birds, the four-chambered heart evolved in which one side of the heart pumps oxygenated blood and the other deoxygenated blood.

Enlarged Brain and Related Structures

The earliest mammals had as one of their major adaptations a significantly enlarged brain for their body size compared with that of the reptiles. The enlargement was particularly observable in a part of the brain originally concerned with smell, the *cerebrum*. The cerebrum assumed new and expanded functions in the mammals. Sensory information—visual, auditory, taste, and smell—were recorded and remembered in the outside part, the *cerebral cortex*. This increased memory and ability to receive and act upon environmental information with effective behavior became an important component in mammalian adaptation. In Chapter 5, we discuss how this trend intensified in the primates and especially in the apes and ourselves.

The shape of the skull also changed in mammals. The neurocranium expanded to hold the larger brain. A new design of the head articulating to the vertebral column became perfected in the mammals. Instead of a centrally located bony projection, the *condyle,* on the back of the skull, two condyles developed on both sides of the opening for the spinal cord. This formed a more stable joint and enabled faster, more accurate movements of the head, needed in animals that dispatch prey with their teeth. A *hard palate* evolved to separate the nasal air passages from the oral food passages, thus allowing mammals to maintain their oxygen supply while eating.

The mammalian jaw, or **mandible,** became a stronger structure, being formed by only a single bone. Greater force could be exerted in biting and chewing. Two of the old reptilian jaw bones assumed a new

metabolic rate–the rate at which energy is expended in all the chemical reactions in an animal's cells and tissues.

mandible–the lower jaw of mammals, composed of a fusion of the reptile dentary and articular bones.

function in the mammals. They became ear bones: the *malleus* (hammer bone) and the *incus* (anvil bone) of our middle ear. The malleus attaches the eardrum to the incus, and the incus connects to the *stapes* (stirrup bone), which first evolved in the amphibians. Sound is amplified by this system of bony levers, which constitutes a finely tuned hearing mechanism in the mammals.

triune brain—the division of the human brain by Paul MacLean into three broad divisions based on phylogenetic and functional patterns.

THE HUMAN BRAIN IN EVOLUTIONARY PERSPECTIVE

Like other parts of our anatomy, the brain has been evolutionarily constructed using structures inherited from earlier ancestors. Within our brains we have parts that basically think like our fish, amphibian, reptilian, and mammalian ancestors, although evolution has also undoubtedly acted to change particular details to fit into the functioning of the whole brain.

Paul MacLean of the National Institute of Mental Health developed the concept of the three-part or **triune brain** (Figure 4–10), each part of which is a legacy of a different stage of development in the human evolutionary story. These three stages are built on the most ancient "neural chassis"—the spinal cord, mid- and hind-brains—that are inherited from our fish and amphibian ancestors. With these most ancient parts of our

Figure 4–10 • Cross-sections of the human brain showing *(a)* regions of the triune brain, *(b)* the limbic system, and *(c)* the striatal (or R) complex including the corpus striatum (caudate nucleus and putamen). The club on the tail of the caudate, C, is continuous with the amygdala of the limbic system. Diagonal shading indicates a cut through the corpus callosum. (After MacLean, 1990)

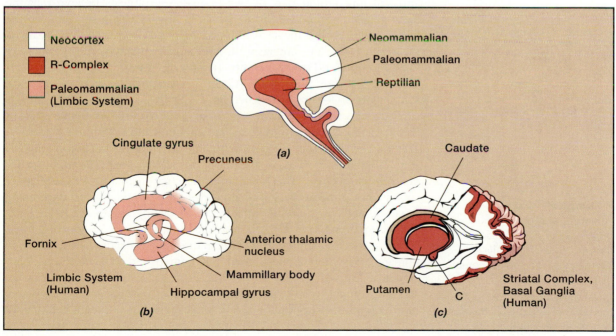

brains, we breathe, run our hearts, and have instincts for survival and reproduction. The first part of the triune brain is the reptilian brain. While we use MacLean's triune brain model for descriptive purposes, it does have a number of critics. In a recent book, *Comparative Vertebrate Neuroanatomy: Evolution and Adaptation* (1996) two neuroanatomists, Butler and Hodos, state that over the past three decades recent work "unequivocally contradicts this theory" (page 86). For example, these findings do not "support the evolutionary history of the limbic system as described by the triune brain hypothesis. The present evidence indicates that the limbic system evolved before the advent of any amniote vertebrates, let alone mammals" (pages 455–56).

The R-Complex

The reptiles of 250 million years ago possessed several evolutionary advances in brain function over their amphibian forerunners. The **R-Complex** ("R" standing for reptilian) is in the base of the forebrain of all reptiles, birds, and mammals and is made up of several structures, termed **basal ganglia.** A *ganglion* (Greek, meaning "knot" or "swelling") is a concentration of nerve cell connections, identified as the *corpus striatum* (Latin, meaning "striped body"), *olfactostriatum* (Latin, meaning "smell striped part" from its olfactory function), and *globus pallidus* (Latin, meaning "pale sphere"). The R-Complex is rich in *dopamine,* which is necessary for releasing energy; the neural transmitter *serotonin; cholinesterase,* a protein that helps to transmit signals across synapses; and the opiumlike *endorphins.*

What parts of our thoughts and actions can be traced to this ancient and still functioning part of our brains? Neurologists believe that the basal ganglia are involved in transmitting or processing signals from the motor cortex to the muscles, because disorders in physical skills result when other, similar ganglia in the midbrain are damaged. But MacLean (1990) has pointed out that destruction by disease or injury of large parts of the R-Complex does not result in motor deficits, nor does electrical stimulation of R-Complex structures result in movement. MacLean has carried out experiments on lizards and monkeys that demonstrate a "basic role in displays used in social communication" for the R-Complex. This part of the brain must also be able to interpret behavioral signals from other animals, and, as a result of this ability, it recognizes other animals as individuals. The R-Complex is active in maintaining social (or "dominance") hierarchies and territories (see Chapter 6), in expressing ritualistic behaviors, and in initiating or mediating aggressive behavior.

It is important to recognize, however, that there are connecting tracts between the R-Complex and other more evolved parts of the brain in humans and other higher animals. In human behavior, therefore, neocortical ("learned") input affects the expression of R-Complex output. Not surprisingly, we do not always see exact correspondence between lizard and human display behavior, although the R-Complex is functioning in the same manner in both species' brains. But in some cases, as in

R-Complex—the most primitive, "reptilian" part of the "triune brain" model of Paul MacLean; the site of certain ritualistic, stereotypical, and social communication behaviors.

basal ganglia—structures in the forebrain of vertebrates that form part of the R-Complex.

a comparison of the stiff-legged agonistic displays of the komodo dragon, mountain gorilla, and World War II German soldier (Figure 4–11), there are remarkable similarities.

The Limbic System

The second part of the triune brain is the **limbic system** (from Latin, meaning "bordering, peripheral"), consisting of the parts of the forebrain surrounding the brainstem and the R-Complex system. There are three main subdivisions of structures making up the limbic system, each, apparently, with a different function. The first area (Figure 4–10) includes the *amygdala* (Greek, meaning "almond"), the *hippocampus* (Greek, a mythological sea creature), the *hypothalamus* (Greek, meaning "below the thalamus"), and the *pituitary* (Latin, meaning "mucus-secreting"). This first area of the limbic system is concerned with self- and species-preservation, particularly the activities of fighting, feeding, and self-reproduction. The second area is called the *septum* and is located in the midline just below the the large connecting tract of the brain, the corpus callosum. It is somehow involved in sexual behavior. Both of the first two areas of the limbic system are closely related to the sense of smell, via their neural connection to the olfactory bulbs, the part of the cerebrum that processes smell.

The third section of the limbic system extends through the anterior part of the *thalamus* (Greek, meaning "chamber"), connecting the hypothalamus with the cerebral cortex *cingulate* (Latin, meaning "beltlike")

limbic system–a mammalian adaptation of the primarily olfactory part of the forebrain, important in sexual and maternal behavior.

Figure 4–11 • Agonistic display in the komodo dragon, mountain gorilla, and human being: a function of the ancient R-Complex? (From Eibl-Eibesfeldt, 1975)

FRONTIERS

The Interaction of Climate, Environment, and Evolution

by Lloyd H. Burckle

Many new areas of research have now shown that there is a general correspondence between times of major climate change and episodes of evolutionary change. Why should this be so? One idea is that during periods of worldwide cooler temperatures ("global cooling"), the animal and plant species in the far north and far south, those most affected by colder temperatures, suffer some extinction and tend to be pushed toward the equator. Ecological pressure is placed on the species already resident near the equator as the immigrant species compete for food and space. A great deal of extinction of the resident low latitude species results. When conditions become warmer, species are free to repopulate the higher latitudes again, and evolution acts to increase the diversity of species. In this scenario most of the newly evolved species in the world derive ultimately from higher latitude populations.

Even if this scenario is accurate, and it is not by any means the only explanation for evolutionary change, there are many other factors that may complicate the story. For example, there have been periods, unlike the present, during which climatic cooling was not the same at both the North Pole and the South Pole. If, because of continental drift, a continent was centered at one pole, and the open ocean was centered at the other, the pole without the insulating effect of water would suffer greater temperature change, and hypothetically would witness the greater effect on its animal and plant communities. Further changes can occur on land as ice builds up during periods of cold. These episodes are known as glaciations. The massive build-up of ice on land takes up so much of the earth's water that sea level is lowered worldwide. Islands can become connected with mainland areas, and previously open land connections can become blocked by ice formation. These changes in land routes can have important effects on dispersal of species and their subsequent evolution.

What causes the changes in the earth's climate that we see? Major changes are dictated by astronomical cycles related to the earth's relationship to the sun. These cycles lead to periodic and predictable changes in global climate. However, the severity and mosaic pattern of that climate change is dictated by other factors as well. Surface and near-surface earth movements, known as tectonism, are one of the most important factors. Tectonic effects include mountain building, continental drift, and long-term vertical uplift or subsidence. Only recently have geologists and climate modellers come to appreciate the role that tectonism plays in climate and climate change (and, by extension, its effect on evolution).

Another important factor affecting climate is weathering, or the physical

gyrus. Much of the influence of the limbic system on behavior derives from the hormonal proteins that its structures produce. The pituitary gland produces *ACTH* (adenocorticotrophic hormone), which affects anxiety, attention span, and visual memory.

The Neocortex

The third and most uniquely human part of the triune brain is the **neocortex** (Latin, meaning "new covering"). Human behavior is a function of an expanded mammalian part of the triune brain—the cerebral cortex.

The **cortical homunculus** (Latin, meaning "little man") was discovered by a British neurologist, John Hughlings Jackson, who in the 1860s researched the behavior of individuals suffering from epilepsy. He discovered that seizures always started with uncontrolled movements of one part of the body. By recording where in the brain an injury oc-

neocortex—the evolutionary "new" part of the cerebral cortex.
cortical homunculus—the localized map of the entire body as represented in the cerebral cortex.

and chemical wearing away of the rock of the earth's surface. Increased rates of weathering, caused by higher continental elevations (in turn related, of course, to tectonic activity), cause greater amounts of calcium carbonate from chemical weathering of rocks to be deposited into the world's oceans. This, in turn, reduces the amount of carbon dioxide in the atmosphere, and in a reverse greenhouse effect, reduces global temperature. The relationship among mountain and plateau uplift, increased chemical weathering, and global climate cooling seems to hold both for the recent periods of earth history during the Tertiary and for much of geological history.

The Tertiary Period is particularly important for primate and hominid evolution and provides a good illustration of the interaction of tectonic change, regional climate, and evolution. Within the past 50 million years, Antarctica separated from South America and Australia, while the north polar regions became landlocked. India collided with Asia some 40 to 50 million years ago and initiated the rise of the Himalayas.

In addition to the formation of this large mountain barrier, uplift of the Tibetan plateau was initiated. The American West also witnessed uplift during this time, the most significant result being the Colorado plateau. Finally, regions such as eastern and southern Africa underwent broad vertical uplift, which caused fracturing and rifting at the earth's surface.

The climatic effects of these tectonic changes included the thermal isolation of the south polar region and the initiation of major glaciation in Antarctica after 54 million years ago. This ice sheet increased 34 million years ago, leading to a global drop in sea level. The rise of the Himalayas not only caused increased weathering and reduction of atmospheric carbon dioxide, thus reducing global temperature, but their height redirected wind patterns in the entire Indian Ocean area, creating a seasonal, or "monsoonal" rain pattern in Africa and southern Asia. Uplift of the Colorado and Tibetan plateaus, besides influencing local climate, diverted high-level jet stream and low-level winds to

the north, causing further cooling, particularly in the northern hemisphere. Two more recent global cooling events are recorded at 14 million years ago, when the Antarctic ice sheet greatly enlarged, and at 7 million years ago, when the Greenland ice sheet was initiated. Many interrelated changes in environment accompanied these broad changes in climate. The subtropical and temperate belts, for example, had been of broad extent some 50 million years ago, but they have moved progressively closer to the equator through the Tertiary, and have created a series of new climatic zones in their wake. The interplay among climate, tectonics, and evolution is an active field of research, and we can expect to see much progress as research proceeds.

Lloyd H. Burckle is senior research scientist at Lamont Doherty Earth Observatory, Columbia University, New York.

curred, and what part of the body was subsequently affected in the epileptic fit, Hughlings Jackson was able to map out the whole body along a strip of brain tissue. Figure 4–12 shows a refined version of what was termed a "homunculus" because it represents in miniature the human figure. Areas of the body with the greatest area of cortex are represented larger in the homunculus.

Hughlings Jackson had discovered the **motor cortex,** a loop of brain in front of the *central sulcus,* and therefore termed the *precentral gyrus.* One writer described the motor cortex as "the keyboard of an instrument whose strings are the muscles, which finally play the melody of movement" (Blakemore, 1977:79). There are larger "keyboard" areas for certain parts of the body, where more finely tuned muscular control is required, such as for the thumbs and lips in humans.

Other researchers discovered that a similar "sensory homunculus" was present directly behind the central sulcus, and thus it was named

motor cortex—the part of the cerebral cortex located in the precentral gyrus that controls voluntary movements of the body.

Figure 4–12 • Frontal section of the brain through the precentral (motor) and postcentral (sensory) gyri.

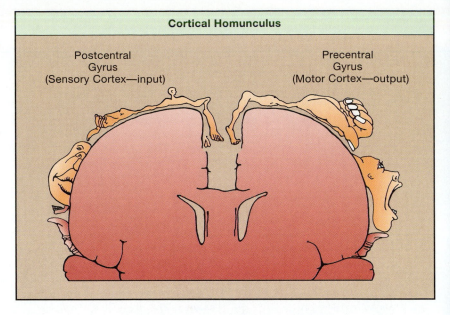

Cortical Homunculus

Postcentral Gyrus
(Sensory Cortex—input)

Precentral Gyrus
(Motor Cortex—output)

the *postcentral gyrus.* This area is the **sensory cortex.** Sensations from the skin of touch, heat, cold, and pain are perceived in the brain in a clearly organized pattern (Figure 4–12). As in the motor cortex, the proportion of cortical area allotted for sensations correlates with the importance of particular sensations in the animal's adaptation. Human brains have a very large sensory area for the hands, as do most primates, whereas dogs, for example, have larger sensory areas for perceiving touch on the nose.

Understanding the structure and function of the human brain is one of the most challenging frontiers for modern science. The model of the triune brain is one way to understand some very complex structures in an evolutionary framework. The model will certainly need to be modified as new discoveries are made.

MAMMALS AND ADAPTIVE RADIATION

The evolution of diverse mammals during the Cenozoic Era is another example of an adaptive radiation. Since their origin, mammals have diversified into a number of habitats. Changes in the limbs have been of primary importance in the mammalian adaptive pattern (Figure 4–13), and in the different groups of mammals they formed the basis for adaptations to different ways of life. The process of moving the front and hind limbs under the body, begun in the therapsids, was completed. The toe joints were reduced to three in all digits except the first (the thumb or *pollex,* and the big toe or *hallux*), where there are two joints—the same pattern that we possess.

sensory cortex–the part of the cerebral cortex located in the postcentral gyrus that senses touch, temperature, and pain on all parts of the body.

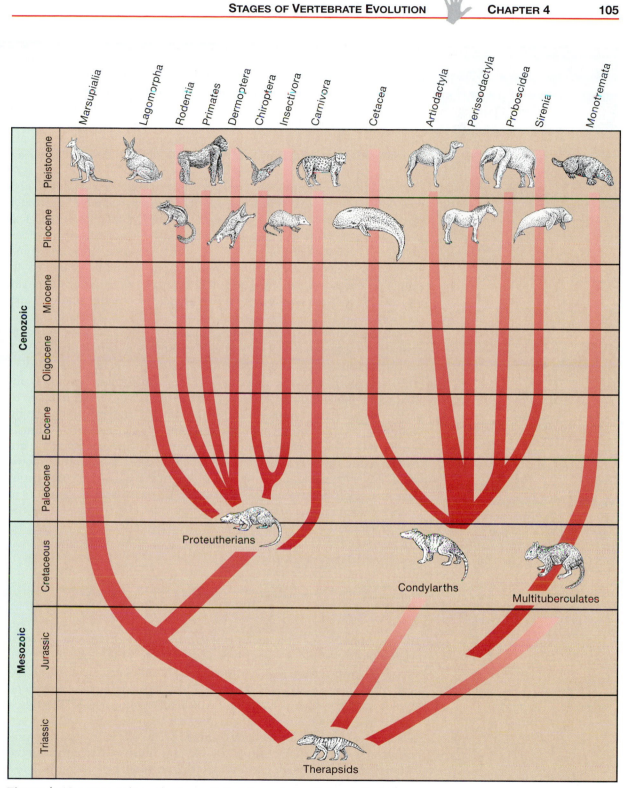

Figure 4–13 • Mammalian adaptive radiation through the Cenozoic Period.

Figure 4–14 • Tree shrew.

Figure 4–15 • Flying lemur or colugo, *Cynocephalus volans,* whose order, Dermoptera, is closely related to the insectivores and primates.

Insectivora—order of insect-eating mammals that includes shrews and tree shrews; similar to early Mesozoic mammals.

The most primitive living order of placental mammals is the **Insectivora,** composed of small, usually forest-dwelling animals with high metabolisms, such as tree shrews (Figure 4–14). They are probably very similar to the ancestors of all placental mammals in the Cretaceous Period. Using modern shrews as an analog, our Mesozoic ancestors were likely very small, voracious, and nocturnal animals. Our earliest primate ancestors constituted one of the first stems off this basic mammalian trunk.

Excepting the insectivores, primates, and rodents (rats, squirrels, and their kin), which have remained morphologically primitive, the other placental mammals have radiated into a large number of ecological niches—that is, particular morphological and behavioral specializations for specific habitats (Figure 4–13). The first of these radiations came about in the Paleocene Epoch, beginning about 70 million years ago. In simplified terms, we can categorize the Cenozoic radiation of mammals into five major adaptive zones: aerial, aquatic, fossorial, arboreal, and cursorial.

Bats and some other small gliding mammals (the dermopterans), such as flying squirrels and flying "lemurs," constitute the only members of the aerial radiation. Biochemical studies, and more recently fossil discoveries, indicate that the dermopterans (Figure 4–15) may be closely related to the primate stem (see Chapter 5). Mammals have also adapted to marine niches. This group includes the whales and porpoises, along with the sea cows and carnivorous seals and otters. Fossorial mammals are burrowers, such as moles and aardvarks. The arboreal mammals are evolutionarily the most conservative of the entire class, and our own order, Primates, is the most arboreal of the mammals. Cursorial, or running, mammals are by far the largest ray of the adaptive radiation of Cenozoic mammals. Foremost among the cursorial mammals are the hoofed mammals: the odd-toed *perissodactyls* (horses and rhinoceroses) and even-toed *artiodactyls* (pigs, antelopes, deer, hippopotamuses, and giraffes), and the carnivores.

UNDERSTANDING HUMAN MORPHOLOGY

The vertebrates, and particularly the mammals, provide an essential background for understanding human evolution. The human body is a mosaic of many anatomical structures and physiological mechanisms derived from ancestors at many stages in a long evolutionary development. At each stage those traits were important parts of the species' adaptation to its environment. Clearly, there was no orthogenetic, or predetermined, trend toward the human condition. The story of our early preprimate evolution, with all its twists and turns, is a much more complicated and, indeed, exciting one than a simple plodding progression towards ourselves.

Many of the main adaptive grades (roughly a stage in evolutionary development) in our vertebrate heritage have been recognized for some time, having been discovered by several generations of comparative anatomists, embryologists, and paleontologists. Yet, nonprimate data continue to provide important contributions to our understanding of human evolution. A number of biological anthropologists and evolutionary biologists are working with nonprimate vertebrate data to solve anthropological problems. These contributions are coming today primarily from functional morphology, in which comparative data from other vertebrates are essential to the interpretation of hominid behavioral capabilities. Vertebrate paleontology is also providing important information on the context of human evolution: the environmental conditions, regional connections, and ages of fossil faunas that tell us about the world of our ancestors.

The human body is not a well-designed machine unique unto itself. Each part has a long history of evolutionary change behind it. It is therefore important in human anatomy, and its practical applications in medicine, to appreciate the evolution and development of structures as well as their present functional configurations. Comparative anatomical, paleontological, embryological, and biochemical data provide compelling evidence of human beings' connections with and evolutionary differentiation within the animal world. Regardless of how dramatic the later developments of human evolution may seem to be, their bases lie in the adaptations inherited from our chordate and vertebrate ancestors.

 SUMMARY

1. We can trace the ancestry of humans through the vertebrates by using data from comparative anatomy, embryology, and paleontology. Contrary to an anthropocentric view of evolution, humans and their ancestors were until quite recently minor components of life on earth.
2. The evolution of vertebrates proceeded through a series of ancestral stages, many of which are represented by living forms today.
3. Early fish evolved skeletons of cartilage and bone, which allowed an increase in animal body size. The development of biting jaws among the placoderm fish was an adaptation to a predatory way of life.
4. Land vertebrates evolved from lobe-finned fishes that possessed air bladders and were capable of limited movement on land.
5. By developing the drought-resistant amniote egg, early reptiles evolved during the Carboniferous Period as animals free from life in the water. Mammal-like reptiles evolved many features of the skull, jaws, teeth, and limbs characteristic of the later mammals.
6. Early mammals differentiated from the reptiles in their adaptations (a) to maintaining a constant internal body temperature (homeothermy), (b) to giving birth to live young, and (c) to possessing a considerably larger brain, consisting of the new additions of the limbic system and the neocortex. The adaptive radiation of mammals into five major zones began about 70 million years ago from ancestors similar to the insectivores of today. Later primate and human evolution is best understood with this backdrop of the whole of vertebrate evolution.

CRITICAL-THINKING QUESTIONS

1. Define and give examples of homologous and analogous structures.
2. Discuss "our fish heritage," and the role it played in the evolution of vertebrates.
3. Explain the development of the different bone types found in the human body.
4. What are the primary characteristics that set off the class Mammalia from all other classes of animals?
5. Briefly discuss the role homeothermy played in mammalian evolution.
6. Describe the functions of the limbic system and how they relate to the "triune brain."

SUGGESTED READINGS

Cartmill, M., W. Hylander, and J. Shafland. 1987. *Human Structure*. Cambridge, Mass.: Harvard University Press. An evolutionary perspective on human anatomy. Detailed but understandable.

Falk, Dean. 1992. *Brain Dance*. New York: Morrow. A popular account of the human brain and its evolution.

Hildebrand, M. 1974. *Analysis of Vertebrate Structure*. New York: John Wiley. A good general introduction to comparative anatomy of vertebrates.

MacLean, Paul. 1989. *The Triune Brain*. New York: Academic Press. A detailed discussion of MacLean's theory of the triune brain. Comprehensive.

Savage, R. J. G. 1991. *Mammalian Evolution*. New York: Longmans. A well-illustrated general introduction to the evolution of the mammals.

Strickberger, M. 1996. *Evolution,* 2nd ed. Boston, Mass.: Jones and Bartlett. An extensive, up-to-date overview of the evolution of vertebrates.

CHAPTER 5

Introduction to Primates: Origins and Evolution

With the evolution of flowering plants, including trees, in the latter part of the Mesozoic Era, forests became complex environments. There were more niches available for exploitation. One group of mammals radiated to fill the new tree-living niches. These were small creatures who climbed in the trees by grasping. They are called primates.

WHAT IS A PRIMATE?

The term **primates** was coined by Linnaeus in 1758 to name the order of mammals that includes monkeys, apes, and humans. "Primate" comes from the Latin *primas,* meaning "of the first rank." Linnaeus considered the order that contained humans to be first among the animals.

Primate species are numerous throughout the Old and New Worlds, from Africa and Asia to South and Central America (Figure 5–1). Almost all of the primates are tree living or *arboreal,* one of the main exceptions being humans. As a group they are subdivided into two major taxonomic groups. The **prosimians** (Latin, meaning "before monkeys") are the most primitive of living primates; that is, they retain many characteristics of their earliest ancestors. Most species of prosimians are small, solitary, and active only at night. **Anthropoids** (Greek, for "humanlike"), often called the "higher primates," include the monkeys, apes, and humans. They share derived characteristics that distinguish them from their earliest primate ancestors. As a group anthropoids are generally larger in body size than prosimians, and they are organized into social groups that are active during the day (Figure 5–2).

The anatomist Sir Wilfred Le Gros Clark (1964) set out a number of trends that typify most, if not all, primates.

primates–the order of mammals that includes living and extinct monkeys, apes, and humans, as well as more primitive taxa.

prosimians–primates typified by small body size and frequently nocturnal adaptations in the living forms.

anthropoids–"higher" primates, including the monkeys, apes, and humans.

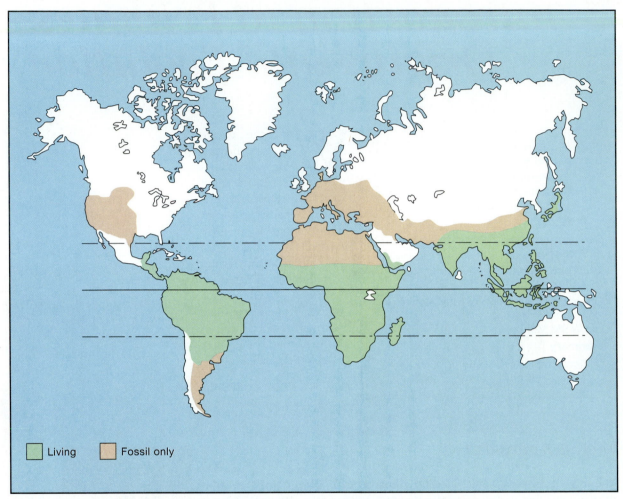

Living   Fossil only

Figure 5–1 • World distribution of nonhuman primates. Living primates are basically tropical to subtropical, as indicated by the area bounded by the broken lines on either side of the equator. Fossil primates are found in regions of the world that were once tropical.

stereoscopic vision–the ability to perceive depth by virtue of the fact that the fields of vision of each eye partially overlap, thus giving the brain information sufficient to reconstruct an accurate impression of depth or distance.

1. Primates tend to have a well-developed *visual sense,* which includes good depth perception. The latter ability is correlated with overlapping fields of vision for each eye (binocular vision) which, when integrated in the brain, yield a perception of three dimensions, **stereoscopic vision.** Primates have eyes that face forward near the front of their head, a condition known as *orbital frontality.* Prosimians show less orbital frontality than do anthropoids.

2. *Color vision.* The ability to see and discriminate a wide range of the color spectrum is another characteristic of all primates except the nocturnal prosimians. Color vision in primates may have arisen by selection for a fruit-eating diet that required the ability to determine the ripeness and edibility of particular food.

3. Primates in general have *larger brains* for their body sizes than do other mammals. This is particularly true for anthropoids, and among

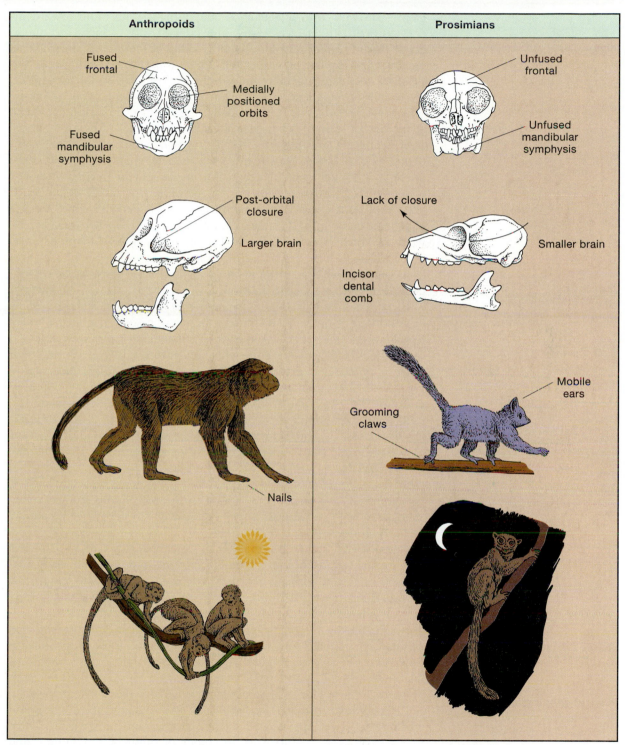

Figure 5–2 • Prosimians and anthropoids compared.

them, especially true of the apes and humans. The trend toward increased brain size, which relates in a general way to increased intelligence, may result from a predatory lifestyle requiring primates to outsmart and capture prey (Cartmill, 1982). It may have been further developed in higher primates because of their complex social adaptations to life in well-integrated groups. Human ancestors underwent extensive brain development due to their increasing reliance on a peculiar social adaptation of learned behavior, known as *culture.*

4. *Increased parental investment in offspring.* Primates show a tendency to give birth to fewer offspring than do many other mammals. There is a greater degree of parental investment in looking after offspring, throughout the relatively longer period of infant dependency after birth. As a consequence, infant mortality is generally low. Aspects of primate anatomy and physiology reflect this reproductive strategy. Almost all primates have only two breasts for suckling infants whereas other mammals have a series of nipples.

5. The period of development of the primate fetus, *gestation,* increases from prosimians to anthropoids.

6. Primates show a diversity of modes of locomotion. Figure 5–3 is a classification of the various types of locomotion seen in primates today (Napier and Napier, 1967). The earliest primates probably were arboreal quadrupeds (Figure 5–3a), somewhat similar to but less specialized than modern prosimian **vertical clinging and leaping** forms (see Figure 5–8). Vertical clinging and leaping is a type of locomotion typified by grasping a vertical tree trunk with the hands and feet encircling the trunk, and then jumping to another such perch (Figure 5–3d). Prosimians thus possess hands and feet capable of grasping. Some of the traits associated with these adaptations for locomotion are an *opposable thumb and big toe,* capable of being flexed or "opposed" against the other digits, *flat nails* instead of claws to support sensitive finger and toe tips, *fingerprint ridge patterns* to increase friction in grip, and relatively *short fore- and hindlimbs* of nearly equal length, a generalized mammal trait (Figure 5–2).

Body size increased in a number of descendant primate groups, and new locomotor adaptations appeared: (a) fore- and hindlimb lengths increased in ground-running primates, which increased stride length and speed (Figure 5–3b); (b) in the tree-living apes ("arm swingers"), forelimbs increased in length, which increased both speed and reach (Figure 5–3e); (c) in the frequently ground-dwelling African apes (gorilla and chimpanzee), longer forelimbs facilitated a unique form of locomotion called *knuckle walking* (Figure 5–3c); and (d) length of the lower limbs increased in the human lineage, which allowed for greater stride length in a new form of terrestrial locomotion, bipedal walking (Figure 5–3f).

7. *Low-crowned molar and premolar teeth* adapted to grinding and crushing food, as opposed to slicing, cutting, and piercing food. Primates have been described as an "order of omnivores" (Harding and Teleki, 1981). Animal protein in the form of insects and small vertebrates probably made up a large part of early primate diet, along with fruit and

vertical clinging and leaping– the method of locomotion characteristic of many living prosimians, and inferred to have been a method of locomotion in some early primates.

(a) Arboreal Quadruped

(b) Terrestrial Quadruped

(c) Knuckle Walker

(d) Leaper

(e) Arm Swinger

(f) Biped

Figure 5–3 • Primate locomotor categories.

other types of vegetation. Later and generally larger primates have evolved adaptations that emphasize one of several components of this basic dietary adaptation. The dentitions of primates clearly correlate to their diets. In general, primate teeth show some degree of flat, rounded structure in their molars, which indicates their function in crushing and chewing food. In contrast, monkeys tend to have shearing crests on their molars, adapted for cutting tough plant food.

8. Primates are generally *tropical* animals. However, the Japanese macaque has been able to extend its range into cold regions and has an adaptation that includes heavy fur; *Homo sapiens* has extended its range by means of culture.

9. Most primates are *active in the daytime*. This is understandable from the standpoint of the primate emphasis on the sense of sight. Food is located, predators are avoided, and movement is effected by visual referents. Most primates nest for the night in a secure location.

Suborders of Primates

Although the basic division among the living primates is that between prosimians and anthropoids, there is a third suborder of extinct, primitive primates, the plesiadapiforms, which we will discuss below. Within the suborder Prosimii are found the infraorders Adapiformes, containing most of the prosimians, and Tarsiiformes, containing only one living form, the tarsier. Within the anthropoid suborder are found the platyrrhine infraorder, containing the New World monkeys, and the catarrhine suborder, containing the Old World monkeys, and the hominoids: the apes and humans (Appendix 3).

THE FIRST PRIMATE RADIATION: PLESIADAPIFORMS

The significant changes in the earth's environment, fauna, and flora that occurred at the boundary of the Mesozoic and Cenozoic Eras are currently a subject of considerable debate. Flowering plants, characterized by a covered seed coat, had first appeared in the Cretaceous Period at the end of the Mesozoic. They diversified to form forests of great complexity, opening up new niches for animal life. Among the faunal changes the most noticeable is the disappearance of the dinosaurs, large and small, by the end of the Cretaceous Period, 65 million years ago. This mass extinction may have been quite sudden, perhaps caused by meteoritic impact(s) with the earth, or more gradual, caused by significant temperature and climatic change over several million years. In whatever manner it occurred, the extinction of the dinosaurs left many ecological niches vacant that were subsequently reoccupied by the birds and mammals.

During the Paleocene and Eocene, there were no mammals larger than a medium-sized dog. Among the successful of the early mammals were the archaic primates, the **plesiadapiforms.** The term comes from

plesiadapiforms—archaic primates of the Paleocene and Early Eocene Epochs.

the Greek word *plesi-* meaning "like" and *Adapis,* the first fossil primate to be named (by Cuvier in 1821), originally thought to be an ungulate ancestor and named for the ancient Egyptian bull god Apis—thus *ad* (Greek, meaning "toward") Apis.

The plesiadapiforms were among the most common animals in the Paleocene and early Eocene Epoch sites of North America and Europe some 50 to 65 million years ago (Figure 5–4). Over 60 species in 30 genera are known (Rose and Fleagle, 1981). They lived in environments of dense lowland forests along rivers, lakes, swamps, and at the edge of the midcontinental sea that divided eastern and western North America. Comparable environments are to be found today in Southeast Asia and subtropical parts of the southeastern United States.

There are two superfamilies of plesiadapiform primates: the **paromomyoids** (Greek, *par-* meaning "near," *Omomys* meaning "raw meat eating" and "molar") and the **plesiadapoids.** Both groups were part of a placental mammalian radiation into arboreal niches of which megabats ("flying foxes") and dermopterans ("flying lemurs") were also a part (Pettigrew et al., 1989). Recent work on new postcranial fossils (Beard, 1990) has shown that the paromomyoids were a group whose primary locomotor behavior was that of gliding, similar to the modern flying lemurs.

The plesiadapoids are the more generalized of these archaic primates, and they may represent the ancestral group from which later primates arose. They lack the adaptations to gliding seen in the paromomyoids. Both pairs of their central incisors, upper and lower, are enlarged, and the uppers have a characteristic three-pronged mitten shape. Like later primates, the plesiadapoids had a forearm that could easily supinate and pronate (see Appendix 1), and their ankle-joint articulations allow a wide degree of movement seen in living animals adapted to a climbing life in the trees.

During the Eocene the plesiadapiforms underwent significant decline, and by the end of the Eocene Epoch they were extinct. Their demise is most likely explained by the presence of more specialized small mammals that more successfully exploited the archaic primate niches. Rodents, which continuously grow front teeth used for gnawing, likely outcompeted many of the plesiadapiform primates. Other groups that may have competed with the plesiadapiforms were the bats, the dermopterans ("flying lemurs"), and their own relatives, the prosimian primates.

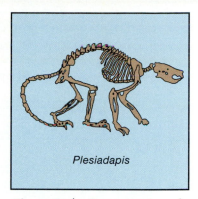

Plesiadapis

Figure 5–4 • Reconstruction of *Plesiadapis.*

paromomyoids–plesiadapiform primates that had gliding adaptations.

plesiadapoids–plesiadapiform primates that were generalized archaic primates and may have been ancestral to later primates.

THE SECOND PRIMATE RADIATION: PROSIMIANS

The end of the Paleocene Epoch marked a period of global warming that caused greater rainfall and higher temperatures over much of the earth (Figure 5–5, Appendix 2). Evergreen tropical forests extended over much of Africa, North America, and Eurasia at this time. The spread of tropical forests and warm temperatures facilitated the spread and adaptive radiation of primates into new areas.

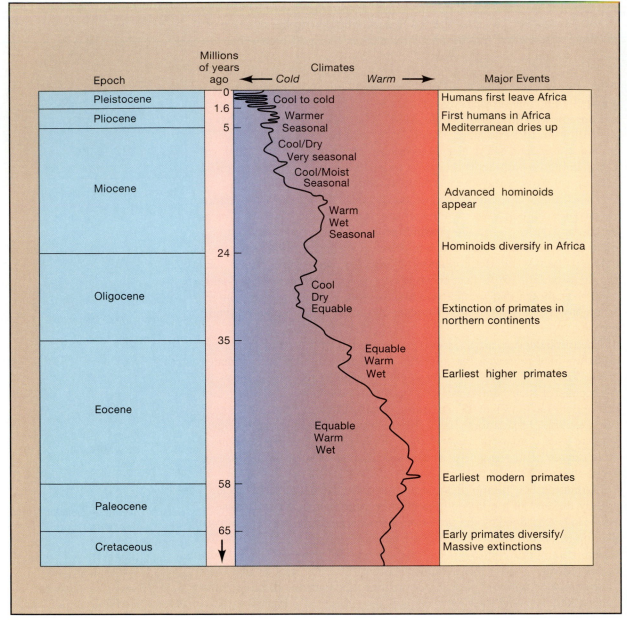

Figure 5–5 • Geological time and paleoenvironmental record of the Cenozoic.

The Eocene Epoch, beginning some 58 million years ago, was a period of worldwide expansion of the early primates. These were prosimians, and they possessed such distinguishing characteristics as a postorbital bar that completed the lateral or outside ring of bone around the eye socket; a thumb that diverged from the other digits, allowing opposability and grasping; and nails, rather than claws, on their digits.

Primates may have first diversified in Africa and spread northward as climates warmed at the Paleocene/Eocene boundary (Gingerich, 1990). In Morocco, North Africa, there is evidence of the evolutionary split between the lines leading to the modern lemurs and lorises, also known as strepsirhines (Greek, meaning "twisted nose") on the one hand, and those leading to the group including tarsiers and anthropoids, also known as haplorhines (Greek, meaning "single nose") on the other. These two lineages are represented in the fossil record by the lemurlike **adapids** (Figure 5–6), animals larger than their plesiadapiform predecessors and about the size of the modern Malagasy lemurs, and the early tarsierlike prosimians, the **omomyids.** One of the earliest of the tarsierlike omomyids, named *Altiatlasius,* is dated to about 60 million years ago (Sige et al., 1990). *Altiatlasius* was about the size of a mouse lemur or a galago (50 to 100 grams). Both adapids and omomyids had the elongated limbs characteristic of today's clinging and leaping species, although in other respects they are much more primitive. The common ancestral population of these two Paleo-Eocene prosimian lineages likely lies among the plesiadapoids.

The pulse of climatic cooling at the end of the early Eocene, coupled with mountain formation in western North America and Europe, made for diversifying environments over the ranges of prosimians. The Eocene primates of North America and Europe evolved in their own distinctive ways. North American Eocene sites seem to record a greater diversity of omomyids whereas European sites show a greater diversity of adapids. Though the prosimians have left a trail of their evolutionary history with scattered fossils through the Eocene and into the Pleistocene, prosimian dominance was well on the wane by the beginning of the Oligocene, some 37 million years ago. They disappeared from the fossil record in North America during this period.

The living prosimians are relics of what was once a widely distributed and ecologically diverse group. Today, in the mainland areas of Southeast Asia and tropical Africa, the prosimians have been displaced from the daytime world by the anthropoids, as a result of competition for natural resources. With the exception of the isolated case of Madagascar, a large island off the southeast coast of Africa, now only nocturnal prosimian species survive.

In Africa and Southeast Asia, prosimians range into tropical woodlands, deciduous forests and rain forests. In addition, the largely day-active lemuroid groups live in the dry spiny forests and the rain forests of Madagascar (Figure 5–7). Three species of bush babies ("galagos") are found in habitats throughout the forests of central to southern Africa. Two additional prosimians in the lorisid family, the potto (*Perodicticus*) and the angwantibo (*Arctocebus*), live together with the galago over much of their forested range. In Asia the nocturnal prosimians include the slender loris (*Loris*) and the slow loris (*Nycticebus*), as well as the leaping form, the tarsier.

Napier and Walker (1967) described prosimian locomotion as primarily a form of vertical clinging and leaping (Figure 5–8). Among the

Figure 5–6 • Reconstruction of the Eocene adapid *Notharctus* from North America.

adapids—lemurlike prosimians, among the earliest strepsirhines.

omomyids—tarsierlike prosimians, among the earliest haplorhines.

Figure 5–7 • Ring-tailed lemur in native habitat in Madagascar.

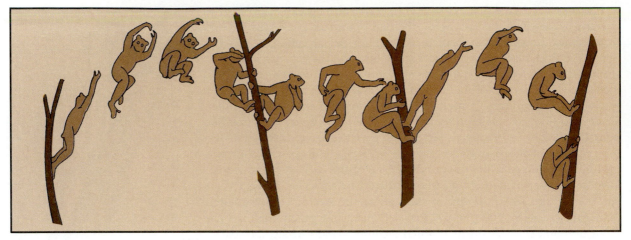

Figure 5–8 • Vertical clinging and leaping in prosimians.

prosimians exist the extremes in locomotor speed. The tarsier and galago are "vertical-clinger-and-leapers," moving by rapid jumping and clinging to branches, while the potto and slow loris move, as the latter's name implies, at a casual pace with caution along the branches. The limb skeleton of each reflects their locomotor capabilities. The tarsier, perhaps the most dramatic jumper, has extremely elongated hindlimbs. The lower portion of the hindlimb has a largely fused tibia and fibula. This adaptation increases the stability of the lower limb and at the same time adds greater strength to withstand compressive shock in landing after long jumps. Two of the tarsier's tarsal (foot) bones, the heel bone or *calcaneus* and ankle bone or *talus*, are also elongated. This elongation of tarsal bones provides greater leverage in jumping and gives the tarsier its name.

BEHAVIOR AND SOCIAL ORGANIZATION OF PROSIMIANS

We do not know how the ancient prosimians behaved or how their social groups were structured. We have, however, studied extensively the behaviors of modern diurnal and nocturnal prosimians and, on the basis of these studies, we can create models of what archaic prosimian behavior may have been like. Modern prosimian behavior is most probably quite different from that of the earliest ancestors who coped with substantially different environments from today in places of the world where prosimians are no longer found in the wild. Thus, behavioral model building of archaic behavior based on the behavior of living forms must proceed with great caution.

Charles-Dominique (1977) noted that "all lemurs are social, even those which are not particularly gregarious." Although it is generally true that the males and females of these nocturnal species avoid contact with one another except during the breeding season, their successful reproduction depends upon the continuing knowledge of one another's whereabouts. This knowledge is imparted by urine or fecal marking, commonly practiced by most prosimians throughout their individual **home ranges**—that space which a group of animals occupies all through the year. Other prosimians possess glands on the neck and chest from which the males deposit scent on branches as well as on nearby females. Pair-bonding is reinforced by tactile signals, such as grooming and side-by-side contact, both of which increase in frequency as the annual breeding season approaches. Even during solitary foraging, the nocturnal prosimians maintain a network of social interactions through scent markings and vocal calling and, at times, direct contact.

The adult female of each species generally occupies a distinct home range. During the day, female lorises often sleep alone or with immature offspring. The galagos forage alone at night in overlapping home ranges, but females often sleep in groups of two or three, with their young. Males of all these species usually forage and sleep by themselves. The home ranges of one or more of the females overlap with that of a single male. The male keeps constant vigilance throughout his range, periodically visiting females and mating with those who are in estrus. Young males, in order to find a spot devoid of another "central" male, may travel substantial distances from their natal home ranges to establish themselves. Females, on the other hand, usually remain near the area of their birth throughout their lives.

The day-active (diurnal) prosimians are found only on Madagascar, where they have avoided ecological competition with the higher primates. Diurnal prosimians are gregarious in their social behavior. Of these Madagascar prosimians the best studied have been the ring-tailed lemur (*Lemur catta*) (Figure 5–7) and the sifaka (*Propithecus*).

The ring-tailed lemurs form social groups numbering between 5 and 22 animals of all ages and sexes. The core of the group consists of females and their young, with the several adult males spatially peripheral to the core. Adult males often transfer between groups and will aggregate temporarily into all-male groups. Lemur home ranges may be exclusively utilized by a single group, or they may overlap with other groups, which mutually avoid one another by adjusting their foraging patterns and times.

Dominance rank interactions are displayed by both the adult males and females of the troop. In lemurs, however, adult females are dominant, and, as in most other primate social units, the female dominance hierarchy is generally more stable than that of the males. Aggressive behavior between the males is common, but only during the mating season do these aggressive interactions result in physical injury. During the breeding season the male dominance hierarchy breaks down and the males interact in a free-for-all for sexual access to the females in **estrus.**

The sifaka social group consists of adult males and females, but group size tends to be smaller, ranging between 2 and 12 animals. Some sifakas occupy the drier spiny forests of southern Madagascar and establish and

home range—the area that a group or population inhabits and ranges over, the boundaries of which, unlike a territory, are not defended.

dominance rank—the relative hierarchical position of an individual in a social group.

estrus—the period of maximum sexual receptivity and ovulation that may be marked by physiological and behavioral changes in females. Corresponding changes may also be observed in males.

FRONTIERS

Predation, Feeding Strategies, and Primate Origins

by Matt Cartmill

Several new accounts of primate origins have been put forward. Until recently, the main contenders were the conflicting stories offered in various versions over the past two decades by Frederick S. Szalay (1972) and myself (Cartmill, 1974, 1982). Szalay's account offered to explain primate origins in terms of the shared derived features of modern and archaic primates, whereas my explanations centered on the traits peculiar to "primates of modern aspect." Both of these accounts are now being challenged by new findings and interpretations.

Robert Sussman (1991) has put forward the idea that posits the central adaptation of fruit-eating in the earliest primates. The visual and grasping adaptations of the early primates Sussman sees as adaptations to feeding at the ends of branches, and he suggests that the radiation of the early primates may have been a side effect of great diversification of flowering plants at the end of the Eocene Epoch (Sussman and Raven, 1978). However, as I have pointed out, the known teeth of the earliest primates do not suggest fruit-eating, and Sussman's theory also does not explain the characteristic visual specializations of the primates. It would make sense for a visually predatory animal to have a wide range of sharp stereoscopic vision directly in front of it, whereas such specializations are not obviously needed when the prey is a banana.

Tab Rasmussen (1990) suggested a new hypothesis that incorporates some of both Sussman's and my ideas. Finding that a South American primatelike opossum eats both fruit and insect prey, Rasmussen suggests that early primates may have climbed out into the terminal branches in search of fruit (as Sussman thinks), and developed their visual peculiarities to help them catch the insects that they encountered there (as my theory implies).

Continuing research on the comparative behavior and adaptations of other tree-living mammals will help to sort out and test the explanations that have been offered for the evolution of grasping feet and flattened nails in the first primates. It would also help if we knew something about the order in which the various primate peculiarities were acquired. If the first primates had grasping feet and blunt teeth adapted for eating fruit, but retained small, divergent orbits like those of *Plesiadapis,* Rasmussen's account would gain added plausibility. If they had convergent orbits and the sharp, slicing molar teeth of insect-eaters, that would support my ideas. The oldest fossil primates we know of at present resemble modern primates in both their foot bones and their eye sockets, and so they do not help to answer this question. We can only hope that new fossil finds will help us to tease apart the various strands of the primate story, and give us some clearer insights into the evolutionary causes behind the origin of the primate order to which we belong.

Matt Cartmill is Professor of Biological Anthropology and Anatomy at Duke University. He is past editor of the American Journal of Physical Anthropology *and the author of* A View to a Death in the Morning: Hunting and Nature through History *(Cambridge, MA: Harvard University Press, 1994).*

defend their home ranges, called *territories,* with ritualized aggression towards other groups, aggression that seldom results in actual physical violence. In other areas of Madagascar, however, sifakas show no defense behavior when their home ranges overlap. As with the lemurs, male social dominance hierarchy disappears during the annual breeding season.

Another species of Madagascar lemur, the indri, exhibits a particularly interesting social organization that is similar to the organization of the marmosets, small monkeys of South America. The indri form groups that may include siblings and unrelated younger males, in addition to monogamous adult males and females and their immature young

(Richard, 1985a:296). How these additional individuals function in the indri group is as yet unknown. It may be, however, that these hangers-on are put to work baby-sitting newborns of the troop. Although the prosimians are anatomically more primitive than the monkeys and apes, they do display many similar behavioral patterns that parallel those observed in their more advanced cousins, the anthropoids.

THE THIRD PRIMATE RADIATION: ANTHROPOIDS

The latter half of the Eocene Epoch to the beginning of the Oligocene Epoch (47 to 35 million years ago) was a period of global cooling and of increasingly open, less forested habitats. Faunas worldwide changed to include more browsing and terrestrial forms. Anthropoids appear suddenly in the Late Eocene–Early Oligocene sediments of Africa, and possibly Southeast Asia, without any obvious antecedents.

The earliest fossil record of possible anthropoids comes from Late Eocene deposits in Burma. Specimens have been attributed to two species (*Pondaungia cotteri* and *Amphipithecus mogaungensis*) that show the anthropoid-like characteristics of deep mandible and low-crowned molars. But because the specimens are so fragmentary, experts disagree on whether they represent the first anthropoids or just large prosimians.

The first undisputed anthropoid is *Catopithecus browni* from the Fayum Depression of northern Egypt (Simons, 1990). It dates from below or near the Eocene–Oligocene boundary, some 37 million years ago. The skull and mandible of this species show the same number and kinds of teeth as those found in the Old World monkeys, apes, and humans. The number and kinds of teeth may be expressed as a *dental formula*, written to show the teeth present in one side of the upper and lower jaw.

In the case of *Catopithecus*, as well as humans, the formula is written 2.1.2.3./2.1.2.3. This means that each side of the upper and lower jaws contains 2 incisors, 1 canine, 2 premolars (or bicuspids), and 3 molars. The skull of *Catopithecus* also shows the presence of a postorbital bar, a fused frontal bone in the midline, and likely a fused mandible in the midline. All these are higher primate characteristics, which indicate that the species is definitely an anthropoid. Details of the teeth and ear region (absence of a tubular **ectotympanic bone**), however, have led Simons (1990) to suggest that *Catopithecus browni* is descended from adapoids rather than omomyoids, an opinion that is different from that now held by many specialists (Figure 5–9).

The Fayum is a low-lying desert region of the northernmost Egyptian Sahara and it is the primary spot on earth to have provided a window on the period when the first anthropoids arose. The fossil-bearing sections of the Fayum date from the late Eocene to middle Oligocene Epoch, between approximately 31 and 37 million years ago.

ectotympanic bone–a separate bone covering the ear canal.

Figure 5–9 • Different views on the phylogenetic relationships between the fossil prosimians and later anthropoids.

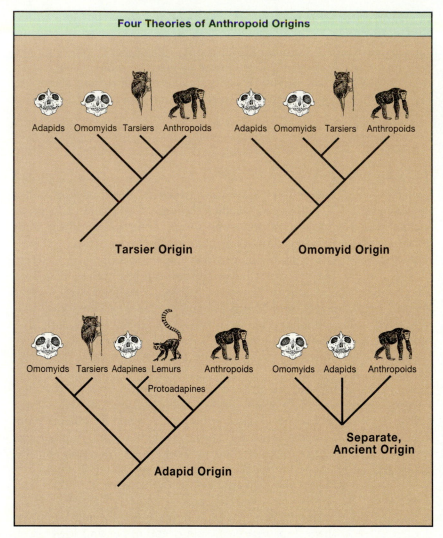

The environmental setting in the Fayum has been reconstructed through painstaking geological and paleontological work by Bown et al. (1982). The fossil plants preserved in the Fayum provide an important glimpse at the world of the early anthropoids. Mangrove trees, which live in low-lying swamps near the sea, large broad-leaved trees characteristic of dense rain forest, and climbing, vinelike plants known as lianes, are abundant. There was abundant rainfall, in marked contrast to the desert conditions found today.

The Oligocene primates that lived in the Fayum shared it with many large and small mammals. Among the primates there are the parapithecids (*Apidium* and *Parapithecus*), small anthropoid primates only slightly advanced over their prosimian relatives, that were more common than the primitive anthropoids. In fact, *Apidium* is the most common small animal found in the middle and upper levels at the Fayum.

In the early levels of the Fayum, the smallest of the Fayum anthropoids, known as *Oligopithecus savagei,* is morphologically similar to and related to *Catopithecus.* It was the size of a large marmoset, approximately 20 to 35 centimeters (8.5 to 15 inches) in head and body length. The species is not well known, but Simons (1972), Kay (1977), and Fleagle and Kay (1987) consider it most closely allied with and a possible ancestor to the later, larger **propliopithecoids** in the Fayum, *Aegyptopithecus* and *Propliopithecus.* On the other hand, Szalay (1970) and Delson (1977) suggest that it was actually a more generalized species, not a propliopithecoid or early apelike anthropoid itself, and should be included with *Apidium.*

There are two, and possibly more, species of propliopithecoids preserved in later levels at the Fayum. *Aegyptopithecus zeuxis* was the largest species (Figure 5–10), the size of a modern gibbon. It was thus about 40 to 65 centimeters (1.5 to 2 ft.) in combined head and body length. *Propliopithecus* has two named species, *P. haeckeli* and *P. markgrafi,* and was substantially smaller, about the size of a modern African swamp monkey or talapoin. *Aegyptopithecus* and *Propliopithecus* also had a dental formula that is the same as that of all living apes and Old World monkeys, distinguishing these species from the contemporary parapithecids, whose jaws show three premolars.

Aegyptopithecus shows a significant amount of sexual dimorphism, with the males about a quarter larger than the females. Using modern primates as a guide, this degree of sexual dimorphism suggests that the mating structure of these early anthropoids was a single-male group with several females and offspring. Other possible correlates of behavior, such as territoriality, are as yet unknown.

propliopithecoids—anthropoid (catarrhine) primates from the Oligocene of Egypt, sometimes considered the earliest hominoids.

Figure 5–10 • Reconstruction (left) and skull and mandible (right) of *Aegyptopithecus zeuxis.*

ORIGINS AND EVOLUTION OF THE MONKEYS

The evolutionary origins of the monkeys involves the split between the primate infraorders of **platyrrhines** (Greek, meaning "flat-nosed") and **catarrhines** (Greek, meaning "downward nose"). New World monkeys, which have noses with laterally facing nostrils, make up the former group, and Old World monkeys belong to the latter, along with apes and humans.

The origin of the Old World monkeys has not been controversial because generally acknowledged ancestral forms from the Oligocene exist in Africa. But the evolutionary origin of the New World monkeys has been problematical. There are no fossil primates known at all from South America during the Paleocene or Eocene Epochs, when open sea separated it from North America, which was teeming with prosimians (omomyoids and adapoids). By the beginning of the Cenozoic, South America was also separated from Africa by a substantial expanse of Atlantic Ocean.

Monkeys appear suddenly in the fossil record of South America, in the late Oligocene. The **cebid** genus *Branisella* occurs at the Bolivian site of Salla with a potassium-argon date of approximately 26 million years ago (MacFadden et al., 1985). The fact that monkeys appear full-blown in South America with no apparent ancestral source there indicates that they migrated from elsewhere. Opinions on the origin of the platyrrhine monkeys have been divided between those favoring an evolutionary origin from North American prosimian ancestors (Rosenberger, 1992) and those favoring an African origin (Fleagle and Kay, 1987). Dispersal from North America would have been across the strait of Panama or the Caribbean Sea, but there are no good North American candidates for direct ancestors of New World monkeys in the Eocene, and no North American Oligocene monkey fossil record at all. Dispersal from Africa might seem less likely, because it would have required transport of monkey ancestors across the South Atlantic Ocean, estimated to have been only 200 kilometers wide during the Oligocene (Figure 5–11). This apparently unlikely event, however, is probably what happened.

Parapithecids as known from the Fayum may be good candidates for the ancestral populations of the New World monkeys. Both parapithecids and New World monkeys have three premolars, a major distinction from the catarrhines, which all have only two. The age of the earliest *Parapithecus*-bearing levels in the Fayum is dated to 31 million years ago (Fleagle et al., 1986), predating the earliest monkey-bearing fossil sites in South America. The data strongly suggest that platyrrhines had an African origin and dispersed to South America by rafting on floating mats of vegetation across the open ocean. In modern times, large rafts of vegetation, some large enough to support standing mid-sized trees, are known to break off from river banks of large tropical rivers and drift out to sea. Such a raft emanating from perhaps the Congo (formerly Zaire) or Niger Rivers of western Africa may have launched primates on their new evolutionary career once they reached South America.

platyrrhines–New World monkeys.

catarrhines–Old World monkeys, apes, and humans.

cebid–New World monkeys excluding marmosets and tamarins.

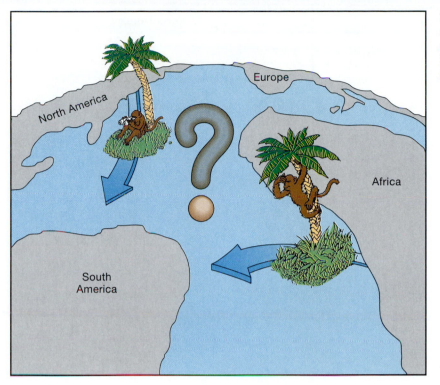

Figure 5–11 • Hypothetical possible routes of dispersal of the ancestors of the New World monkeys from Africa and North America, respectively.

New World Monkeys

The French naturalist Buffon (1767) was the first to recognize the primates of the New World and differentiate them from those better known monkeys and apes in the Old World. He based his early, simple classification primarily on their external morphological features, of which the three most visible characteristics were an absence of cheek pouches and ischial callosities, and more widely spaced nostrils (Figure 5–12).

Later in the nineteenth century came the discovery of the **callitrichids,** marmosets and tamarins, distinguished by the lack of the prehensile tail common to a number of other New World primates, the lack of third molars, their three-cusped upper molars, and also the presence of claws. These claws function in much the same way as do those of rodents, opening up the possibilities for very small animals to vertically ascend and descend large trees and to engage in cling-and-leap locomotion.

The modern species of New World primates are all arboreal and, with one exception, the night or owl monkeys (*Aotus*), are diurnal. They range as far north as the Yucatán in Mexico and as far south as the southernmost expansion of the tropical rain forests of South America. Most occur within the reaches of the Amazonian rain forest basin.

Quadrupedalism and leaping appear to represent the earliest arboreal locomotor adaptation in the evolution of this group (Gebo, 1989a). The fossil remains of early New World primates show a widened foot, a

callitrichids—marmosets and tamarins.

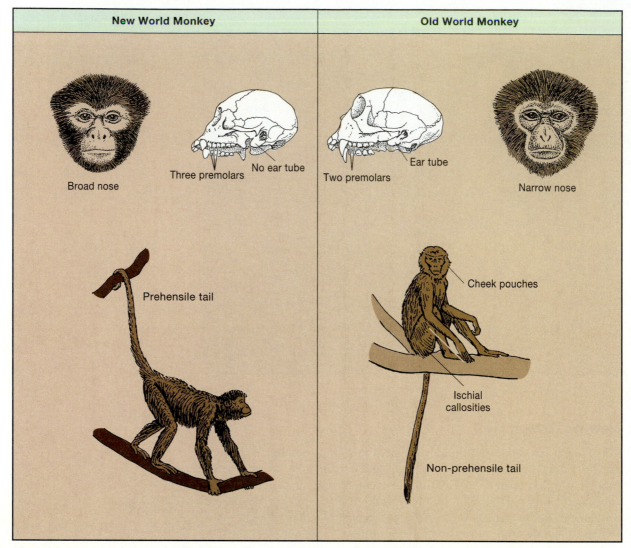

Figure 5–12 • Morphological differences in the New World and Old World monkeys.

lengthened great toe for purposes of grasping, and an increased mobility of the limb joints. This pattern was later modified by some cebids, such as the spider monkey (Figure 5–13), which developed tail-assisted suspensory movement, including a greater mobility in the upper limb. These adaptations allowed them to carry out an arm-swinging form of locomotion paralleling, though not precisely analogous to, true brachiation (Jungers and Stern, 1980).

On the other end of the spectrum, the marmosets and tamarins and the night monkey have only a minor ability in arm-swinging. These animals are generally quadrupedal, using a squirrel-like gait, and confine their locomotor activities to larger tree limbs. Midway between the smaller marmosets and the tail-assisted brachiators are a third group of fairly acrobatic species, such as *Lagothrix* (the woolly monkey) and *Alouatta* (the howling monkey), which occupy the smaller branches in the forest canopy.

Old World Monkeys

The earliest fossil record of Old World monkeys is a species found on the eastern shore and nearby islands of Lake Victoria, Kenya, known as *Victoriapithecus maccinnesi*. It shows the double-crested pattern of the lower molars that characterizes Old World monkeys. It dates from the early Miocene, some 18 to 20 million years ago. Of almost comparable, but likely middle Miocene, age is a North African species, *Prohylobates tandyi.*

Monkeys are scarce in comparison with apes in the earliest fossil sites in which they are known. This is quite the opposite of the modern situation, in which apes are rare in terms of both population numbers and species diversity. Modern-day monkeys have likely taken over many of the ecological niches occupied in the Miocene by the numerous species of small-bodied apes.

The superfamily of Old World monkeys, **Cercopithecoidea,** is made up of a large number of species whose appearance differs widely. The living cercopithecoids are divided into two subfamily groups: the **cercopithecines,** the baboons, macaques, and relatives; and the **colobines,** the leaf-eating monkeys. Among many species and even within subspecies, remarkable variety in coat coloration and hair patterns have evolved, paralleled only among the New World marmosets. In other morphological characteristics, however, the cercopithecoids have few divergent specializations compared with the prosimians, the New World monkeys, or the hominoids (Figure 5–14). Size differences are not as great as those found in the other primate groups: The smallest cercopithecoid, the talapoin, weighs about 1.2 kilograms, and the largest, the mandrill, about 30 kilograms.

The Old World monkeys are basic quadrupedal animals showing few locomotor specializations, with the exception of the relative elongation of the hindlimb as seen in the colobines, the specialized leapers in this group. Primate quadrupedalism in general has been much less studied than the more exotic types of locomotion such as leaping or brachiation. Quadrupedal locomotion does vary, however. Within one genus, *Cercopithecus,* Ashton and Oxnard (1964) noted that some species preferred quadrupedal walking and running on larger branches, while other species used the smaller branches more frequently in acrobatic leaping.

In the Old World monkeys, leaping is less developed than in the prosimians. Their leaps have a downward direction, a spread-eagle, midair posture, and a crashlike mode of landing. Old World monkeys also show some inclination towards side-raised upper-limb positioning, as seen in the New World primates and the apes. The shoulder blades of

Figure 5–13 • The spider monkey.

Cercopithecoidea–Old World monkeys.

cercopithecines–Old World monkeys with generally omnivorous or graminivorous diets, frequently ground-living, and sometimes lacking tails.

colobines–leaf-eating monkeys, mostly arboreal.

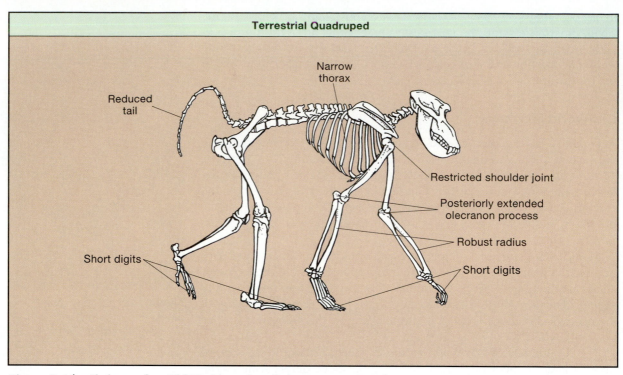

Figure 5–14 • Skeleton of an Old World monkey (baboon, genus *Papio*).

all the Old World monkeys lie at the sides of their relatively narrow chests and, as a consequence, their collar bones have remained proportionately short. In the lower trunk the pelves are quite similar. The ilium forming the blade of the pelvis is long and narrow in a cranial-caudal direction, and the pubic bones are rounded, which allows for a birth canal that is slightly larger in size than the usual head diameter of a newborn.

Limb proportions, as measured by the *intermembral index* (the length of the forelimb divided by the length of the hindlimb, multiplied by 100), differ far less in the Old World monkeys than in other primate groups. The active arm swingers—the Asiatic gibbons and the larger-bodied orangutans—show the longest relative arm lengths. The longest relative leg lengths belong to the bipeds and the leaping Asiatic tarsiers and Madagascar sifakas. In the hands and feet the Old World monkeys are also relatively unspecialized and do not show the opposable capability seen in many prosimians. Old World monkeys do not possess prehensile tails, though they may use their tails for balancing and perhaps for assisting in vertical climbing. Tail length varies considerably among species in the Old World monkeys.

In most species males are generally significantly larger in body size than females. In the terrestrial baboons they are often twice the size of females. Certain Old World monkeys exhibit sexual differences in such features as the shape of the ischial callosities, on which both males and females sit or sleep during the night, the size of the cheek pads, and the size of the nose. No such comparable sexual dimorphism can be seen in the living New World monkeys or prosimians.

The skull of Old World monkeys shows proportions different from those seen in most other primates. The most striking differences appear in the relative length and protrusion of the jaws, the extreme of which is seen in baboons. Jaw prognathism is the result of the large size of the canine teeth and first lower premolar, which are significantly sexually dimorphic in all but the smallest Old World monkeys. The dentition of the Old World monkeys (as well as the apes and humans) shows the typical dental formula 2.1.2.3. Old World monkeys, however, as we have seen, have the two-ridged molar cusp pattern, which differentiates them from the hominoids.

The subfamily of colobines is divided into two subgroups, the colobus monkeys of Africa and the Asian leaf monkeys or langurs. The Colobinae form a group distinct from the Cercopithecinae, characterized by a number of morphological adaptations for a predominantly leaf-eating (folivorous) diet. Additional morphological features that distinguish them from the cercopithecines are related to locomotor specializations in leaping and arboreal suspension. Colobines are capable of greater forelimb abduction, including shoulder rotation with the elbow joint fully extended. This larger range of forelimb movement allows them to sit on branches and, from overhead, pull down smaller twigs containing food (Tuttle, 1975). They also use their forelimbs and hands to grasp overhanging limbs in order to steady themselves (Morbeck, 1979).

 **SUMMARY**

1. True primates originated during the Paleocene as tropical animals that evolved hands and feet for grasping as a form of locomotion in newly available arboreal niches. As a way of catching prey as well as locomoting rapidly in the trees, they developed stereoscopic vision and, in many forms, color vision.
2. The ancestry of the primates is perhaps most closely related to that of the insectivores, which today are represented by one common form: the tree shrew of Southeast Asia, once thought to be a primate itself.
3. An omnivorous diet distinguished the earliest or archaic primates, including the well-known plesiadapiforms.
4. The evolution of the archaic primates was followed by a series of three major adaptive radiations. During the first radiation, which occurred during the Paleocene and Eocene, the plesiadapiforms diversified. The second radiation, which began at the end of the Paleocene, produced the arboreal prosimians, the ancestors of the living lemurs, galagos, and tarsiers. The third radiation occurred in the Oligocene, during which anthropoid primates appeared and spread out of Africa.
5. In South America, the platyrrhines diversified as ancestral forms to all of the modern New World monkeys, which possess both unique (as in the prehensile tail) and parallel characteristics (as in larger brains).

CRITICAL-THINKING QUESTIONS

1. What is a primate?
2. Describe the general characteristics of plesiadapiforms.
3. Briefly discuss the behavior and social organization of the prosimians.
4. What anatomical differences distinguish anthropoids from prosimians?
5. Discuss the differences between nocturnal and diurnal primates.
6. Compare and contrast Old World and New World monkeys.

SUGGESTED READINGS

Ankel-Simons, F. 1983. *A Survey of Living Primates and Their Anatomy.* New York: Macmillan. An introduction to the diversity of living primates and their adaptations.

Conroy, G. 1990. *Primate Evolution.* New York: W. W. Norton. A general text on primate evolution and morphology.

Fleagle, J. 1988. *Primate Adaptation and Evolution.* New York: Academic Press. A general text on primate evolution and morphology.

Fleagle, J., and A. Rosenberger. 1990. *The Platyrrhine Fossil Record.* New York: Academic Press. A review of the fossil record of the New World monkeys.

Szalay, F., and E. Delson. 1979. *Evolutionary History of the Primates.* New York: Academic Press. A detailed treatment of primate evolution for the advanced student.

Primates: Patterns in Social Behavior

Chapter 5 examined primate evolution by looking at the fossil record and the morphological adaptations of modern primates. This chapter explores aspects of the **social behavior** of the anthropoids, the monkeys and apes. Such studies of modern primates, both in the wild and under laboratory situations, are instructive in two broad areas. First, in a general sense behavior is ecologically constrained. Thus, behavior is ecologically adapted, and variations in behavior patterns can be explained by how a species exploits its natural resources. Survival or life history strategies of a species must be successful in the species' environment if an animal is to eat, mate, and avoid predators. Second, the study of behavior sheds light on evolutionary problems. Behaviors that are universal among modern primates provide us with some clues as to the kinds of behaviors that our ancestors may have practiced. With such clues we can develop models of ancestral behaviors. The social behavior of modern prosimians, discussed in the last chapter, provides us with information on those basic primate behavioral adaptations from which the more complex behaviors of the higher primates have evolved. We turn our attention in this chapter to social behavior of the anthropoids.

social behavior—actions and interactions of animals within groups.

field studies—in primatology, studies of species in their natural habitat, uninfluenced or influenced to a minor degree by interactions with humans.

semi–free-ranging studies—in primatology, the study of primate groups that are in some way affected by or are dependent on humans, yet live more or less "normal" social lives.

laboratory studies—in primatology, controlled studies of captive primates.

FIELD STUDIES

Arguably, the first successful study of a primate species done in the wild was C. R. Carpenter's work on the howler monkeys of Barro Colorado Island, Panama, in 1934. Since then, **field studies, semi–free-ranging studies,** and **laboratory studies** on primates of both the Old and the

Figure 6–1 • Irven DeVore in Nairobi National Park.

New Worlds have expanded dramatically. Interest in general social behavior of a wide variety of primate species was followed by more specific studies on communication, mother–infant behavior, matrilineal kinship, and dominance, as well as the relationships of behavior to ecology. Long-term studies (more than one year in length) have been undertaken on genealogical relationships and life histories of animals of such species as the common chimpanzee (Goodall), the gorilla (Fossey), the savanna baboon (Strum), the orangutan (Galdikas), and the Japanese macaque (beginning with Itani).

In the late 1950s, K. R. L. Hall studied the chacma baboons of South Africa; Sherwood Washburn and Irven DeVore studied the yellow and olive baboons of the Serengeti Plains in Kenya (Figure 6–1); Hans Kummer and Fred Kurt studied the desert baboons (*Papio hamadryas* of Ethiopia); and Phyllis Jay Dolhinow studied the langurs of North India. During the 1970s, studies on almost every genus and most species followed, all of which have increased our awareness and concern for those conservation measures that might help stem the alarming trend of habitat destruction, which threatens the survival of many species throughout the world (Southwick and Smith, 1986).

ADVANTAGES OF GROUP LIVING

One of the most important primate characteristics is sociality. In primates social behavior is organized around the continuous interactions of a group of animals. Some members of the group may continue to interact with certain other members throughout their life span. Long-term interactions, such as those seen between a mother and her offspring, support group cohesiveness and make social living possible. Because group living demands complicated social interactions, each animal must spend a substantial amount of time learning about other animals and the roles they play. The individual's ability to recognize other individuals and act according to what is known about them based on past experience forms the basis for group interaction. Primate group living on a year-to-year basis also demands a great measure of social control over each individual's actions, as individual deviant behavior, for the most part, must be constrained if the group is to survive as a unit.

All animal species that interact among themselves on an ongoing basis share the same advantages and costs of group living. Costs and benefits can be calculated for many different social adaptations. Among the social primates, for example, costs and benefits can be determined for diurnal as well as nocturnal species (Figure 6–2). Perhaps the first advantage is that social living sets the stage for **observational learning** by individuals and, thereby, reduces the necessity of novel experimentation by any single animal. Knowledge of group traditions and the adaptive solutions to recurring problems allows an animal to learn how to survive within its ecological setting. In this regard the advantage of sociality is that such information is transmitted more easily among animals

observational learning–learning by seeing and hearing.

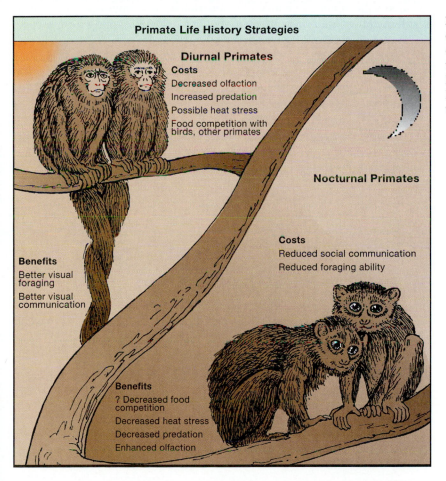

Primate Life History Strategies

Diurnal Primates

Costs
Decreased olfaction
Increased predation
Possible heat stress
Food competition with birds, other primates

Nocturnal Primates

Costs
Reduced social communication
Reduced foraging ability

Benefits
Better visual foraging
Better visual communication

Benefits
? Decreased food competition
Decreased heat stress
Decreased predation
Enhanced olfaction

Figure 6–2 • Reasonable hypothesis of the costs and benefits of diurnality and nocturnality for two species of New World monkeys, the dusky titi monkey (top, left) and the owl monkey (bottom, right).

reproductive fitness–relative reproductive success of certain individuals over others as measured by selection in a particular environment; the ability of one genotype to produce more offspring relative to this ability in other genotypes in the same environment.

infanticide–killing of infants.

living in a group. Through the socialization process, the group makes available to its members more knowledge than a single individual could acquire in its own lifetime.

A second advantage of social behavior is that it increases the possibility of resistance to diseases and parasites. The development over time of such resistance is less likely among solitary animals than among those animals who are social.

A third advantage is that social behavior functions to increase the overall **reproductive fitness** of group members. Generally, group living is organized by a dominance hierarchy in which all members are ranked according to various criteria. This hierarchical structure of groups may result in reduced reproductive fitness of subordinate members relative to fitness in individuals of higher dominance rank. But even a subordinate, group-living individual probably has a higher fitness, because of the availability of mates, than do individuals living a solitary existence (Figure 6–3).

Furthermore, social groups are more efficient in finding food resources, as foraging becomes more effective with larger numbers of individuals looking for food. For females an additional benefit of social groups is the reduced chance of **infanticide** by nongroup males, since resident males often protect group females and their young from attack.

These benefits must be weighed against the costs of social group living:

1. Reduced fecundity (reproductive output) of individuals, due to the stress of ongoing social interactions (Dunbar, 1989), which balances against increased reproductive fitness due to the increased number of potential mates in a social group.
2. Greater competition for food, which increases as the size of the group increases, but which is balanced against a higher likelihood of finding food in the first place due to an increase in number of foragers.

Figure 6–3 • Troop of savanna baboons.

3. Increased possibility of killing of infants of those females who shift their residency from one group to another or, on the other hand, whose resident males transfer out of the group; however, there are lower frequencies of infanticide for those females whose group remains stable and whose social history is known to the resident males.

4. Increase in the immediate spread of disease or parasites due to the close proximity of group members, balanced against the long-term advantage that group-living, sexually reproducing organisms have in acquiring resistance to disease and parasites.

DEVELOPMENT OF BEHAVIORAL MODELING

As information from numerous field studies has accumulated, syntheses or models of behavior have been needed to explain various patterns of primate social organization (Figure 6–4). Variations in social patterns have had to be integrated with the ecological and **demographic** data collected by field workers.

Some of the first attempts to synthesize primate behavioral data borrowed theory from ethological studies of other animals, mainly birds and the social insects. One of ethology's pioneers was Konrad Lorenz. He focused on **stereotypic** (species-specific) aspects of behavior that clearly reflected evolutionary patterns. The complex social behavior of mammals, and of primates in particular, remained mostly outside this field of study. The primary reason was that species-specific behaviors, which are primarily genetically programmed, were considered to be relatively minor components of the total behavior patterns of mammals. Behavioral variation within the species was thought to have little evolutionary or adaptive importance.

During the middle 1960s, new theoretical perspectives emerged through the efforts of William Hamilton, George Williams, and J. Maynard Smith. From these perspectives evolved the concepts of **inclusive fitness.** Inclusive fitness is the sum of an individual's reproductive success and that of its relatives in proportion to their shared genes. It involves the success of individual strategies of game playing and optimality. *Game playing* refers to how specific behavior patterns develop that maximize an individual's reproductive success, and *optimality* refers to alternative behaviors available to an individual. Along with this body of work, Dawkins (1989) developed the model of the "selfish gene," which argued that the basic unit of selection was the gene, not the individual. These concepts replaced the earlier ethological views with notions that animal behavior is flexibly opportunistic rather than stereotypic. Behavior is thus designed to maximize reproductive fitness through various strategies of self-interest.

These ideas were incorporated in a new field in animal behavior called **sociobiology** (Wilson, 1975). Sociobiology turned its attention on the behavioral adaptations that are most important to an animal's reproductive strategies. It argued that the evolution of sociality must be

demographic—relating to the age composition, proportions of the sexes, size, and other statistical parameters of a population.

stereotypic—referring to repetitive behavior reproduced without significant variation.

inclusive fitness—the relative reproductive potential of an individual within a group of related individuals in a population.

sociobiology—evolutionary study of social behavior emphasizing relative reproductive rates of success of individuals within a population.

Figure 6–4 • Common types of primate social groups. Social groupings vary from monogamous partnerships, as observed in gibbons, to opportunistically mating multi-male, multi-female troops, as seen in the baboons and macaques. Single-male units vary from the pattern of the orangutans, to one-male troops, as observed in the south Indian langurs, to the single-male harems that are the smaller foraging–mating units of the larger aggregate of hamadryas baboons. The most fluid type of social grouping is the fission–fusion societies of the chimpanzees.

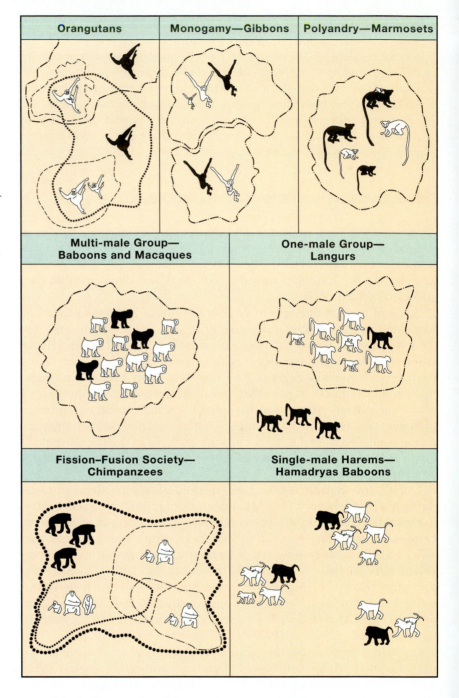

explained at the level of reproductive costs and benefits to the individual (Alexander, 1974). Behavioral variation, especially between the sexes, became the focus of evolutionary significance, and behavioral decisions were viewed in terms of the influence played by social and ecological variables. Within the scope of reproductive strategies, an animal's primary interest involved *sex-ratio manipulation* (how to alter the number of males or females produced in relation to environmental demand); *parental investment* (how much time and energy should be spent on any given offspring); and *parent–offspring conflict*.

The second field of interest to arise from the ethological perspective is behavioral ecology or **socioecology,** which looked at ways in which nonsocial environmental variables, such as the availability of food or the threat of predators, could determine or constrain behavior. Whereas sociobiology measures genotypic success, based on gene propagation or spread, socioecology measures phenotypic success, that is, how successful animals are at food acquisition, resource defense, and mating (Wrangham, 1987a; Terbough and Jansen, 1986; Isbell, 1991).

Causes of Behavior

The question of why individuals perform specific behaviors in given situations requires answers at different levels of understanding. Evolutionary biologists have separated the causes of individual behavior into two main types, proximate and ultimate. *Proximate causes* are directly linked with physiological, neural, or hormonal factors. For example, the expression of aggression may be directly related to stimulation in the part of the brain that causes rage. In primates, however, aggressive behavior is usually modified by further *proximate causes,* such as social group size and individual dominance rank. *Ultimate causes* refers to evolutionary origins. For example, natural selection is the ultimate cause of aggressive behaviors, favoring them as part of the overall defense and reproductive strategies of males and females.

In an attempt to reconcile the notion of behavioral flexibility with that of biological determinism in studying primate behavior, biological anthropologists develop models in which social and environmental factors play key roles in determining behavior within a context of genetic and physiologic influences. All of the elements of genetics, ecology, sociality, and learning are used in explaining behavior. We will now look at specific aspects of behavior, beginning with those that have formed the cornerstones of sociobiology: male and female reproductive strategies.

MALE AND FEMALE REPRODUCTIVE STRATEGIES

Central to the theories of vertebrate social organization today is the consideration of male and female reproductive strategies. The social structure and organization for any species relates to the interplay between male and female reproductive interests, which unfold under unique ecological and demographic circumstances. Female behavior and, consequently, female social organization, relate to habitat characteristics, that is, where females find food and safety. Male behavior, on the other hand, relates to the ability to obtain reproductive access to females. Because of this we would predict that male social organization is primarily

socioecology—evolutionary study of social behavior emphasizing the adaptation of species to their environment and ecological conditions.

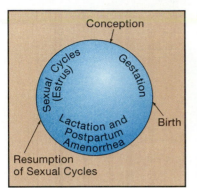

Figure 6–5 • Mammalian reproductive cycle. Ovulation occurs during the period of estrus. (From *Primates in Nature* by Richard. Copyright © 1985 by Freeman and Company. Used with permission.)

social bond–linkage or tendency to associate between one or more individuals in a group.

ovulation–release of a mature egg cell from the female's ovary after which time it can be fertilized by a male sperm cell.

pheromones–hormones that produce their effect by the sense of smell.

perineal–relating to the area between the anus and the external genitalia, the perineum.

steroids–family of chemical substances that includes many hormones, constituents of the body, and Vitamin D.

correlated with the distribution of females but that it may also vary according to the demands of the environment.

Female Behavior

Although Zuckerman (1932) was convinced that the primary reason for the nonhuman primate year-round **social bond** was sexual attraction, most subsequent studies have shown that sexual behavior for any single individual is quite limited over the period of one year. Field work also points up another interesting characteristic of social organization: Matings between close matrilineal relatives (especially between sons and mothers) are almost totally absent. Females have multiple mating partners, if they are available, and they often show a preference for mating with unfamiliar males. Between their selective mating patterns as well as through dispersal from one troop into another, the problems of inbreeding are avoided and genetic heterogeneity within groups is maintained.

Because breeding patterns of many nonhuman primates were observed by early field workers to be seasonal, the female reproductive cycle was termed estrus. A common example of estrus is the domestic dog or cat in "heat." It is during this period that females are most willing to mate with a male, and in most mammalian species it is the only time in their reproductive cycles that they actually do mate. Biologically speaking, estrus is that part of the mammalian reproductive cycle when females **ovulate** (Figure 6–5).

Hormonal change related to ovulation in many species leads to specific external physiological and behavioral changes. Just before ovulation, increases in estrogen and testosterone levels, and physiological changes occurring in response to the elevation of these hormones, may produce other external signals of ovulation: (1) visual signals, (2) olfactory signals, and (3) behavioral signals. **Pheromones** (Greek, meaning "carriers" [of scent messages]) as well as a scent in urine have the effect of signaling receptivity to males. In some primate species, females also have a specialized **perineal** skin that reacts to ovarian **steroids** by swelling and reddening.

This sort of reproductive signaling was remarked upon in 1876 by Charles Darwin, who concluded that the swelling of the perineum functioned as an attractant to males. Among species whose females do exhibit perineal swelling, including baboons (Figure 6–6), many other Old World monkeys, and the common chimpanzee, copulations become much more frequent as the size of the perineal area increases. During the period of maximum swelling, as male arousal becomes more intense, ejaculations are also more frequent. Recent experiments have pointed out that the swollen perineum by itself, independent of any smell-detected vaginal secretions, is the arousing stimulus affecting male sexual behavior.

The term "estrus" is not accurate in describing the reproductive cycle of all monkeys and apes (Loy, 1987). Prosimians, however, are more similar in their reproductive behavior to other mammals: Their reproduc-

Figure 6–6 • Swollen perineal region of female baboon in estrus.

tive activity is exclusively tied to ovulation and is rarely observed during other phases of the cycle. Some species of the higher primates do breed seasonally and may also restrict their entire sexual activity to this one period during the year. However, there are numerous exceptions to this rule. Some species have breeding seasons but continue sexual activity throughout the year. The crab-eating macaque (*Macaca fascicularis*) of Southeast Asia, for example, breeds year round, and copulates throughout the female's reproductive cycle and during her pregnancy.

In primates there is not necessarily a simple cause-and-effect relationship between hormones and sexual behavior. Gordon et al. (1979) showed that, when male rhesus macaques are removed from their normal heterosexual groups, they fail to show any sexual activity at all, even during a mating season when they would normally associate with receptive females. These studies show that primates differ from other mammalian species in that hormonal influences on both sexes act on the brain's motivational systems rather than directly on the specific motor activity of a species' sexual behavior patterns. Consequently, sexual behaviors in the higher primates are affected by context and other external factors.

The estrus cycle is the same reproductive cycle as that of human females but with a number of important differences. The first difference is that human females show very little indication of ovulation. In humans, ovulation may be detected by a slight rise in body temperature as measured by thermometer, by testing for a change in levels of hormones, and by, perhaps, subtle changes or shifts in some behavior patterns. On the other hand, the end of the reproductive cycle, or **menstruation,** which occurs if the female fails to become pregnant, is quite obvious by the copious discharge of blood and tissue of the built-up uterine lining. The second important difference lies in the area of sexual activity, which

menstruation—monthly, cyclic shedding of the lining of the uterus by nonpregnant female primates, particularly noticeable in humans.

lactation–in mammals the period of production of milk following birth of offspring, during which offspring are suckled by the mother.

life history strategies–behavioral decisions that each animal in a species must make to acquire food, avoid predators, and find mates. These decisions may increase inclusive fitness and, thus, vary the reproductive success of different individuals.

predation rate–frequency of killing and eating of individuals of a prey species by one or several predator species.

for humans, as well as for many of the monkeys and apes, is ongoing and continual throughout the entire reproductive cycle including pregnancy and **lactation** (breastfeeding) phases.

Seasonality and Behavior

Given the large differences in primate **life history strategies** and the complexity of ecological relationships, biological anthropologists have not been able to clearly tie environmental variables to the timing of reproductive events among all primate species. Nevertheless, it is obvious that some breeding seasons are environmentally related. Because seasonal reproduction is part of the reproductive strategies of some species, natural selection may favor individuals who time their births to coincide with optimal environmental conditions, guaranteeing a better chance for survival of both offspring and mother. For example, among yellow baboons, young baboons who are born later in the season than other infants are at some disadvantage. About 30% of these late-comers die during their first two years of life.

Where yearly variation in temperature is small and the **predation rate** on both parent and young is low, seasonal availability of food is generally the most important variable to explain the timing of births. For *Cercopithecus* monkeys, food apparently is the primary determinant of when a female should give birth, and rainfall, through its effect on the food supply, plays the major indirect role. In regard to food, however, it is not so much what the mother eats as what is available to newly weaned young. Their diet at this critical time may be the most important causative factor in birth seasonality.

Male Strategies and Behavior

Whereas females in many nonhuman primate species exhibit seasonal reproductive behavior, seasonal changes in male *androgen* levels are less well understood, but it is apparent that in many nonhuman primate species they also vary. The influence, for example, of female receptivity on male cyclicality has been documented for squirrel monkeys (DuMond and Hutchinson, 1967). During the mating season, plasma *testosterone* levels in adult males are considerably higher than at other times of the year, accounting for distinct birth peaks.

In contrast to those species that show a restricted breeding season, others, such as the stumptail macaque of Southeast Asia, breed all year long, and testosterone levels do not show a seasonal pattern. The stumptail macaque might well be the "sexiest" primate on record, with an ejaculation rate for one male of 59 times during a 6-hour period. Observed rates for other macaque species occur at less than 10 times per day (Nieuwenhuijsen et al., 1986).

Carpenter (1942) studied rhesus monkeys colonized on Cayo Santiago Island near Puerto Rico (Figure 6–7). On the basis of his observations he hypothesized that the number of females with which any male mated

Figure 6–7 • Cayo Santiago Island, Puerto Rico.

was directly proportional to the individual male's dominance rank. However, more recent studies have shown that male rank and copulatory frequency are not significantly interrelated. Copulation frequency of young low-ranking males is usually underestimated, because as part of these individuals' reproductive strategies they often conceal themselves from the view of others, knowing that dominant males will usually disrupt their copulation attempts if they can see them.

In young males, copulatory frequency rises sharply between the sixth and twelfth months prior to the descent of their testicles, which occurs as the males reach sexual maturity. Up to this point and a few months beyond, young males attempt mating with willing females openly in view of other group members without interruption from other adults. Starting about a year following testicular descent, however, this sexual freedom for the most part ends because of increasing intolerance of these males by fully adult males, as well as by females. It is this growing intolerance of the presence of the young adult males that in many cases ultimately forces them to the periphery of the group and then forces their ultimate immigration into nearby all-male or other heterosexual groups.

Although paternity will always be to some extent uncertain in **multi-male groups,** males who have mated and then remain in the group during the birth of infants are usually assumed in field studies by primatologists to be the fathers. These males also associate with newborns far more than do more transient males. From the point of view of the infant, "paternal" protection often prevents harassment and aggression by other males or females. From the protector's point of view, protective behavior may serve to either develop or further social relations with the infant's mother. Such non-kin alliances or "friendships" are often maintained for long periods of time.

Adult male–infant behavior may work in another direction to benefit the adult male. Sometimes males "kidnap" infants temporarily to use as buffers or "shields" in **agonistic** encounters with other males. In baboons a very common three-way interaction has an adult male holding or carrying an infant while accompanied by another adult male (Figure 6–8). In this manner potential aggression between these males is often thwarted.

multi-male groups—in reference to primate social organization, groups of primates where several dominant males live together in the same group.

agonistic—in ethology, referring to behavior that appears in aggressive encounters.

Figure 6–8 • Use of an infant as a shield in a potentially agonistic encounter between male baboons.

Figure 6–9 • New World monkey, *Callimico;* father carries single infant.

Male parentage is more easily determined in species that are (at least serially) **monogamous,** and in which males make regular contributions to the care of offspring. In the New World monkeys—among the marmosets, tamarins, titis, and the owl monkeys—males usually do most of the infant carrying and return infants to their mothers only for feeding. Fathers, with the help of previously born juveniles and in some cases even unrelated subdominant males, carry infants on their backs, share food after the infants are weaned, and play with, as well as protect, infants from predators and other dangers (Figure 6–9). Fathers, however, will get out of "baby-sitting" if they can, and will relieve themselves of the chore if they have available helpers (McGrew, 1988). In the marmosets and tamarins, one primary function of paternal care is to aid the mother in carrying multiple offspring, as twinning (producing twins) is common rather than the exception for this group. Among the Old World anthropoids males do not habitually carry infants. In single-male, multifemale **harem species** such as the hamadryas and gelada baboons, males may adopt prepubescent females, carry them about and protect them much as their mothers would, and, ultimately, when they become adults, incorporate them into the "harem."

Under certain circumstances adult males kill infants (Hrdy et al., 1995). The most common instance of infanticide occurs when an unfamiliar male migrates into a troop and usurps the position of the resident dominant male. When the new male has established his position of dominance in the group, he may systematically kill young infants belonging to the group's resident females. Sarah Hrdy's study in 1970 revealed that on the average, every 27 months, a female common langur's infant was killed in this manner. One apparent result of this behavior is that females soon after the death of their offspring begin to ovulate and become sexually receptive. Langur infanticide is explained as part of a male's reproductive strategy that brings females into estrus and thus ensures his paternity for the next round of infant births.

Other examples of infanticide have been observed among baboons, red colobus monkeys, silver leaf monkeys, and the New World red howler monkeys. In these cases infanticidal males were **natal residents** of the troop. Apparently the trigger for this sort of behavior was the male's rise to higher dominance status.

Female Strategies

Hrdy has further shown that females are not passive objects of males' reproductive strategy. In order to avoid male infanticide, instead of relying on the single best male as a mate choice, females, even when pregnant, will often engage in sex with numerous males. Hrdy theorized that females use **promiscuity** to confuse paternity, and she believes that mating with many males increases the number of males who might befriend a female.

In some species, however, females can reduce the risk of aggression by forming long-term breeding relationships with one male. Van Schaik

monogamous—referring to one male–one female pair bonding.

harem species—in primatology, species characterized by social groupings of one dominant male and a number of females and their young.

natal residents—residents of a group that were born in the group.

promiscuity—sexual relations with a number of partners.

and Dunbar (1990) believe that monogamous relationships are best explained by the protection the male provides against infanticide by other males. They cite studies on the incidence of infanticide in gorillas (Watts, 1989), showing that in 8 out of the 11 observed cases of male infanticide a mother and her infant were attacked when they were unaccompanied by a mature male. Perhaps for this reason females live in some form of social group to reduce the possibility of infanticide.

Both birth seasonality and the **inter-birth interval** may play a role in infant survivability. For example, in rhesus monkeys, there appears to be an early onset of maturation, somewhere between four to five years, versus five to six years for the Japanese macaque. Rhesus monkeys also show a shorter inter-birth interval of 14.3 ± 5.5 months as compared with 18.0 ± 6.6 months for Japanese monkeys. The slower reproductive rate for the Japanese monkeys might be favored because of the harsh winters these animals experience, and females with a reduced reproductive rate may better care for their infants for longer periods of time.

The **dominance rank** of the mothers also seems to be an important variable in infant production, infant survival, and offspring maturation rates. One recent study showed that the rate of production of weaned offspring of dominant females is almost twice that by subordinate females.

While we have known these facts for a number of years from studies based on baboons and macaques, it has recently been shown (Pusey et al., 1997) that they hold true for the slower-reproducing chimpanzees as well. It now appears that dominant females are more reproductively successful than lower-ranked females, and, according to Richard Wrangham (1997:774), that "female strategies [are now] seen to have their own logic independent of the males."

One way that dominant females can affect the reproductive success of their low-ranking competitors is by harassing them during copulation. Among langur monkeys, for example, rank plays some role in the frequency of harassment: Females disrupted only 50% of the copulations that involved the top three females in a troop; in contrast, females disrupted almost 96% of copulations involving the three lowest-ranking females. Dunbar (1986) demonstrated with gelada baboons that social stress caused by dominant females harassing subordinate females limited the subordinates' reproductive success, probably by suppressing ovulation.

Higher-ranking females often threaten, chase, and perhaps bite low-ranking females when these females show reproductive behavior. However, Pusey et al. (1997:828) propose that higher rank may influence reproductive success by allowing these females to "establish and maintain access to good foraging areas rather than by sparing them stress from aggression."

In spider monkeys the composition of adult animals in the group shows a heavily biased sex ratio of about 3 females to 1 male. One way to account for this difference in adult sex ratios is to assume that dominance rank must play some role in the timing and sex determination of a newborn. Low-ranking females have a much longer birth interval than

inter-birth interval–the period of time between births.

dominance rank–the relative hierarchical position of an individual in a social group.

do high-ranking ones, about 36 months as compared with 29 months, and they almost exclusively give birth to daughters, whereas high-ranking females produce most of the sons. By chance alone, the ratio of males to females at birth should be about 50:50. The skewed birth ratio, which is correlated heavily with maternal rank, presupposes some post-conception mechanism that results in a differential male mortality *in utero*.

After the birth of the infant, aggressive harassment by adult high-ranking females further reduces the chance of survival of young males. Their attacks resulting in injury occur about 1.7 times more often to young males than to young females (Chapman et al., 1989). One explanation is that under the conditions of intense resource competition, it may be advantageous for adult females to reduce the production and survival of male offspring of other females in order to decrease competition later for their sons. The consequences of these behaviors give an additional advantage to sons of higher-ranking females, who are likely to be competitively superior to the sons of lower-ranking females anyway.

PRIMATE FORAGING AND FEEDING

A group's **foraging strategies** must be modified to accommodate the number of animals in a social group who feed on relatively concentrated food sources (or patches). Having to compete among themselves for food may give rise to higher frequencies of dominance interactions, and the resultant increase in social friction may be considered as one cost of social group living. Alexander (1974), who proposed that predator pressure was the primary determining factor for sociality, believed that intragroup competition in foraging was a cost of group living. When too many animals feed in the same area at the same time, they tend to reduce foraging efficiency by depleting available resources. To solve these problems, there must be some optimal group size for which foraging efficiency is maximized. Optimal group size, however, may vary from group to group, species to species, and year to year (Figure 6–10).

When food sources are scarce and the geographical location of these patches and their annual productivity is unpredictable, a large number of foragers may be advantageous, because it increases the group's chance of finding food quickly (Ward and Zahavi, 1973; Clutton-Brock and Harvey, 1977; Rodman, 1988; Isbell, 1991). As an example, when a few chimpanzees locate a particularly coveted food, they hoot loudly as a signal for others to join them. Sharing of information on preferred food sources among group members is clearly of benefit.

The ideas discussed above have been formally organized into what has become known as **optimal foraging theory.** The theory states that optimal behavior will develop when returns and benefits are maximized in relation to costs and risks within the context of resource availability and socioecological factors. As Robinson (1986) has shown from his field studies of the wedge-capped capuchin, a New World monkey, for-

foraging strategies—behavior patterns that result in the discovery and procurement of food.

optimal foraging theory—a predictive theory based on food-getting behavior selected to balance a group's needs to find food against the costs of getting it.

Figure 6–10 • Foraging unit, the gelada baboon harem.

aging groups do possess considerable knowledge of the resources in their **home ranges** and utilize this knowledge effectively to find seasonal fruit. The capuchin's large home range ensures that some fruiting species is available throughout most of the year and, because the home ranges overlap extensively, intergroup competition makes social living and large group size the practical solution to their feeding problems (Wrangham, 1980, 1983; Rodman, 1988).

PRIMATE DEFENSES AGAINST PREDATION

Whereas a solitary animal must depend solely on its own ability to detect a predator, group living in primates almost always ensures early detection of a predator by many animals (Hamilton, 1971) and the subsequent emission of a warning signal, thereby reducing each member's chance of being attacked. A number of species have elaborated on this defense strategy and, in addition to warnings, have developed some form of cooperative defense against the predator. The African savanna baboon may use cooperative adult male threat behavior to ward off predators (DeVore and Washburn, 1963). Adult males, especially the most dominant ones, typically stay on the group's periphery, and are usually the first animals to confront a predator. In a similar fashion the juveniles and females often form the center of the group (Figure 6–11).

The potential effect of predation on the survival of solitary males may help explain why multi-male associations persist in seasonally breeding species. Van Schaik (1983) believed that predation avoidance offered the only universal selective advantage of group living. They believe that predation is what sets the lower limit for group size, whereas intragroup feeding competition is what sets the upper limit. Broad generalizations about the relative influence of predation pressure on primate social organization, however, may be difficult to prove.

home range—the area that a group or population inhabits and ranges over, the boundaries of which, unlike a territory, are not defended.

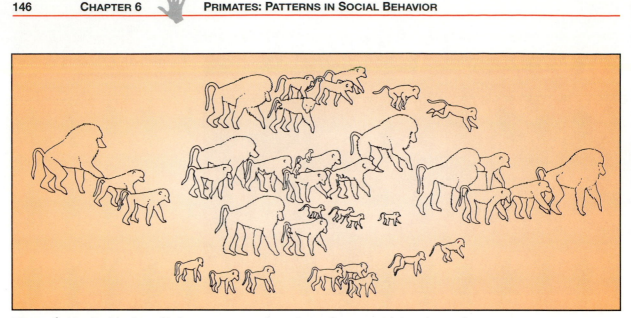

Figure 6–11 • Positioning of baboon troop members during foraging. Adult males tend to lead and follow up the main group.

COMMUNICATION

Considering that nonhuman primates have no spoken language in the human sense, they communicate a great deal. In order to live together peacefully year after year, animals must communicate their needs and emotions by means of various signals. **Communication** usually results in cooperative action of a give-and-take nature. Communication is necessary to all primates, even the less gregarious ones, for purposes of reproduction at least. For highly social primates, precise communication of emotional states and information about the environment is critical to social life. As a result, primates have developed elaborate communication systems that incorporate both specific anatomical structures and specific types of signals that vary depending upon the environmental situation. For instance, high canopy forest monkeys often rely on discrete vocalizations, because individual animals cannot usually see each other in the dense foliage. By contrast, savanna baboons, who are almost always in sight of one another, usually rely on visual or postural cues to communicate their intent.

One trend in primate communication has been to reduce the emphasis on signals based on olfaction (sense of smell) and to increase those based on vision. This change is understandable considering the importance of vision to arboreal locomotion in all primate species. The Old World monkeys and apes rely on visual means of communication and use a more expanded array of facial gesturing and expression than do their New World and prosimian cousins. The expansion of visual signaling in all Old World species, including humans, is in part related to a more elaborate and complex facial musculature (Figure 6–12).

communication–transmittal of information by sensory means.

Figure 6–12 • Facial expression in *Cercopithecus*.

Most primate species communicate using a number of different signals or modes. For example, vocalizations, facial gestures, postures, and touch may all be incorporated in a single message, often simultaneously. For some species, signals are discrete from one another to avoid ambiguity. Vervet monkeys use distinct vocal calls to distinguish between snake and bird predators. Many primates also relay subtle changes in their emotional state during an interaction. For that reason, most expressions of dominance involve signals that are variable in intensity.

The early studies of primate communication systems showed that primates communicated only about their emotional state and that they could relay little information about objects or events around them.

> One might expect that intelligent, long-lived primates who spend most of their lives in close proximity to relatives and fellow group members would readily learn to associate individual vocal characteristics with other attributes of social relevance. (Steklis, 1985:159)

However, more recent studies involving the recording of individual vocalizations and their subsequent playback to the animals have revealed a much greater complexity in the kinds of information relayed. These studies have shown that apes as well as monkeys produce variable vocal signals that can give information about the sender's sex, the kinship group to which the sender belongs, and the sender's social status. For example, wild forest mangabeys respond selectively to the long-distance calls of adult males from outside their group. Presumably group members' responses to these vocalizations are based on their past experience with the individuals making the calls.

Within the vocal repertoire of many species, calls may be age- and sex-specific. The colobine genus *Presbytis* uses between 18 and 21 discrete vocalizations, of which four calls are used exclusively by adult

FRONTIERS

Insights from Field Primatology

by Linda D. Wolfe

Field primatology encompasses social behavior, sexual behavior, demography, activity budgets, foraging and ranging strategies, and the environmental factors that impinge on the lives of the primates. In order for researchers to view the full range of adaptations and social behaviors, species must be studied in their natural habitats. Because primates are long-lived, long-term field studies produce the most valuable insights into behavior.

Much of what we know about behavior comes under the rubric of primate ecology and primate socioecology. Primate ecology involves a field study of ecological adaptations of a particular group of free-ranging primates. During the field study, a primatologist collects and analyzes data on foraging and ranging patterns, specific foods ingested, activity budgets (how the group spends its time during the day), polyspecific relationships (how the primates relate to other species), and the group composition (the individual primates making up the group). Primates consume fruit, leaves, seeds, flowers, gum, insects, and in some cases, meat. Fig, tamarind, acacia, and palm nut trees are among the most important food sources for primates. There is also evidence that at least chimpanzees deliberately eat plants for their medicinal effects (Jisaka et al., 1992). Primates learn to avoid eating plants with high levels of toxins.

Almost since the inception of field primatology in the 1930s there has been interest in primate socioecology, the study of the relationship between primate social systems and the environment through comparative studies (Richard, 1985). The literature on primate socioecology includes both large-scale studies that use multiple variables from field studies to link social systems and the environment, and smaller-scale studies in which the adaptations of members of one species living in different environments are compared. An example of the latter is Mitani's (1992) study of the western lowland gorilla in the northern tropical forest of the People's Republic of the Congo, an area that has not been disturbed by human occupation. Mitani indicates that gorillas in this area have a fission–fusion type of social system rather than the uni-male grouping usually reported for gorillas. He suggests that this related to the patchy distribution of fruit.

A number of researchers have attempted to demonstrate a relationship between primate social systems and the environment (Crook and Gartlan, 1966; Eisenberg et al., 1972; Clutton-Brock and Harvey, 1977; and Wrangham, 1980). None of these attempts has proved entirely satisfactory because evolutionary history (phylogeny) or random changes in the behavior of a species may be more important than current environmental factors in determining present-day social systems. Further complicating the issue is Rowell's (1993) suggestion that primates do not perceive a social system and that analyzing their social behavior with this theoretical construct is not productive. Dunbar (1992) has recently made the suggestion that brain size (neocortical volume), not environmental variables, most accurately predicts primate group size. Finally, there is considerable individual variation in behavior and in behavioral traditions in different troops, which can make cross-species comparative studies difficult.

There is a growing debate among field primatologists as to whether primates other than humans have culture (McGrew, 1992). It is evident that there are behavioral traditions, such as potato-washing (Kawamura, 1959) and branch-shaking displays (Wolfe, 1981) among Japanese macaques, and tool-use and grooming postures among chimpanzees (McGrew, 1992), which may vary from group to group within the same species. If culture is behaviorally based and defined as learned, shared behaviors that are passed on from one generation to the next, then we would have to say that primates have culture. If, on the other hand, culture is based on symbols, and defined as the rules in the mind used to generate behavior, then it would seem evident that other primates do not possess culture. The resolution of the issue of alloprimate culture will ultimately depend on greater communication between cultural anthropologists and primatologists, and a consensus on the definition of culture.

Linda D. Wolfe is Professor and Chair of Anthropology at East Carolina University. She has conducted extensive primatological field research in Asia.

males and one call by adult females. In *Presbytis,* alarm calls of adult females and juveniles of both sexes differ in structure from the harsh bark of adult males. Similar findings were also made for the golden monkey (*Rhinopithecus roxellena*). On the other hand, Marler (1973) found certain structural similarities in the alarm calls of many species living in the same habitat that were endangered by the same predators, indicating how minimizing the difference in specific vocalizations that function solely as alarm signals could mutually benefit different species.

Expanding these notions in terms of the origin of human language, Seyfarth, Cheney, and Marler (1980) have suggested that the simplest sort of "representational" signaling, such as the alarm calls of vervet monkeys that distinguish specific predators, provides a considerable selective advantage, and, therefore, an adaptive advantage to individuals who use it. Success in alarm call signaling might support the further development of this ability into many other social situations. Studies of the titi monkeys of South America have further blurred the distinction between the communications of nonhuman primates and human language: These primates have been known to repeat calls to form what might be considered phrases and to combine them in sequence, mimicking the elementary rules of syntax.

AGGRESSION AND DOMINANCE INTERACTIONS

One of the major functions of communication in group-living animals is to provide group cohesion. Primatologists have looked at the ways primates maintain group cohesion in spite of occasional aggressive acts by members within the group itself (Figure 6–13). These studies have shown that primates resolve most of their conflicts through a series of reconciliation behaviors, which usually follow some aggressive act, by seeking out one's former opponent and attempting to repair whatever damage has been done to the relationship. Kinship plays an important

Figure 6–13 • Primate aggressive interaction between two subadult male gorillas.

Figure 6–14 • Primate appeasement behavior in chimpanzees.

role: Two opponents are much more likely to reconcile if they are matrilineal kin than if they are unrelated. For most primates, kinship functions as a major feature of intragroup behavior and is useful in explaining many patterns of grooming, dominance, and aggression. Some species of primates have specific gestures and social displays to accomplish a reconciliation, such as lip smacking (Figure 6–14) and presenting, commonly observed in baboons and macaques. Other species, such as patas monkeys and some species of *Cercopithecus*, use adjustments in proximity to one another to accomplish the same end.

Some nonhuman primates exhibit behaviors aimed at preventing aggression in the first place. Peripherality among adult males in relation to the center of the group is an extremely good way to do this: It separates the males from one another. But when males cannot avoid interacting, they may exhibit behaviors to help maintain peaceful coexistence (Dohlinow and Taff, 1993). Male–male mounting behaviors, for example, may function in this manner. Because a significant number of these mounts are made by subordinate individuals over more dominant animals, this behavior cannot be explained in terms of an expression of higher dominance rank. Mountings of this type frequently occur before friendly relations are established between two individuals, in which case they may function cohesively by promoting nonaggressive social contact.

Grooming behavior also prevents aggression and at the same time helps maintain group solidarity. In fact, grooming is a good example of a behavior pattern that serves a multitude of social functions. From a hygienic point of view grooming is necessary for the maintenance of good health, because ticks, lice, and other ectoparasites infest many species and grooming generally concentrates on those regions of the body that are difficult to get at by oneself. Also, grooming may be traded for sexual access, for proximity to a mother with a new infant, or for forming an alliance with another animal for assistance in future aggression with a third party. Mothers spend a good deal of time grooming their infants, although as their offspring mature, mother monkeys tend to groom them less, and they groom sons less than daughters.

The patterns of dominance based on the rank of the adult males and females organize most of the social interactions in the nonhuman primate group. Dominance rank is established and maintained by aggressive interactions, yet aggressive behavior is usually not disruptive to social order. In fact, because aggression is most often based on threat rather than actual fighting, it functions positively to maintain social integration and group cohesion. Although the biological elements of aggression are similar in most nonhuman primates, the pattern and degree of the development of aggressive behavior differs between species and within species in different habitats.

The expression of dominance occurs in many ways. One individual may displace another in a favored resting place, or an individual, usually a high-ranking individual (a male or a female), may purposefully break up disputes to restore peace within the group. Interference behavior of this sort may be a defense of self-interest, in that an interfering animal

grooming behavior—slow systematic picking through the hair of another individual to remove foreign matter; important in primate social interactions.

might be supporting kin, a friend, or a potential sex partner. Finally, interference interactions may have the continuing function of improving (or at least monitoring) one's dominance position.

Female dominance rank relationships are generally stable and continue over long periods, because females usually do not emigrate from their natal troops, as males often do. Until puberty, both males and females, even fostered infants, assume the rank of their real or foster mothers. If a mother dies while her daughter is still a juvenile, the daughter's rank may be reduced, although one study showed that about 55% of these orphaned daughters inherited the rank of their mothers. Apparently, the most important factor that determines a daughter's rank is the memory others have of those dominance relations that existed while her mother was still alive. On the other hand, some females from an early age can significantly elevate their rank through their associations with older males and females (Small, 1989).

In most primate species, the males who are at or near the age of puberty often emigrate from their natal group (Pusey and Parker, 1987). Field data indicate that the numbers of males that actually move from group to group range from a low of 30% to as many as almost every male in the group. Because young males often migrate from their natal troops at puberty, and later in life older males may also move from group to group, male dominance hierarchies tend to be unstable over time. Many different males may at one time or another reach the highest position in the group's dominance hierarchy, but sooner or later each of them will ultimately be replaced by younger individuals. Factors other than current dominance rank that affect the behavior and social interactions of adult males include their age, physical strength, residence time, and previous mating successes.

BIRTH AND THE MOTHER–INFANT BOND

All mammalian mothers nurse, protect, and care for their young during lactation. However, the duration and intensity of the mother–infant relationship varies considerably. Among mammals, with the exception perhaps of elephants, the primate (including human) mother–infant bond seems to be the most intense and long-lasting.

Primates are usually born during the night or in the early morning hours before the group begins to wander in search of food. Births at night have the advantage of allowing some time for recovery for both mother and newborn before the group's social life resumes its daily pace. Within hours after birth, the new mother and her infant must be able to move away from the sleeping area with the group in search of food, and the infant must be able to cling to its mother's hair with little or no assistance. An adult male may linger behind the group to assist the new mother or to thwart aggression, but this often depends upon the mother's earlier "friendships" or her kin relationships. The group as a whole rarely modifies its behavior to suit a new mother.

Figure 6–15 • Harlow's experiments on primate mother–infant interaction.

During the first few months of an infant's life, it remains in close proximity to its mother. While traveling, the mother transports the infant under her belly in a **ventro-ventral position.** Infant monkeys attract attention in the social group, and in the first few weeks after birth, mothers receive frequent social contacts from other members of the group. Some mothers appear to be very responsive to other individuals' curiosity about their newborn; others are quite restrictive and intolerant of other animals' presence.

Nonlactating females may "kidnap" an infant for a period of time if they can. However, this "aunt" behavior of caring for and holding the infant may, for a short time, help the real mother. It is certainly a way by which young females learn about infant care before they have offspring of their own. In contrast to earlier views, we now know that much of the increased interaction that occurs between new mothers and other group members is antagonistic rather than friendly. New mothers often direct aggression towards juveniles and experience more aggression from adult males than they do when they are not pregnant or lactating.

If a mother dies, other females in many species may adopt the orphaned infant. Adoption has been observed in both New and Old World monkeys and apes. Parental care by other females to older infants may afford them some protection against the aggressive behavior of other animals. However, when an infant who is still dependent upon its mother's milk is orphaned, the adopter must be a lactating female. Often an adopter is kin. Lynn Fairbanks (1988) demonstrated that even grandmothers form affiliative relationships with their grandinfants, though the intensity of this relationship varies considerably with the dominance rank of the grandmother. High-ranking grandmothers associated with their grandinfants more often, assisted them by providing social support and protection, and groomed them more frequently than did lower-ranking grandmothers. According to Fairbanks, grandmothers contribute to the reproductive success of their daughters by helping them protect the offspring.

The psychologist Harry Harlow demonstrated in his early experiments on bond formation and "love" in monkeys that an infant's clinging plays a vital role in its development (Figure 6–15). In fact, if the infant becomes agitated or frightened, body-to-body contact is more important to it than nursing. The mother is a safe, secure home base from which the infant launches its exploration of its environment, observing its mother's varying reactions to specific individuals and later to specific situations while clinging to her.

The social development of a young primate passes through a series of discrete phases. Each successive phase is linked by transitional steps in which relationships may change considerably. The sex of the infant appears to be a crucial variable during these transitions. In most species, sex differences during the infancy and juvenile period show a mixture of behavioral patterns that resemble those of the adults together with those that are specific to the particular demands of the earlier stage. For example, juveniles may regularly incorporate in their vocalization a mixture of signals, some typically infantile as well as some common to adults.

ventro-ventral position—two individuals facing each other with bodies in contact.

During the transitional phase from infancy to the juvenile stage, young males transfer much of their affiliative behavior away from their mother towards others, usually adult males. Loy (1992) notes this especially in his studies of patas monkeys. The juvenile's successes in achieving a friendly bond with the adults will be limited primarily by the youngster's own rank relative to that of its older friends, the interest or behavioral reciprocity its friends have in the juvenile, and finally any kin relationship the young male might have to a "friend" (Smuts, 1987). If bonds with high-ranking males can be made, the young male's chance of being forced out of the group later is diminished. Female yearlings, on the other hand, usually maintain their close association with their mothers, their kin, and friends.

LEARNING AS ADAPTATION TO SOCIALITY

Primates have the ability to **learn** a great number of things. Consequently, they require more developmental time for learning than any other group of mammal. It is not surprising that the two most important ingredients for learning, one's mother and interactive play, form a substantial part of a primate's lifetime experience. Situational responses are easily learned within the context of the group and the affectional bonds and stability that the group affords.

The ability to learn can be explained in part by the expansion of that part of the brain known as the neocortex (Chapter 4). Primates have a large brain-to-body weight ratio. But bigger brains are only part of the answer. We have to be motivated to learn, and effective learning requires strong motivation. Psychiatrist David Hamburg has described the primate learning process as an emotionally pleasurable experience. Natural selection has endowed that part of the brain that moderates pleasurable responses, the limbic system, with the ability to motivate individuals to do what they have to do in order to survive. This system makes it pleasurable to form social bonds and thus makes it easy to learn them. In laboratory situations, for instance, infant monkeys will establish contact relationships with their mothers regardless of the treatment the infants receive from them.

A young primate's learning is **imitative,** usually of its mother's actions or reactions to individuals or objects. Typically these concern what foods to eat and where to find them, where to sleep and where to find water, and which animals can be approached and which should be avoided. However, the major part of a young primate's education is not the simple facts about its physical environment but learning to live successfully with other members of its group. Depending on the species, the infant increases its independence from its mother after a time, and the usually gradual process of separation called weaning begins. As weaning progresses, the mother may refuse her infant the nipple and refuse to carry her infant. Nevertheless, through this transitional stage the infant continues to be influenced by its mother, most importantly by

learn–remember information or experience and retain for use in future behavior.

imitative–relating to information gained through observing other individuals and not through one's own experience.

play—behavior that is not directed toward any clearly defined end result such as food getting, and which is frequently characteristic of young mammals.

her personality and social rank. As infants become older, they leave their mothers for longer periods of time, widening their explorations and increasing their social relationships, usually through play with their age-mates, but frequently through interactions with older adults.

An important component of learning in the young primate is **play** (Figure 6–16). Play is not a frivolous activity, but a behavior pattern that is practiced for skill acquisition and problem solving in adult life. Play provides the secure, largely carefree environment and the emotional motivation needed to sustain an individual's attention to a specific object or activity. Play is pleasurable, and, because it involves a seemingly endless series of imitations, repetitions, and experimental variations supervised by adult animals, young animals are seldom hurt during play.

Initially, as young primates leave their mother for periods of time their play is solitary and it consists primarily of locomotion explorations, which ultimately become explorations of the environment. Because primates are extremely curious animals, over time their play helps them explore and become familiar with the entire area over which their group wanders. However, for exploratory play to remain interesting it must constantly change. But there are only so many trees to climb and so many ways to climb them, and considering how much time a young primate spends in play, the environment's novelty soon disappears.

Social play then becomes the logical continuation of the process. Peers are perfect play subjects. They are familiar and secure; they are mobile and not always predictable. Hence, peers are endlessly interesting. Whereas observers readily see the importance of social play for learning the basic social skills needed in adult life, this probably is not the reason young primates play. Most likely it is because it is more emotionally pleasurable and, therefore, more "fun" to play with one another

Figure 6–16 • Young bonnet macaques at play. (From Paul Simonds)

than with a twig. Once again, natural selection has produced a situation in which the critical learning necessary for an individual's survival is easy and enjoyable. Under these circumstances, new information is rapidly assimilated into an individual's body of knowledge.

In order to play socially the young primate must be social; that means it must make adjustments in its own behavior so that it can get along with others. Play allows the young animal to learn from its experiences which behaviors are acceptable and which are not. This knowledge is important later to adult membership in the group. In this sense, social play serves as a model of later adult social interactions. For example, the social skills required in juvenile play fighting are the same as those required in adult real fighting. An individual must be able to rapidly and correctly appraise a situation and through effective communication use this information to its advantage. This development of effective communication is the basis of all adult interaction. Fortunately, play has an advantage: While using all these social skills it allows the players to make mistakes, misinterpret intent, and communicate ineffectively without suffering serious punishment. In contrast, generally speaking, adults making these kinds of errors must pay for them.

However, there is danger in play, because it makes young animals inattentive to external events and may attract predators. Hausfater (1976) observed play groups of African vervet monkeys that typically occurred at some distance from the adults. Juveniles of this species were often stalked and killed by adult baboons. The adults of other species may exhibit more vigilant behavior while their young are engaged in play. Squirrel monkey mothers, for example, respond quickly to the alarm calls of their close associates, the capuchins. Although loud vigorous play may provoke the curiosity of a predator, it also seems to alert the adults that play is going on and, perhaps because of this, juvenile vocalizations stimulate greater vigilance in predator detection by the adults.

SUMMARY

1. One of the most important behavioral characteristics of anthropoid primates is that they live in year-round social groups. From studies of primates in the wild we have come to understand many of the reasons for variability in the social organization and behavior that have been observed.

2. Two levels of explanation are useful in understanding behavior patterns: Proximate explanations concern an animal's immediate motivation for behavior, and ultimate explanations look at the evolutionary significance of such behavior. Within the context of the group, primates have evolved solutions to problems involving reproduction, predation, and feeding. Life history strategies are the resulting behavioral responses of social animals to these problems.

3. In an attempt to explain primate social behavior the first question that needs to be asked is, "Why are primates social at all?" Answers to the

question involve analysis of the costs and benefits of social group living. Some of the costs are loss of individual freedom of behavior, increased competition for a limited food supply, and increased stress. The benefits include increased reproductive fitness, improved mechanisms for predator avoidance, and enhanced efficiency in feeding.

4. Primatologists have borrowed from studies of other animal species in their attempts to synthesize primate behavioral data. The ethological perspective has focused on aspects of behavior that are controlled by genetics. Sociobiological analysis has looked at an individual's reproductive strategies, and socioecology has looked at ways in which animals are successful in finding food and in defending themselves and their resources from attack by other animals.

5. Although genetics, natural selection, and evolution can explain a great deal of what occurs behaviorally in a primate social unit, primates, more than perhaps any other group of mammals, depend on their ability to learn through social interaction how to develop those behavior patterns that will prove to be successful in adult life.

CRITICAL-THINKING QUESTIONS

1. Why is group living advantageous for primates?
2. Compare and contrast male and female reproductive strategies.
3. Discuss some of the commonalities between nonhuman primate communication and human communication.
4. Why is it important that there be a strong mother-infant bond in primates?
5. How does play influence learning in a young primate?
6. What important functions do grooming behaviors accomplish?

SUGGESTED READINGS

Bramblett, C. 1994. *Patterns of Primate Behavior.* Prospect Heights, Ill.: Waveland Press. A good treatment of primatological field work and deductions arising from it.

deWaal, F. 1989. *Peacemaking Among Primates.* Cambridge, Mass.: Harvard University Press. A readable account of primatologist Frances deWaal's research among the bonobos of central Congo.

Loy, J. D., and C. B. Peters (eds.). 1991. *Understanding Behavior: What Primate Studies Tell Us About Human Behavior.* New York: Oxford University Press. An edited volume that emphasizes the "primateness" of human behavior, especially the social and ecological aspects of that behavior.

Mason, W. A., and S. P. Mendoza (eds.). 1993. *Primate Social Conflict.* Ithaca, N.Y.: State University Press. A book on causes and resolution of conflict among primates, with lessons for humans.

Quiatt, D., and V. Reynolds. 1993. *Primate Behavior: Information, Social Knowledge, and the Evolution of Culture.* Cambridge, England: Cambridge University

Press. A book that looks at the continuity of nonhuman primate behavior and human cultural behavior within society.

Small, Meredith. 1993. *Female Choices: Sexual Behavior of Female Primates*. Ithaca, N.Y.: Cornell University Press. A primatological study from a female perspective, looking at what strategies evolution has produced for choice of mates in female primates.

Smuts, B. B., R. L. Cheney, R. M. Seyforth, R. W. Wrangham, and T. T. Struhsaker (eds.). 1987. *Primate Societies*. Chicago: University of Chicago Press. An edited volume for advanced students dealing with theoretical issues of primate behavior and adaptation.

Strum, S. C. 1987. *Almost Human: A Journey into the World of Baboons*. New York: W. W. Norton. An introduction to the study of baboons by primatologist Shirley Strum based on her long-term studies in western Kenya.

CHAPTER 7

Introduction to the Hominoids

hominoids—modern apes, modern humans, and their immediate ancestors.

suspensory—positional behavior; ability of hominoids to hang (from branches) using one or both fully extended forelimbs.

Hominoids (Latin for "like humans") are members of the zoological superfamily Hominoidea, which includes the many lineages of fossil and recent species of apes and humans. As we saw in Chapter 5, the first apes appear in the fossil record during the Miocene Epoch some 20 million years ago. Hominoids first appear in Africa in dense lowland forested environments.

The Living Hominoids Minus People: Apes
What Is an Ape?
Anatomy of a Climbing Heritage
Proconsulids: The Earliest Hominoids
Hominoids with Thick Molar Enamel Appear
Ape Evolution in Eurasia
Evolutionary Relationships Among Hominoids
Summary
Critical-Thinking Questions
Suggested Readings

knuckle walking—a terrestrial quadrupedal form of locomotion characteristic of chimpanzees and gorillas involving the placement of the flexed second phalanges instead of the palms on the ground for support.

fist walking—a terrestrial quadrupedal form of locomotion characteristic of orangutans involving the placement of the flexed first phalanges instead of the palms on the ground for support; similar in function but probably not homologous to knuckle walking.

THE LIVING HOMINOIDS MINUS PEOPLE: APES

By the middle Miocene, about 15 million years ago, apes had expanded from Africa into Europe and Asia (Figure 7–1). During this period, forests and dense woodlands connected Africa and Asia, so as hominoids expanded their ranges they came into contact with an increasing diversity of environments. By 10 to 14 million years ago, there were fewer species of apes, but they were found throughout Africa and Eurasia. During the late Miocene, the radiation of apes began to draw to a close: By about 5 million years ago, most of these species had become extinct, with only a few forms surviving to the present day (Figure 7–2). What remained were the ancestors of the living gibbons, orangutans, and the common ancestor of humans, chimpanzees, and gorillas. As the apes were declining, monkeys were successfully expanding in number of species and in geographical range—a likely result of broad ecological competition between the two groups.

The hypothesis of monkey–ape competition in the late Miocene may explain why today we have five separate hominoid adaptations, all quite different from one another and from their more "monkeylike" early ancestors. Today among the hominoids there is a small-bodied **suspensory** species, the gibbon (Figure 7–3); a large-bodied **knuckle-walking** terrestrial form, the gorilla; a smaller knuckle-walking terrestrial form, the chimpanzee; a large-bodied arboreal and terrestrial **fist-walking** form,

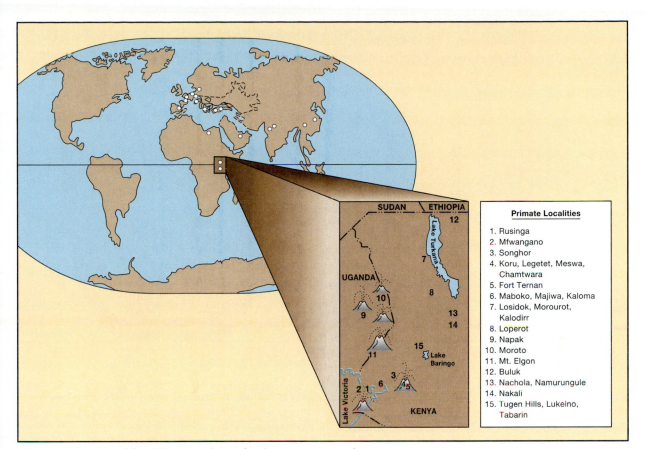

Figure 7–1 • Map of fossil hominoid sites for the Miocene Epoch.

the orangutan (Bornean, meaning "old man of the forest"); and a bipedal terrestrial form, the hominids.

Traditionally, all the living apes were grouped together in the family Pongidae, although a number of authors preferred a taxonomic system that split the Southeast Asian gibbons and siamangs into a separate family, the Hylobatidae (Le Gros Clark, 1960). Likewise, some researchers include both the gorilla and the chimpanzee within their own family, Panidae, separate from the Asian Pongidae. Included in this group is the smaller West African **bonobo,** or pygmy chimpanzee, *Pan paniscus.* Recent molecular studies, however, consistently show the chimpanzee and gorilla to be at least as distinct from each other as each is from humans. For this reason, they are taxonomically classified in their own families here—Panidae for chimpanzees and Gorillidae for gorillas (see Appendix 3). This leaves within the family Pongidae only the orangutan, presently found on the Indonesian islands of Borneo and Sumatra. While the molecular evidence places the orangutan closer to the African apes than to the gibbons (Figure 7–4), both the molecular and fossil evidence show that the orang has a long separate history from its African cousins.

bonobo–*Pan paniscus,* a species of chimpanzee distinct from the common chimpanzee, *Pan troglodytes,* and living in a different, nonoverlapping range—the Central Congo (formerly Zaire) forest basin; also termed the "pygmy chimpanzee" but its differences from the common chimp are more in terms of morphology and shape than size.

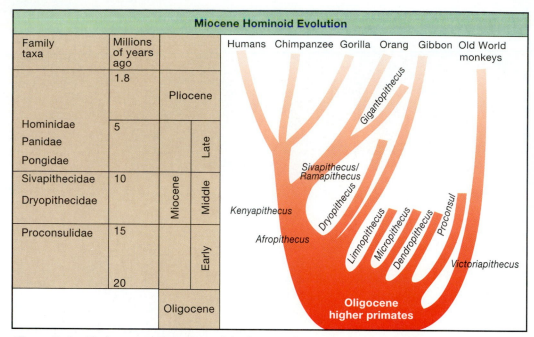

Figure 7–2 • Phylogeny and timeline of the hominoids.

prognathism–forward-protruding jaws (maxilla plus mandible) or lower face.

Apes today are generally found in tropical rain forests from sea level to heights of 4,000 meters, where the few remaining mountain gorillas make their home in the Virunga Volcanoes of Congo (formerly Zaire), Uganda, and Rwanda. The apes have fared poorly at the hands of fate and of humans. Few in number and pushed to the limits of their environmental resources, the living apes face a dismal future today in the wild. On a sliding scale of evolutionary success in the primates, apes rate near the bottom, barely holding their own. Their seriously threatened condition makes it important not only that we study them in the wild while there is still time, but also that primate conservation efforts go hand in hand with the scientific study of the species.

What Is an Ape?

The great apes are larger than monkeys, and as adults they exhibit marked sexual dimorphism (Figure 7–5). In terms of cranial anatomy the Hominoidea are all largely similar at birth (Schultz, 1924; Biegert, 1963). Changes in infant cranial structure are mostly determined by brain size and housing for the special senses (sight, hearing, taste, and smell). However, as the teeth erupt, the mechanical requirements of the developing teeth and jaws begin to show their effect on the cranial anatomy (see Figure 12–1); the face becomes more **prognathic,** a trend that continues until adulthood. With the eruption of the permanent canine teeth (substantially larger in the males), the patterns of growth of the different

Figure 7–3 • View of a gibbon brachiating.

Figure 7–4 • Molecular phylogeny of the apes.

skull regions begin to change dramatically, giving rise to the adult pattern of sexual dimorphism (Schultz, 1969). The cranial anatomy of the gorilla, for example, is dominated by the large upper and lower canines, the large prognathic jaws that give support to them, and the massive

Figure 7–5 • Ape sexual dimorphism in skulls of gorillas: (*a*), (*b*), (*c*), and (*f*) are male skulls; (*d*) and (*e*) are female.

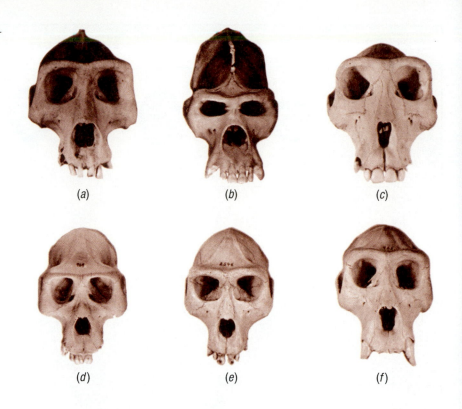

(*a*)   (*b*)   (*c*)

(*d*)   (*e*)   (*f*)

muscles of mastication–four paired muscles that connect the skull to the mandible and move the jaw upward and to the sides in chewing.

sagittal crest–a bony crest running along the length of the top of the skull, formed by the attachment areas of the *temporalis* muscles from opposite sides.

brachiation–hominoid ability, the result of specialized anatomy of the forelimb and upper torso, to move under (branches) by swinging.

muscles of mastication that attach to the jaws (Figure 7–6). The skull itself is covered by the *temporalis* muscles and, in the cheek region, by the *masseter* muscles. As gorillas mature, the left and right *temporalis* muscles meet at the top of the skull and attach to it, producing a bony **sagittal crest,** the largest of its size in any primate.

Apes differ from monkeys in a number of other significant traits (Figure 7–7). Primary among these is their ability to raise their arms above their heads, as we do when we do chin-ups or hold on to a strap while standing on a bus. Apes raise their arms when they hang from tree limbs or climb in trees. In addition, all apes lack tails, have larger brains than monkeys—both in absolute terms and relative to their body size—and have *bunodont molar teeth* (molars with lower and more rounded cusps).

All apes are capable of a wide range of arm movement, "arm-swinging," or **brachiation** (from Latin for "arm"). The direct ancestors of modern apes developed the ability to suspend themselves by their arms from tree branches and even to swing from branch to branch as a unique form of locomotion. Washburn (1963) stressed the importance of the apes' ability to hang with one hand, grasping a branch while feeding with the other hand. He realized that apes' locomotion was in reality an orboreal feeding adaptation: Its adaptive advantage is in obtaining food in trees (primarily fruit) from the ends and the tips of branches. Knowledge of tropical forest ecol-

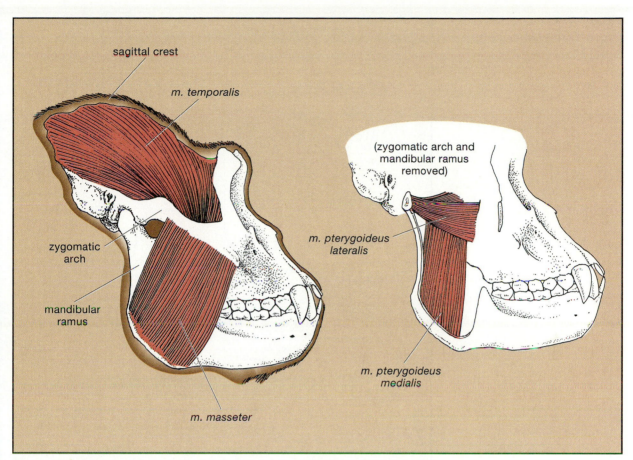

sagittal crest

m. temporalis

(zygomatic arch and
mandibular ramus
removed)

zygomatic
arch

m. pterygoideus
lateralis

mandibular
ramus

m. pterygoideus
medialis

m. masseter

Figure 7–6 • Muscles of mastication and associated cranial structures in the gorilla.

ogy shows that the best and sometimes the only digestible foods in a tree
are at the edges. These include fruits, nuts, flowers, and, perhaps on a
more regular basis, new leaves—those whose internal chemistry has not
yet built up the defense systems that make the most mature leaves indi-
gestible to the average vegetarian.

Brachiation reaches its greatest efficiency in the small-bodied Asian
apes: the gibbons and siamangs. In fact, Napier and Napier (1967) describe these forms as the *true brachiators,* as opposed to the great apes,
which they describe as *modified brachiators.* Movement through the
trees in these two forms is rapid because of the greater elongation of the
forelimbs and fingers of the hands, with the exception of the shortened
thumb, which apparently functions to increase the breadth of the grasping hand in vertical climbing, an important additional gibbon locomotor
component. On the ground and in the trees, gibbons and siamangs are
also unique in that both occasionally adopt bipedal posture in locomotion (Figure 7–8).

Figure 7–7 • How an ape differs from an Old World monkey.

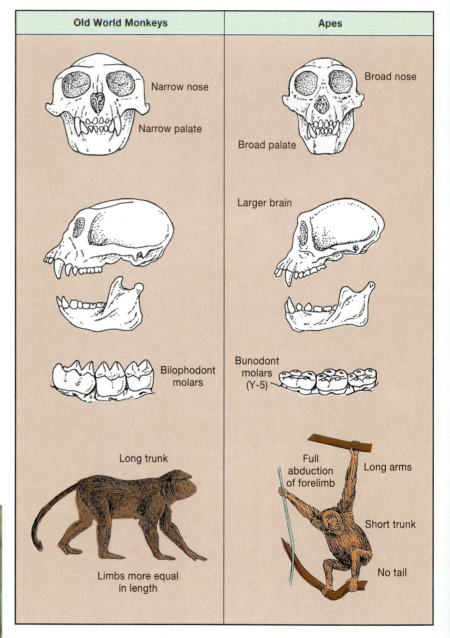

Old World Monkeys	Apes
Narrow nose	Broad nose
Narrow palate	Broad palate
	Larger brain
Bilophodont molars	Bunodont molars (Y-5)
Long trunk	Full abduction of forelimb / Long arms / Short trunk / No tail
Limbs more equal in length	

Figure 7–8 • Bipedal locomotion by the gibbon when on the ground.

The great apes move much more carefully (and slowly) because of their larger size. They usually support their weight with their hindlimbs while in the trees. On the ground, these animals generally move quadrupedally and, on occasion, bipedally. The orangutan (*Pongo pygmaeus*) often travels arboreally, but generally climbs rather than swings along branches. The brachiating anatomy that we have described for gibbons and siamangs is much the same for the orangutan, except that the orang's size is a limiting factor to rapid arboreal locomotion. Infant and juvenile orangutans are much more mobile than adults, both in the trees and on the ground.

When moving on the ground, apes rarely run with their hands *palmigrade* (flat on the ground), but either knuckle walk, as with chimpanzees or gorillas (Figure 7–9); fist walk, as with orangutans (Figure 7–10); or walk on two hind limbs, as with gibbons (Figure 7–8) and humans. While the orangutan's quadrupedal locomotion is usually accomplished with the fists in a clenched position, orangs have been observed occasionally to use a palm-down stance like monkeys.

British paleontologist Richard Owen (1859) first recognized knuckle walking as a form of ape locomotion, but the distinctive anatomy of knuckle walking seen only in the hands of African apes was recognized somewhat later (Keith, 1899). On anatomical grounds it was argued that the two African apes were phylogenetically more closely related to each other than either was to the orangutan (Andrews, 1987). In the skeletal elements of the wrist of African apes (as well as in that of humans) the primitive *os centrale* (Latin, meaning "central bone") fuses with the *scaphoid* (Greek, meaning "shiplike," in reference to its shape) (Figure 7–11). Additionally, the unique shape of the heads (distal end) of the metacarpals are especially related to knuckle walking (Tuttle, 1967). Since the African apes and humans share some of these skeletal characteristics, might this indicate that the common ancestor of all three living species was a knuckle walker as well? Both Washburn (Washburn and Moore, 1980) and Begun (see Frontiers, p. 171) stress the possibility of a knuckle-walking stage in human ancestry. Washburn and Moore discussed the potential advantages of this form of locomotion when they wrote (1980:64):

> This method of walking was the key to eventual upright walking, and to human evolution. By knuckle walking, an ape on the ground could move [quickly] from one isolated group of trees to another. If danger threatened, it still could climb to safety; the knuckle gait did not interfere with the structures that enabled it to climb or move around in the trees. Knuckle walking got the new ground dwellers around the possible fatal dangers of being slow, inefficient bipedalists, as most monkeys are. [Additionally] an ape whose hands were not totally involved in locomotion was freer to use them in other ways, a great advantage.

While this viewpoint has been criticized on anatomical grounds (Tuttle, 1975) and as yet no fossil evidence has emerged to demonstrate conclusively early hominid knuckle walking, the question is intriguing and, as Begun points out, still remains open.

Anatomy of a Climbing Heritage

The hominoids all share similar anatomy of the forelimb, shoulder, and upper back, traits that trace their arboreal climbing heritage. Members of the human lineage also share these anatomical structures—similarities that were recognized early on by Tyson (1699). The evolutionary origins

Figure 7–9 • Knuckle walking in the gorilla.

Figure 7–10 • Fist walking by an orangutan.

Figure 7–11 • The hand skeleton of *Homo sapiens,* showing the *os centrale* fused with the scaphoid, as compared with the hand skeleton of *Adapis parisiensis,* an Eocene prosimian, in whom the *os centrale* is a separate wrist bone. Humans and the African apes share this characteristic, which is not shared with the orangutan.

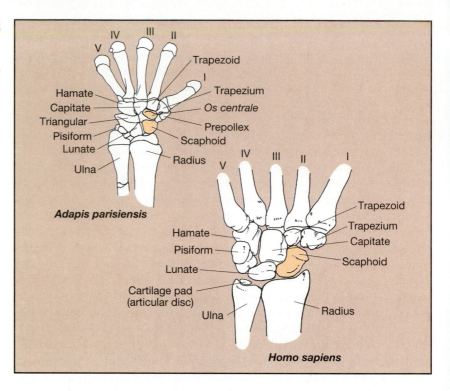

of this climbing morphology, as well as the ancestry of the living apes, is far from clear because the fossil record is nearly nonexistent. This scarcity of fossils that can be directly connected to modern apes is possibly due to the fact that these species, as well as their fossil antecedents, lived in dense tropical forests where the acidic forest floors tend to chemically erode their skeletal remains. But equally important is the fact that modern forests still cover most of the forest areas of the past, making paleontological investigations of these important areas difficult. Where adequate sediments have buried the fossil levels, even forest-living animals of the past, including fossil apes, have been discovered. By the Pliocene and early Pleistocene an early form of the hominid *Australopithecus* (see Chapter 8) showed all of the anatomical characteristics of a climbing heritage, although it was clearly also adapted to a bipedal mode of terrestrial locomotion. The ancestors of modern apes must surely have shared the anatomical characteristics of brachiation with *Australopithecus,* but we have, as yet, no fossils to show it.

In the hominoids, the anatomical adaptations made for climbing and suspensory locomotion (Figure 7–12) have been well described by such prominent anatomists as Sir Arthur Keith (1896) and Adolf Schultz (1936). These include changes that increased rotational movement at the wrist joint, permitting a 180° *pronation* (turning the hand into a palm-down or "prone" position); at the elbow joint, allowing for 180° *exten-*

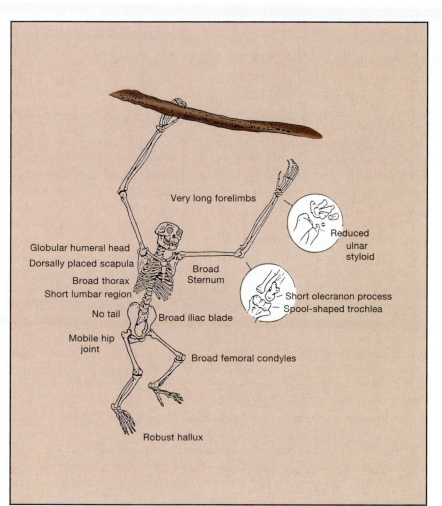

Globular humeral head

Dorsally placed scapula

Broad thorax

Short lumbar region

No tail

Mobile hip joint

Very long forelimbs

Broad Sternum

Reduced ulnar styloid

Short olecranon process

Spool-shaped trochlea

Broad iliac blade

Broad femoral condyles

Robust hallux

Figure 7–12 • Anatomy of climbing: loss of ulnar articulation with the carpals, reduced olecranon process at the elbow, and change in position of the scapula; broadening of the thorax, elongation of the clavicle, and change in the shape of the shoulder joint; strengthened deltoid and other muscles of abduction; shift from strength of triceps in quadrupeds to biceps in brachiators.

sion ("unbending the elbow"); and at the shoulder joint, permitting full *abduction* of the forelimb (lifting the arm away from the body and over the head (see Appendix 1). Additionally, the sternum and thorax (chest region) broadened, and the lumbar (lowermost) section of the vertebral column shortened. Effectively, these changes allow hominoids to raise their forelimbs over their heads while at the same time maintaining a vertical posture.

Changes in the hand also occurred, leading to the development of a curved hooklike arrangement of the *metacarpals* and *phalanges,* solving a potential problem of hand fatigue for an animal hanging for a considerable period of time in one spot. Of all of the climbing adaptations that humans share with the apes, only the hookshaped hand was not retained. The human hand developed in a direction that allowed for finer motor coordination and precise gripping ability.

PROCONSULIDS: THE EARLIEST HOMINOIDS

The Miocene Epoch, extending in time from 23 to 5 million years ago, was a time of a great adaptive radiation of apes. In the early Miocene, dating from approximately 23 to 18 million years ago, at least 15 species belonging to 11 genera of hominoids have been recognized. They range in size from the diminutive, cat-sized *Micropithecus* (3.5 kg) to the large *Afropithecus,* the size of a female gorilla (50 kg). These apes are known as **proconsulids** (Greek, "pro" ["before"] "Consul," the name of a well-known chimpanzee in the London zoo in the 1940s), and they show a diversity of locomotor types, dietary adaptations, and body sizes (Figure 7–13).

The proconsulids are a monophyletic group; that is, they evolved in one adaptive radiation from ancestral catarrhines, most likely the propliopithecoids (see Chapter 5), at a time near the Oligocene–Miocene boundary. Important among the dental traits that herald this change are upper molars of squarish shape with a distinctive belt of raised enamel on the tongue side (the lingual **cingulum**); lower molars with a broad posterior basin (the trigonid basin) surrounded by five prismlike cusps (forming a so-called **Y-5 pattern**); and a strongly developed last cusp on the lower molars (the *hypoconulid;* see Appendix 1). The teeth of the proconsulids show that they had a range of dietary patterns, from primarily fruit-eating, indicated by low, rounded molar cusps, to leaf-eating, indicated by a greater development of molar sharing crests and cusps than seen in earlier primate fossils. The proconsulids also share many primitive catarrhine cranial traits with the Old World monkeys. These include a tubular ectotympanic bone in the ear region. The relative size of the brain compared with overall body size also seems to be similar in the proconsulids and the living Old World monkeys.

Postcranial remains (those other bones of the body except the skull) clearly diagnostic as hominoid are mostly unknown before 18 million years ago (Pilbeam, 1996). Even at that date, postcranial fossils attributable to the proconsulids show very few similarities to modern hominoids. Proconsulid vertebral columns probably had six lumbar vertebrae, and at least the last thoracic vertebrae had lumbarlike articulations. The thorax appeared to be narrow and deep, features most similar to quadrupedal-pronograde monkeys (Figure 7–14). However, there appears to be a range of adaptations within this general pattern. For example, there were suspensory species such as *Dendropithecus macinnesi* (similar to the modern spider monkey), gibbonlike species of *Limnopithecus* and *Simiolus,* and a terrestrial quadruped, *Proconsul nyanzae.* Based on studies of differences in canine size, the proconsulids show considerable sexual dimorphism in body size (Kelley, 1987).

Fossils represented by facial, dental, and vertebral remains were recovered beginning in the early 1960s from a site in Uganda, Moroto II. The surprisingly modern anatomy of the lumbar vertebrae, resembling features found only in modern hominoids, contrasted with the more primitive features of the skull and teeth. The vertebrae indicated a lower back region

proconsulids–family of early Miocene hominids known mostly from sites in eastern Africa.

cingulum–a "belt" (from Latin), referring to a raised ridge of enamel encircling a tooth crown.

Y-5 pattern–a pattern in the lower molars of five distinct cusps, separated by a backward (distally) facing Y-shaped groove; characteristic of hominoids, as well as of more primitive catarrhines (see Figure 7–7).

Dendropithecus macinnesi

Proconsul africanus

Proconsul major

Figure 7–13 • Reconstruction of some proconsulids, showing differences in size and posture.

Figure 7–14 • Skeletal reconstruction of *Proconsul*. (After Alan Walker)

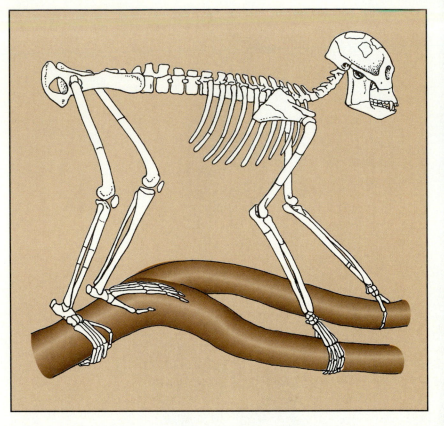

breccia—from Italian, meaning "broken"; a geological term used to refer to the sediment found in cave deposits composed from rock fragments of widely varying sizes cemented together.

that was shorter and stiffer than that observed for the proconsulids and more compatible with a brachiating form of locomotion and an arm-hanging posture. Later explorations of the Moroto site in 1994 and 1995 brought to light new postcranial remains that confirmed the original diagnosis. This fossil primate was large, weighing somewhere between 40 and 50 kg. The fact that this species differed from known proconsulids and modern monkeys suggested to researchers that they had recovered a new hominoid, for which they proposed the name *Morotopithecus bishopi*, after the late geologist W. W. Bishop, who did the original work at the Moroto locality. *Morotopithecus* provided yet another surprise in its early Miocene age. Using a dating technique that compares the ratio of one kind (isotope) of organ gas with another encapsulated in rocks of volcanic origin, the age of a local lava associated with the fossil remains was dated to more than 20 million years. How does *Morotopithecus* fit in with other early Miocene African hominoids? According to Daniel Gebo et al. (1997), these new finds appear to be more closely related to living hominoids than are later species, such as *Kenyapithecus,* which possess primitive postcrania and whose "purported proximity to the living hominoids has rested almost entirely on dental and facial characters" (1997:403).

During the early 1990s the remains of yet another new species of fossil hominoid were recovered from **breccia** in Namibia by a team led by

FRONTIERS

Miocene Apes and Modern Hominoids

by David R. Begun

The results of the last twenty years of research in Miocene hominoids has produced some dramatic changes in interpretations of hominoid evolution. Hominoid evolution is much more complicated than was once thought; at least 25 different genera from between about 20 to 6 million years ago are now known. Living hominoids are but a mere shadow of the former diversity of this group.

The earliest well-documented Miocene hominoid is *Proconsul,* who dwelled in Kenya and Uganda up to about 20 million years ago. Many fossil hominoids are known from these sites. Most are probably related to *Proconsul,* but some, like *Dendropithecus,* may represent a different kind of hominoid, or may not be a hominoid at all. The common ancestor of modern hominoids must have been very similar to *Proconsul.*

The Middle Miocene lasted from about 16.5 to about 11.5 million years ago. The Kenyan site of Maboko, dating to about 15 million years ago, preserves a new type of hominoid with thick molar enamel, known as *Kenyapithecus,* first described from the somewhat younger site of Fort Ternan, also in western Kenya. *Kenyapithecus* is more advanced than early Miocene hominoids in molar morphology but retains many primitive features also found in *Proconsul.* However, certain characteristics of the shoulder joint in *Kenyapithecus,* combined with its thickly enamelled molars, suggests a

greater dependence on terrestrial sources of food, which tend to contain more grit and therefore tend to wear teeth more rapidly. More will be known about the cranial and postcranial anatomy of *Kenyapithecus* when a large sample from the Nachola area of northern Kenya is analyzed. Dentally and postcranially similar hominoids are also known from the Middle Miocene in Europe and Turkey. These forms, called *Griphopithecus,* may, together with *Kenyapithecus,* be the earliest members of the lineage that includes the living great apes and humans.

By the end of the Middle Miocene and into the Late Miocene, modern great ape anatomy becomes evident. Two forms appear at nearly the same time—*Sivapithecus* in South Asia (India and Pakistan) and *Dryopithecus* in Europe. It was the discovery of a remarkably complete face, GSP 15000 [see Figure 7–18], more than any other development, that convinced most paleoanthropologists that *Sivapithecus* was not a "dryopithecine" but an early member of the lineage of the orang.

The interpretation of *Dryopithecus* has also changed considerably due to new discoveries. Three partial crania and large numbers of jaws, teeth, and limb bones from various sites in Europe show that *Dryopithecus* has characteristics only found in African apes and humans, and one other Miocene hominoid, *Ouranopithecus,* from the Late Miocene of Greece. The new interpretation that links *Dryopithecus* and *Ouranopithecus* from Europe, rather than Asian *Sivapithecus,* more closely to African apes and humans, is almost exactly the opposite of the interpretation of these genera 25 years ago.

A major conclusion from recent research in Miocene hominoids concerns our understanding of the relations among living hominoids and the place humans occupy among them. Most paleoanthropologists who focus on morphology believe that chimps and gorillas are the closest, citing such specializations as knuckle-walking and thinly enamelled teeth. But the significance of these characteristics is not so clear-cut. Enamel thickness is a poor indicator of evolutionary relationships because it changes so often in response to dietary requirements. Knuckle-walking, which is unique among living forms to African apes, is commonly considered to be a recent specialization of the African apes. A more controversial, but in my mind more likely, view is that knuckle-walking characterized our ancestors too. After all, humans do share unusual features of the hand and wrist only with African apes, such as fewer wrist bones, more stability of the joints of the wrist, and shorter hand and finger bones. One real possibility is that humans retain these characteristics because we evolved from a knuckle-walker that needed them to ensure wrist and hand stability while walking on the knuckles. When humans shifted to two feet we may have lost many features still found in knuckle-walkers, while other characteristics were suitable to the tasks important to early bipeds, such as enhanced manipulation, and were thus retained.

David R. Begun is Professor of Anthropology at the University of Toronto. He studies hominoid morphology and evolution, especially that of the European Miocene.

Glenn Conroy (Washington University Medical School). The new genus, named *Otavipithecus namibiensis* by its discoverers, is so far the first Miocene hominoid found south of equatorial East Africa, expanding significantly the known hominoid range. The first published remains of this fossil, whose size is somewhat smaller than that of a pygmy chimpanzee, consist of a single partial mandible (jawbone). It shares dental features of relatively thin enamel with the European hominoid known as *Dryopithecus*. A recently discovered first cervical vertebra (the atlas) is morphologically intermediate between those belonging to modern cercopithecoids and hominoids and may indicate the starting point at which quadrupedal hominoids became more upright in posture. In contrast to the early age of *Morotopithecus,* this fossil, dated by faunal remains to about 13 million years (later middle Miocene), is a relatively recent one. *Otavipithecus* at present is best interpreted as a sister group of other Miocene large-bodied hominoids (Conroy et al., 1992a; 1992b; 1996).

HOMINOIDS WITH THICK MOLAR ENAMEL APPEAR

During the middle Miocene in Africa, hominoids appeared that for the first time possessed molar teeth with thick enamel (Figure 7–15). This most likely represented an adaptation for the biting and crushing of hard foods. Species inhabiting dry forest, open savanna, and woodland in

Figure 7–15 • Evolution of thickness and rate of formation of molar enamel thickness in hominoids.

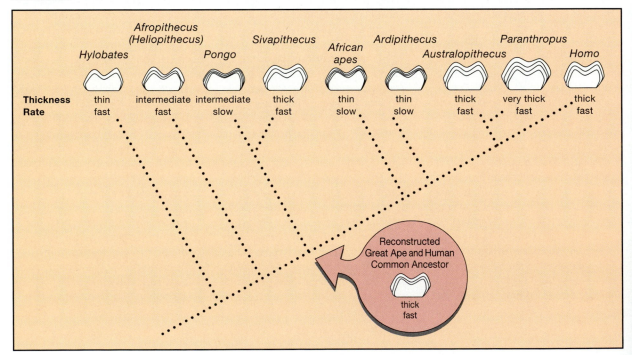

Africa, originally known as *Kenyapithecus,* are characteristic of these hominoids. Fossil remains of this species, known primarily from the teeth and jaw fragments, have been discovered at the Kenyan sites of Maboko (*ca.* 15 million years ago), Fort Ternan (13–14 million years ago), and Samburu Hills (9 million years ago).

From the 1960s to the 1980s, these hominoids, along with fossils discovered in India and Pakistan called *Ramapithecus,* were considered by many researchers to be direct human ancestors. Some characteristics that these apes share with humans are thick molar enamel; a more orthognathous or "straight-faced" profile; and somewhat reduced canine tooth size compared with that of most other apes. The most likely case, however, based on the resemblances of known cranial and dental features, is that these fossils belong to a group of Asian fossil hominoids called *Sivapithecus* (Conroy, 1990) that will be described later in this chapter. Characteristics including thick molar enamel, robust mandible, and large upper premolars suggest a possible relationship with the common ancestor of the modern great apes (Fleagle, 1988:371–72), even though analysis of the postcranial remains examined by Benefit and McCrossin (1993) shows that the knuckle-walking terrestrial locomotion characteristic of the modern African apes is lacking.

The fossil record of African apes after the middle Miocene is a blank except for a possible gorillalike fossil canine tooth reported by Pickford et al. (1988) from the Pliocene deposits of the Western Rift Valley of Uganda. Interestingly, there are no fossil apes in the Pliocene hominid sites of eastern or southern Africa, implying that these areas were either isolated from the forests of Central and West Africa by corridors of open vegetation, or were too arid and unforested to have served as appropriate ape habitats. Future paleontological work in Central and West Africa may improve our understanding of the history of modern ape habitats and their fossil record.

APE EVOLUTION IN EURASIA

Eurasian hominoids, having migrated from Africa, appear in the fossil record for the first time beginning in the middle Miocene about 17 million years ago. The Eurasian fossil apes are more distinct from one another than are the earlier proconsulids (Fleagle, 1988). There are five major groups of Miocene fossil apes: (1) the oldest and most primitive gibbon-sized primates, the **pliopithecids;** (2) the enigmatic late Miocene primate represented by a single genus and species, *Oreopithecus bambolii;* (3) and species of the genus *Gigantopithecus,* the largest primate that ever lived. The smaller species, *G. giganteus,* about the size of living gorillas (125 kg), was found in deposits of the latest Miocene in India and Pakistan. Its larger descendant, *G. blacki,* whose estimated weight approaches some 300 kg, has left remains in middle Pleistocene caves in southern China. Finally, (4) there are different genera and species of groups called the **sivapithecids,** named by Pilgrim (1915) for

pliopithecid—medium-sized, folivorous hominoids known from the middle-late Miocene of Eurasia.

sivapithecid—family of middle to late Miocene hominoids found mostly in Asia. Species of this group may be ancestral to modern orangutan.

the Hindu god *Siva;* and (5) the **dryopithecids,** named by Lartet (1856) (from Greek, *"dryo-"* meaning "oak"). Many of these fossils are known only from jaw and teeth remains. As a consequence, separation of individual fossils into different groups is commonly based on differences in enamel thickness (thin versus thick), mandibular shape, and subnasal structure. Even applying these criteria, classification of specific fossils varies among researchers.

The majority of Miocene apes probably belong to a separate radiation from the one that led to the living hominoids. Currently only *Oreopithecus, Morotopithecus,* and, possibly, *Dryopithecus* show any significant postcranial resemblances to living hominoids. According to Pilbeam (1996), there are essentially no Miocene fossil hominoids that are "directly relevant to the extant apes and especially to the chimp-gorilla-human clade." Hence, there is no fossil record directly relevant to the question of hominid origins, except for Pliocene hominids, the earliest of which date back only to about 4.5 million years ago (Pilbeam, 1996:157).

The dryopithecids apparently lived in densely forested environments, commonly in Europe and possibly China, during the middle and late Miocene, at the end of which time they became extinct. These, the first fossil hominoid remains ever to be discovered, were found in 1856 at a site located in the Paris Basin of France. Subsequently, as more fossils were discovered, the genus and subfamily names were applied to a wide range of Miocene hominoids (Simons and Pilbeam, 1965).

While fossil remains of the dryopithecids' jaws and teeth are well known, the cranial remains that do exist have not, as yet, been described fully. The few pieces that represent the postcranial skeleton, on the basis of a reduced olecranon process (elbow) and the deep humeral trochlea of the elbow, suggest that some of these species were suspensory (Morbeck, 1983) (Figure 7–14). Recent evidence from Hungary suggests to Begun (1992) that dryopithecids had facial anatomy similar to the modern African apes and probably shared a more recent common ancestry with African hominoids than with Asian sivapithecids (Figure 7–16). In summary, the middle-to-late Miocene European hominoids most likely represent a separate radiation of apes that became progressively cut off from the forests of Africa and Asia as the Miocene Epoch drew to a close.

The widespread sivapithecids, especially the genus *Ramapithecus* (now included within the genus *Sivapithecus*), were originally discovered in India from sediments of the Siwalik Hills, an area that follows the base of the Himalayas from western Pakistan to northeast India. In the early 1930s, G. E. Lewis suggested that *Ramapithecus* showed hominid affinities because of its parabolic dental arcade (incorrectly diagnosed) and the relatively reduced height of the canine tooth. Since the 1970s Elywn Simons, David Pilbeam, and colleagues from the Geological Survey of Pakistan have uncovered hundreds of new fossils representing over 100 individuals. Of these, however, only a very few postcranial remains have been found in direct association with the fossil teeth.

dryopithecid–family of middle Miocene hominoids found mostly in Europe.

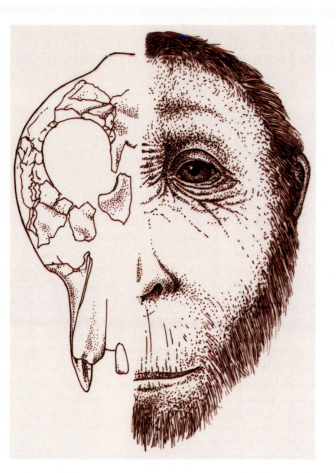

Figure 7–16 • Dryopithecid facial anatomy. (After David Begun)

Sivapithecids are best known from the later Miocene in Asia, with some species spreading into eastern Europe. This family of fossil apes was composed of a wide-ranging group of species, possibly five from Eurasia and one from Africa (*S. africanus,* previously described as *Kenyapithecus*), the largest of which approached the size of a male orangutan (Conroy, 1990:235). Dentally, *Sivapithecus* shows a relatively small amount of canine sexual dimorphism compared with modern anthropoids, thick fast-developing molar enamel, an absence of a cingulum, and relatively low flat molar cusps that allowed the teeth to wear flat. These dental features resemble those of modern anthropoids whose diet consists mainly of hard objects such as nuts, seeds, and fruit with pits. A reconstruction of their paleoenvironment shows a mixed woodland and dry forest habitat.

Europe was also home to two other descendants of early Miocene proconsulids. The first group, the pliopithecids (Greek for "lesser ape"), were small-bodied, forest-living, climbing and suspensory hominoids frequently found associated with *Dryopithecus*. Members of the family Pliopithecidae are the earliest hominoids to appear in Eurasia, at about 16 million years ago. The best-known species was *Pliopithecus vindobonensis,* whose size was closest to that of modern siamangs. Although they were gibbonlike in their postcranial adaptations, details of their teeth and cranial anatomy are too primitive to indicate a close relationship with modern gibbons. The canine teeth show a high degree of sexual dimorphism, and the well-developed shearing crests of the cusps of the premolar and molar teeth indicate that *Pliopithecus* ate foliage.

The second group, the Oreopithecidae, is enigmatic in that fossil remains of this form have been very difficult to place phylogenetically. There is irony in this, because these fossils are the best-known skeletal remains of all the Miocene hominoids. *Oreopithecus* (Greek, "forest ape") was first discovered at an 8-million-year-old site at Mount Bamboli in Italy. Members of this group lived in swamp forests and may have come down out of the trees only seldom. *Oreopithecus* is unique in its postcranial anatomy. It possessed a broad thorax, short lumbar region of the vertebral column, long forelimbs, and short hindlimbs. In comparison with the rest of the Miocene hominoids, *Oreopithecus* shows the clearest early adaptations for suspensory, "forelimb-dominated" locomotion. In its locomotor adaptations it is most similar to the modern orangutan. However, its very different cusp pattern on the molar teeth shows that it had no close phylogenetic connection with any modern hominoids. Harrison (1986) showed possible African ties to middle Miocene *Nyanzapithecus* and to the earlier proconsulid *Rangwapithecus*. These ancestral connections also demonstrate that a bridge from Africa to Europe existed that allowed the migration of these forest-living hominoids. The unique features of *Oreopithecus,* however, along with other data about the ancient climate, show that this bridge was cut toward the close of the Miocene.

EVOLUTIONARY RELATIONSHIPS AMONG HOMINOIDS

The question of when our earliest hominid ancestors diverged from our closest living relatives, the African apes, has been one of the most controversial in biological anthropology. Our understanding of the evolutionary relationships of the Miocene hominoids has undergone a revolution in recent years. At one time most researchers of human evolution, such as Elywn Simons and David Pilbeam (1965), believed that there was a straightforward connection between Miocene forms and living species. *Proconsul africanus* was hypothesized to be ancestral to the chimpanzee, *Proconsul major* to the gorilla, possibly *Sivapithecus indicus* to the orangutan, and *Ramapithecus* to hominids. Greenfield (1980) termed this hypothesis the **Early Divergence Hypothesis,** which stated that the branching of the lineages leading to the modern apes occurred prior to the early Miocene (Figure 7–17). Developments in two areas of biological anthropology, however, changed this general opinion. First, biomolecular studies showed that humans shared a recent common ancestor with African apes, diverging from one another only some 4 to 6 million years ago (Sarich and Wilson, 1967). Therefore, *Ramapithecus,* dating from 13 to 8 million years ago, could not be a direct hominid an-

Early Divergence Hypothesis— hypothesis that postulates an ancient evolutionary split (more than 15 million years ago) of African apes and humans from a common ancestor.

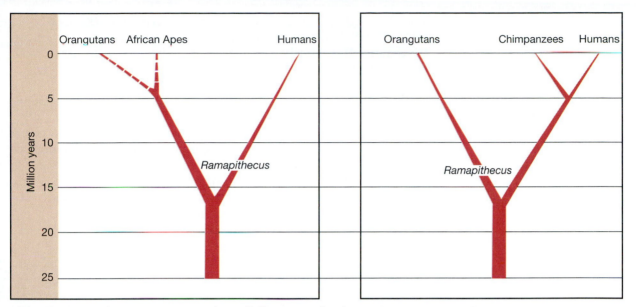

Figure 7–17 • Early Divergence Hypothesis (left) compared with Late Divergence Hypothesis (right).

cestor, because according to the molecular clock, the hominid–ape split had not yet occurred. Second, discoveries of more complete remains, as well as of many new fossil apes from the Miocene of Africa and Eurasia, also began to cast doubt on this simple, straightforward interpretation. A relatively complete fossil facial skeleton of *Sivapithecus* (Figure 7–18), discovered in Pakistan, showed that this taxon shared many facial characteristics with the orangutan. This realization removed the best candidate for a Miocene ape uniquely ancestral to the hominid lineage and

Figure 7–18 • Face of *Sivapithecus* (GSP 15000, center) compared with orangutan (left) and chimpanzee (right).

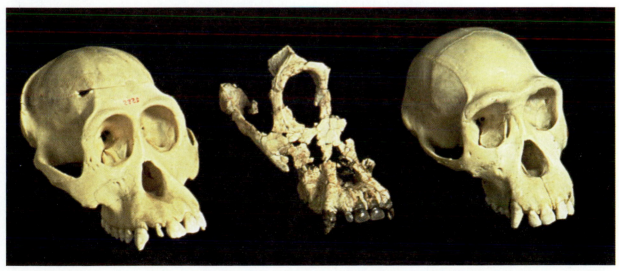

argued strongly against the Early Divergence Hypothesis (Pilbeam et al., 1980). The Early Divergence Hypothesis has been replaced by the **Late Divergence Hypothesis,** a term also coined by Greenfield (1980). Both fossil evidence and molecular evidence played important roles in the acceptance of this hypothesis.

For some years it has been known how close the genetic relationships are between apes and humans (Goodman, 1961, 1962, 1973; Hafleigh and Williams, 1966). Data that have supported this position have been amassed from DNA studies, **globin** sequences, **fibrinopeptide** sequences, and immunology (Table 7–1).

The molecular data argue for a single grouping of hominoids, with a separation from the cercopithecoids some 20 million years ago, and, subsequently, for four major changes that led to the evolution of the hominoids. First is the separation of the gibbon and its relatives from the line leading to the great apes and hominids. This lineage split from the common great ape–hominid line between 12 and 15 million years ago. *Dionysopithecus,* known in the late Miocene of China, suggests the presence of this lineage in the fossil record.

Second is the subsequent divergence of the orangutan from the lineage leading to the African apes and hominids. There is now overwhelming evidence that there is a common lineage leading to the African apes and *Homo,* with *Pongo* (orangutans) as a sister group. The divergence of *Pongo* occurred, according to molecular estimates, between 10 and 13 million years ago. This corresponds with the known

Late Divergence Hypothesis– hypothesis that postulates a recent evolutionary split (5 to less than 15 million years ago) of the African apes and humans from a common ancestor.

globin–protein of hemoglobin that comprises red blood cells.

fibrinopeptide–blood protein related to blood clotting.

Table 7–1 • Differences in Amino Acid Sequences of Human and Chimpanzee Polypeptides

Protein	Amino Acid Differences
Fibrinopeptides A and B	0
Cytochrome C	0
Lysozyme 1	0[1]
Hemoglobin (alpha)	0
Hemoglobin (beta)	0
Hemoglobin (A gamma)	0
Hemoglobin (G gamma)	0
Hemoglobin (delta)	1
Myoglobin	1
Carbonic anhydrase 1	3[1]
Serum albumin	6[1]
Transferrin 1	8[1]
Total	19

[1]These proteins have been compared immunologically; the remainder have been compared by direct amino acid sequencing.

Adapted from "Evolution at two levels in humans and chimpanzee" by King and Wilson, *Science*, 188:107–16. Copyright © 1975 American Association for the Advancement of Science.

range of *Sivapithecus* and *Ramapithecus* in the fossil record (Andrews and Cronin, 1982).

Third is the split of the gorilla from hominids and *Pan* (chimpanzees). It seems likely now that the common chimpanzee-gorilla-hominid lineage existed for some time before the gorilla lineage split off from it, possibly as early as 9 million years ago (Caccone and Powell, 1989). Earlier data were unable to separate the time of divergence of the gorilla and the chimpanzee lineages (e.g. Sarich and Wilson, 1967). However, Horai and colleagues (1995) have sequenced the entire mitochondrial genome in these hominoids, and their data show a clear chimp–hominid clade (grouping) with a long time of separation after divergence of gorillas. Other work on DNA (Table 7–2) has suggested that humans and chimpanzees share a common lineage to the exclusion of the gorilla, which diverged about 8 million years ago (Sibley and Ahlquist, 1987; Sibley et al., 1990). Other studies (Spuhler, 1989) have supported this arrangement, but some (Templeton, 1985, 1986) have not. There has been debate about whether the techniques of analysis (e.g. Marks et al., 1988) have skewed the results, but it also seems likely that different molecules evolved at different rates, and that this factor may contribute to the lack of resolution of the sequence of African ape and hominid divergences (Holmquist et al., 1988). According to Pilbeam (1996:159), "in the case of the hominoids it is difficult to explain the genetic patterns reported here as supporting anything other than a chimp-human clade, given what is known of molecular biology and molecular evolutionary process." The confirmatory fossil evidence for the evolutionary histories of the modern chimp and gorilla lineages, however, at this point is virtually nonexistent.

The fourth change is the split of the hominid and chimpanzee lineages. According to the molecular data, this occurred between 5 and 8 million years ago (Cronin, 1983). Molecular work further reveals genetic differentiation within the modern *Pan* species: the bonobo (*Pan paniscus*) and

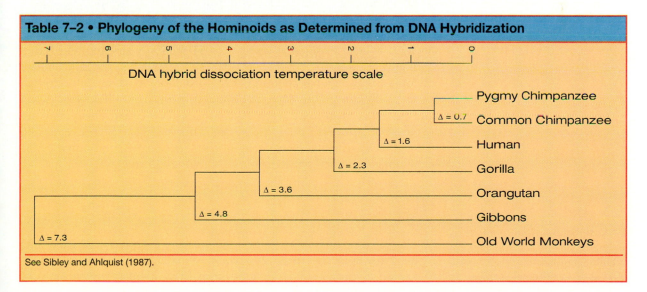

Table 7–2 • Phylogeny of the Hominoids as Determined from DNA Hybridization

DNA hybrid dissociation temperature scale

Δ = 0.7 — Pygmy Chimpanzee / Common Chimpanzee

Δ = 1.6 — Human

Δ = 2.3 — Gorilla

Δ = 3.6 — Orangutan

Δ = 4.8 — Gibbons

Δ = 7.3 — Old World Monkeys

See Sibley and Ahlquist (1987).

the common chimp (*Pan troglodytes*), which shared a common ancestor about 2 million years ago. The living populations of the gorilla are somewhat less divergent genetically and may have separated into western and eastern populations about 1 million years ago.

DNA hybridization data are now available on several primate species (Sibley et al., 1990). This technique compares the temperature (measured in degrees centigrade) required to break apart the two strands of the DNA molecule of any species (called the *dissociation temperature,* Tm) with the reduced temperature it takes to break apart a "hybrid" DNA: DNA whose two strands come from two separate species. This technique assumes that the hybrid DNA of species more distantly related will dissociate at a temperature lower than the hybrid DNA of species that are more closely related. This assumption is based on the fact that more distantly related species will have fewer nucleic acid sequences in common, and, thus, the strands of the hybrid DNA will bond together less completely. Chimpanzee–human hybrid DNA dissociates at a temperature somewhere between 0.7 and 1.5°C lower than the dissociation temperature of either human or chimpanzee DNA by itself.

DNA hybridization results have proven to be extremely useful in primate phylogenetic analysis. For example, hybrid human–capuchin monkey DNA (a New World monkey) dissociates at a temperature about 10.5°C G lower than the pure DNA of either species. If we assume that the platyrrhine/catarrhine divergence occurred about 35 million years ago, then the human–chimpanzee difference of 1.5°C translates to about a 5 million year divergence time. Similarly, a difference of 6.3°C between human and green monkey DNA (an African cercopithecoid) translates to a time of separation of 21 million years, and the human–gibbon difference of 3.5°C translates to a divergence estimate of 11.7 million years. All are in excellent agreement with the time of divergence calculated using the immunological data.

An integrated biomolecular and paleontological perspective argues increasingly for an entirely African origin for the common ancestral hominid-chimpanzee-gorilla and hominid-chimpanzee lineages. These lineages, which diverged at about 9 to 11 million years ago and 5 to 8 million years ago, respectively, arose close to the dates of significant late middle Miocene global cooling (11 to 14 million years ago); the formation of the Western Rift Valley in Central Africa (*ca.* 8 million years ago); and the "Messinian Event," the drying up of the Mediterranean Sea, between about 6.2 and 5 million years ago (Boaz, 1997). These events, and the significant climatic effects that resulted, may have contributed to the evolutionary origins of these various hominoid lineages.

 **SUMMARY**

DNA hybridization–method of assessing genetic relationships by splitting and "reannealing" strands of DNA from different species.

1. The earliest members of the hominoid group appeared in Africa during the early Miocene, over 20 million years ago. These fossil forms, known as proconsulids, differed from fossil monkeys in molar cusp

morphology (the hominoids shared a Y-5 pattern), in locomotor abilities (the hominoids were more dexterous climbers), and, in some later forms, in unique patterns of locomotion (such as brachiation and knuckle walking).

2. Hominoids spread throughout the Old World by 15 million years ago. In Europe they appeared as the dryopithecids and in Asia as the sivapithecids, in addition to a number of smaller species that were possibly ancestral to the modern gibbons. By 5 million years ago most of these early species had become extinct, possibly because of unsuccessful competition with a growing number of monkey species.

3. Brachiation, a form of arboreal locomotion characteristic of all modern hominoids, involves specific anatomical changes in the upper torso and forelimb. These changes permitted hominoids a much greater degree of rotational freedom and use of the forelimb in climbing and feeding activities. Brachiation also involved a loss of the tail.

4. The four surviving hominoid groups, the lesser apes or hylobatids, gorillas, chimpanzees, and orangutans, have limited distribution today in tropical rain forests of Africa and Southeast Asia.

5. Molecular studies of living apes have changed our ideas about their phylogenetic relationships with the Miocene forms. Middle Miocene species such as *Ramapithecus* and *Kenyapithecus* (now taxonomically included with *Sivapithecus*), once considered to be hominid ancestors, are now thought to be related to, if not ancestral to, the orangutans.

6. The Early Divergence Hypothesis predicted independent lineages for the modern apes and humans extending back over 15 million years. Molecular studies involving such techniques as electrophoresis, immunology, protein sequencing, and DNA hybridization, as well as a more complete fossil record, now support a Late Divergence Hypothesis and a more recent date for a point of common ancestry of the chimpanzees and humans, with an earlier split of this group from gorillas.

CRITICAL-THINKING QUESTIONS

1. What morphological characteristics distinguish a hominoid from a monkey?
2. What are the advantages of the hominoids' unique brachiating patterns of arboreal locomotion?
3. Describe the family Proconsulidae. When and where were members of this group found?
4. Discuss the evolution of the hominoids outside of Africa during the middle to late Miocene.
5. Describe the four major cladistic events in hominoid evolution.
6. What can the cusp patterns and tooth enamel thickness of hominoids tell us about the environment in which ancient animals lived?

SUGGESTED READINGS

Boaz, N. T. 1997. *Eco Homo*. New York: Basic Books. A look at the relationship between environmental change and change in the plants and animals of the middle to late Cenozoic with special emphasis on the primates.

Conroy, Glynn. 1990. *Primate Evolution*. New York: W. W. Norton. Primate evolution is reviewed in this volume using the known Cenozoic fossil record. Conroy's taxonomy of the primates differs from Fleagle's because of the differing conceptual notions these authors have of primate relationships.

Fleagle, John. 1988. *Primate Adaptation and Evolution*. New York: Academic Press. An overview of the adaptations primates have made from those characterizing the group's origins 65 millions years ago to those of present-day species.

Australopithecines

The origins of the hominid family is one of the most active areas of current investigation in human evolution. As paleoanthropologists have discovered successively older and more primitive fossil remains of hominids, the definition of the family **Hominidae** and its distinction from apes has had to be constantly reassessed. Past definitions have been based primarily on characteristics of *Homo sapiens,* our own species, which is the best-known member of the family. The fossil record now presents several species of hominids that, in varying degrees, are unlike modern humans. Where to draw the line between human and ape has had to be spelled out in ever greater detail. This chapter covers the **Australopithecines,** the earliest group of hominids that share important traits with *Homo sapiens.*

Hominidae–the zoological family in which humans and their more recent fossil antecedents are classified; bipedal hominoids with increased brain-to-body-size ratio.

Australopithecines–small-brained, bipedal members of an early genus of the family Hominidae; *fl.* late Miocene (~4.0 million years ago) to early Pleistocene (~1.0 million years ago), and replaced by members of the genus *Homo.*

DEFINITION OF HOMINIDAE

The ancient Greeks defined people in the natural world as "featherless bipeds." The term "biped" split people off from all four-footed animals, and "featherless" removed people from the largest category of bipedal animals, the birds. But such living animals as the kangaroo, gerbil, and gibbon and such fossil animals as the *Tyrannosaurus,* pterodactyl, and an Eocene bipedal insectivore also fall into this category.

The British anatomist Sir Wilfrid E. Le Gros Clark provided (1964) what has been the most widely accepted definition of Hominidae (Table 8–1). Hominidae, or hominids, are relatively *large-brained* and *bipedal* members of the order Primates. They have *orthognathous facial skeletons* that protrude less than those of apes, and *canine teeth reduced* in size in relation to their other teeth, compared with those of apes. However, as more primitive hominid fossils have become known, some of these distinctions have become less absolute. The earliest hominids now known show characteristics only slightly more advanced than those of

Table 8–1 • Characteristics Defining the Family Hominidae

Skeletal adaptations to erect bipedalism, especially proportionate lengthening of lower extremity and changes in proportions and morphological details of the pelvis, femur, and foot skeleton

A well-developed pollex (thumb)

Loss of opposability of hallux (big toe)

Increasing flexion of basicranium (base of the skull), with increasing cranial height

Forward positioning of occipital condyles (the bony prominences surrounding the foramen magnum)

Restricted nuchal (neck) area on occipital bone for attachment of posterior neck muscles

A strongly developed pyramid-shaped mastoid process of the temporal bone

Reduced forward projection of the face in the area below the nose opening and fusion of premaxilla bone

Canines spatulate in form, showing little or no interlocking, and lacking sexual dimorphism

No diastemata (gaps) in the tooth row related to the canine teeth

First lower premolars bicuspid and nonsectorial (nonshearing)

Tooth wear largely even and horizontal on the crowns

Dental arcade evenly rounded

In later stages of evolution reduction in size of the molar teeth

Accelerated replacement of deciduous teeth in relation to the eruption of the permanent molars

"Molarization" of the first deciduous molar

In later stages of evolution, marked and rapid expansion of cranial capacity, associated with reduction in the size of the jaws and in the attachment areas for the muscles of mastication, and with presence of a mental eminence (chin)

From Le Gros Clark (1964).

apes. Nevertheless, these early hominids were well-adapted bipeds, notwithstanding significant climbing abilities, and bipedalism still serves as the most useful distinguishing characteristic of the family.

THE EARLIEST HOMINIDS

Despite intensive searching for more than a hundred years, fossils that document the common ancestor of the ape-human grouping have eluded discovery. The hominoid fossils of this time period are fragmentary and predate the earliest known definitive hominids (Table 8–2). The sites from which these fossils come are in Africa and date between 5 million and 11 million years ago.

An isolated upper molar tooth from Ngorora, Kenya, is the earliest possible fossil evidence for hominids in Africa. It is dated to about 11 million years ago. The specimen is similar to that of a modern chimpanzee except that it is larger and likely has a thick enamel capping on

Table 8–2 • Major Fossils Attributed to Australopithecines

Taxon	Locality	Specimen Number	Body Part	Geological Age
Ardipithecus ramidus	Middle Awash, Ethiopia	ARA (Aramis Location) VP-6/500 "Ardi Ram"	Dentition, partial skeleton	4.3–4.4 million years
Australopithecus anamensis	Kanapoi Allia Bay, Kenya	NA	Various cranial, postcranial, and dental specimens	3.9–4.2 million years
Australopithecus afarensis	Laetoli, Tanzania	LH (Laetoli Hominid) 4	Mandible with teeth	3.6–3.8 million years
	Hadar, Ethiopia	AL (Afar Locality) 288-1 ("Lucy")	Partial skeleton	3.2–3.4 million years
		AL 333 ("The First Family")	Various cranial, postcranial and dental specimens of some 14 individuals	
		AL 444-2	Complete skull	
Australopithecus africanus	Taung, South Africa	Taung 1 ("The Taung Child")	Complete skull and mandible with teeth	circa 2.5 million years
	Sterkfontein, South Africa	STS (Sterkfontein Type Site) 5 ("Mrs. Ples")	Skull lacking teeth	circa 3.0 million years
Australopithecus aethiopicus [also considered *A. boisei*]	Omo, Ethiopia	Omo 18-67-18	Mandible with tooth roots	2.8 million years
	West Turkana, Kenya	KNM WT (Kenya National Museum, West Turkana) 17000 ("The Black Skull")	Skull lacking teeth	2.5 million years
Australopithecus [or *Paranthropus*] *boisei*	Olduvai Gorge, Tanzania	OH (Olduvai Hominid) 5 ("Nutcracker Man" or "Dear Boy")	Complete skull with teeth	1.8 million years
	East Turkana, Kenya	KNM ER (Kenya National Museum, East Rudolf) 406	Skull lacking teeth	1.9 million years
Australopithecus [or *Paranthropus*] *robustus*	Swartkrans, South Africa	SK 47	Skull with partial dentition	circa 2.0 million years
	Drimolen, South Africa			

the crown of the tooth. Both of these characteristics differentiate the tooth from that of modern African apes, and, in this respect, the tooth resembles the teeth of modern humans. However, because thick enamel is a primitive characteristic for the great-ape–hominid ancestor, as we saw in Chapter 7, it does not confer definitive hominid status on the Ngorora

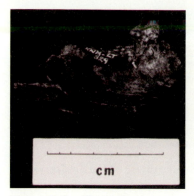

Figure 8–1 • The Lothagam mandible, Baringo Basin, Kenya, the earliest clear example of Hominidae in the fossil record.

specimen. Without associated postcranial bones it is impossible to determine the body size of the Ngorora hominoid and thus to decide whether its molar teeth were relatively enlarged, as in hominids. A second hominoid specimen found at Ngorora is a premolar that Hill and Ward (1988) have suggested represents the last surviving *Proconsul*. The Ngorora molar, however, belonged to a different species of hominoid. It also differs from the gorilla-like Samburu Hills hominoid, being at least 1 million years younger. It may represent the earliest hominid or, more likely, it may be one of several still poorly known late Miocene East African species of apes. Another isolated molar tooth, also from Kenya, comes from the site of Lukeino, dated to about 6 million years ago. In overall appearance it is also chimpanzee-like, but for the same reasons as with the Ngorora specimen its affinities are difficult to determine with certainty.

The earliest fossil evidence generally accepted for Hominidae is the *Lothagam* mandible (Figure 8–1), dated at somewhat more than 5.5 million years ago. This specimen consists of a right portion of a jaw with the first molar and the root of the last premolar preserved. The thickness of the mandible and the squared shape of the molar, as well as a number of structural details, show that this specimen was similar to those of later hominids and significantly different from those of apes. A second jaw discovered at Tabarin, Kenya, and dating to about 5.0 million years ago, confirms that hominids were present in East Africa by the end of the Miocene Epoch.

The earliest fossil evidence for Hominidae, the definition of which ironically is based on a postcranial locomotor adaptation, bipedalism, thus consists of dental and mandibular remains. There is no clear indication of whether the Lothagam and Tabarin hominids were in fact bipeds, since relevant portions of the postcranial skeleton, especially lower limb bones, are lacking.

The earliest possible lower limb bone that may be hominid is the end of a fibula, the outer bone of the lower leg from the Libyan fossil locality of Sahabi, dated at 5 to 6 million years ago. The specimen shows the stout shaft and reduced fibular head seen also in humans. A femur fragment from the northern Ethiopian site of Middle Awash, dated at less than 4 million years ago, is clearly hominid in its long, straight neck and small greater trochanter (Appendix 1). The straightness of the head, neck, and shaft indicates that weight was transferred in a more or less vertical manner, as expected in a biped.

WHAT THE EARLIEST HOMINID LOOKED LIKE

When paleoanthropological research succeeds in uncovering remains of hominids more primitive than are currently known, what sort of creature will they reveal? Equally intriguing is the question of what the common African ape-hominid ancestor was like.

If hominids share a common ancestor with chimps and gorillas, which of the three is the least changed from the common ancestor, and which is the most derived? Comparing only the living species of *Homo, Pan,* and *Gorilla,* the answer to this question has seemed to be that humans are the most derived and that chimps and gorillas are the most primitive, because they are more similar to each other than to people. The deduction follows, therefore, that our common ancestor would have been a knuckle-walking, apelike form (Washburn and Moore, 1980). Zihlman et al. (1978) suggested that the common ancestor would have been very similar to a small chimp, specifically the pygmy chimpanzee or bonobo, *Pan paniscus.*

With the extension of the hominid fossil record back to more than 4 million years ago and with greatly expanded morphological and molecular studies, this situation has now changed. As we saw in Chapter 7, humans and chimps share a more recent common ancestor than either shares with gorillas (Sibley et al., 1990). If true, this implies that many of the traits common in chimps and gorillas, including possibly knuckle walking, are parallelisms, and not primitive at all. Studies of tooth enamel by Martin have shown that the thick molar enamel of hominids is the primitive condition and that chimps and gorillas have secondarily thinned enamel on the top surfaces of their molars. The thin enamel of African apes, then, does not ally them with thin-enameled Miocene apes. Finally the fossil record of hominids now shows that the earliest known representatives of the lineage were bipedal and small-bodied, about the size of a baboon (Hill and Ward, 1988; Boaz, 1988).

These new observations have cast doubt on the traditional ideas of a chimplike ape-human common ancestor. Tuttle (1975) has suggested that the common ancestor would have been more gibbonlike than chimplike, in keeping with his findings that there are no anatomical remnants of a knuckle-walking heritage in the modern human hand and forelimb. Boaz (1993) suggested that the common ancestor would likely have been a small-bodied, thick-enameled, and perhaps primitively bipedal form, from which chimps and gorillas independently evolved larger body size, thin molar enamel, and a knuckle-walking adaptation. Further research will be needed to resolve this question.

WHY ARE HOMINID FOSSILS RARE?

It has been said that paleoanthropology is a unique scientific discipline in that its practitioners probably outnumber the scientific specimens available for study. Several reasons account for the rarity of hominids and their relatives in the fossil record. Some of these reasons are *taphonomic* (Greek, *taphos* meaning "burial" and *-nomy* meaning "law"), that is, they relate to the conditions under which bones were deposited in a fossil site; and some are *paleoecological,* that is, they relate to aspects of the species' adaptations that affected whether their fossils were

taphonomy–the paleontological study of burial processes leading to the formation and preservation of fossils.

collector bias–the selection choices that an individual makes in assembling a collection of specimens.

microfauna–the smallest members of a fauna, commonly small mammals, such as rodents, insectivores, and prosimian primates.

hominine–subfamily of the Hominidae containing the members sharing derived characters with modern humans; characterized by relatively large brains, small dentitions, and fully modern postcranial adaptations.

preserved or not. **Taphonomy** is the paleontological study of how bones become buried and preserved as fossils. Perhaps the largest taphonomic factor accounting for the rarity of hominid fossils is that hominids, especially early in the record, were small animals. All the various destructive forces of erosion, weathering, and scavenging by other animals, therefore, affected the hominid bones much more than they did the bones of larger animals, such as horses or giraffes.

Paleoecological aspects of this problem relate to the probability that hominids were not common animals in the environment. They were relatively rare animals that had large home ranges (Boaz, 1979a). They were, therefore, unlike prey species, such as antelopes, that were common in the environment and thus contributed their bones to the fossil record in proportion to their population numbers. At Omo, Ethiopia, early hominid fossils, usually single teeth, are approximately 1% of the mammalian fossil record recovered in excavations and fossil surveys of surface exposures (Boaz, 1985).

Finally, there is the problem of **collector bias.** Paleontologists in the past have not always been interested in or aware of the smaller animals at their sites. Fossils of elephants, hippos, rhinos, antelopes, giraffes, and even pigs are larger, more "impressive," and easier to spot in the field. Paleontologists now focus on the smaller elements of fossil faunas, the smallest members of which are termed **microfauna.** These smaller fossils are particularly important in recovering information about ancient environmental conditions as they are usually more sensitive to changing conditions than are larger animals.

THE AUSTRALOPITHECINES

Australopithecine refers to the subfamily of hominids, the Australopithecinae (Table 8–2). It is used as an inclusive term for species of hominids that are more primitive than members of the genus *Homo.* Members of the genus termed *Homo* are **hominines,** from the subfamily term, Homininae. Australopithecines have sometimes been referred to as "ape-men" or "man-apes" (Le Gros Clark, 1967), allusions to their transitional position between humans and apes. They are characterized as a group, and set apart from humans, by their *small cranial capacity,* a *protruding facial profile,* a somewhat *larger overall dentition,* and *different hip and lower limb structure.* In contrast to great apes, the australopithecines were *bipedal,* possessed *smaller and functionally different canine and premolar teeth,* and showed many anatomical details of the skull and face that ally them with more advanced hominids.

The number of species attributable to the genus *Australopithecus* continues to grow with the discovery of new fossil remains. This is a common phenomenon in paleoanthropology as different discoverers of fossils vie to establish the importance of their finds. Whether the taxonomic names that have been given to different fossils represent legitimate species has been and remains a matter of considerable debate. A review by Henneberg and Thackery (1995) offers a conservative prospective on this issue, arguing against the establishment of new species without exhaustive comparison with other known fossils, while, at the same time, giving attention to established ranges of variation in modern primate populations.

Australopithecus africanus

Controversy surrounded the original australopithecine find, a skull of a juvenile hominid from a cave site quarried for lime in northern South Africa known as Taung, meaning "place of the lion" in the Tswana language (Figure 8–2). Nevertheless, the discovery is a singularly important event in the history of human evolutionary studies, because it brought to light a totally unknown, though not unexpected, primeval state of human existence.

Figure 8–2 • Raymond Dart and frontal view of the Taung skull, type of *Australopithecus africanus.*

The specimen was blasted out of a lime deposit by a quarryman with the Northern Lime Company. He immediately recognized that it was not that of a baboon, the skulls of which he had come across in the same manner. He speculated that it belonged to a fossil bushman, possibly an ancestor of the San people who still inhabit the region. The specimen, still imbedded in a large chunk of rock, made its way to Johannesburg and to Raymond Dart, an assistant professor in the Anatomy Department of the University of the Witwatersrand Medical School. Dart broke away from the final preparations of hosting his daughter's wedding to receive and examine the shipment of rock-imbedded bones arriving from Taung. His excitement was warranted, because the specimen turned out to be the first of many australopithecines to be discovered.

Dart described the new specimen soon after its discovery in the February 7, 1925, issue of *Nature.* In the article he suggested that the *Taung child,* as it came to be known, represented "an extinct race of apes intermediate between living anthropoids and man," a "missing link," to use T. H. Huxley's now famous term. Dart named it a new genus and species, ***Australopithecus africanus.*** The name itself, translating as "southern ape from Africa," first stirred debate. A geologist from Oxford wrote that the term was a barbarism, mixing Latin ("*australo-*") and Greek ("*-pithecus*") roots in the generic name. This was merely literary criticism, because taxonomic names do not have to be classically or grammatically correct. The real contention, however, lay in Dart's claim of human ancestry for the Taung child. Sir Arthur Keith, perhaps the most highly respected British paleoanthropologist of the day, branded Dart's assessment as "preposterous" in 1925. He considered that the skull showed the essential anatomical features of an ape, with the possible exception of its smaller front teeth. If this suggestion were true, it would have precluded Taung from human ancestry. Robert Broom, a South African physician and paleontologist, began a study of the fossil vertebrates from the Taung cave in 1937 and established, on the basis of the evolutionary stages of the fossil mammals contained in the cave deposits, that the date had to be earliest Pleistocene or late Pliocene, circa 1.8 to 3 million years old.

Australopithecus africanus – the first species of *Australopithecus* to be named, based on the type of the Taung child; characterized by "harmonious dentition" and relatively "gracile" skull morphology, the species dates to between about 3 and 2.5 million years ago; represented at other sites in South Africa, and probably also in East Africa.

The dating of the Taung site has been a source of continuing controversy. Geological studies (Vogel, 1985; Partridge, 1986) have suggested a date for Taung of only about 1 million years ago. Studies of the monkey fossils at Taung (Delson, 1988), however, suggest a date closer to 2.5 million years ago, and this date seems to accord well with most current assessments.

Further Discoveries of the Australopithecines

After Dart's original 1924 find, and the inevitable taxonomic problems associated with a juvenile *type specimen* (the fossil upon which a taxonomic name is based), there was much interest in recovering more australopithecine remains, this time of adults. A number of anatomists had pointed out that juveniles of many higher primates can closely resemble one another, whereas the adult forms are quite divergent.

Robert Broom (1867–1951) undertook in 1936 an exploration of the region of northern South Africa, the Transvaal. Fossils here are found in breccia, a rockhard substance formed from the debris falling into a cave opening. Broom's techniques were essentially the same as those of the quarrymen who worked in the area—blasting with dynamite. This did not allow a precise mapping of the location of the finds, but it was successful in recovering fossils. Broom managed to find four bone-bearing cave sites, in addition to Taung, which did indeed yield remains of adult australopithecines, including a complete skull from a site known as Sterkfontein (from the Afrikaans language, meaning "strong spring"). These sites have continued to yield fossil bones to the present day.

Partly as a result of the early hominid discoveries in South Africa, Louis Leakey, an anthropologist trained at Cambridge University in England, became interested in exploring for hominid fossils in East Africa. The son of missionary parents, Leakey grew up in Kenya, and with his wife, archaeologist Mary Leakey, undertook fieldwork at the now-famous site of **Olduvai Gorge,** Tanzania (then Tanganyika) beginning in 1931. The Leakeys were mostly unsuccessful in discovering early hominids until 1959, when Mary Leakey found a complete australopithecine skull. Later, between 1974 and 1979, Mary Leakey turned her energies toward reexcavations at the site of **Laetoli.** Twenty-four australopithecine fossils, as well as two trails of hominid footprints, are now known from this site.

During the 1960s and 1970s eastern Africa became an increasingly active area of paleoanthropological research, and the results have greatly increased our knowledge of the australopithecines, as well as of other stages of hominid evolution. The Lake Turkana Basin (Figure 8–3) contains the australopithecine sites of **Omo,** East and West **Lake Turkana,** and the recently discovered site of Fejej. Paleontological studies aimed at discovering early hominids were first pioneered here in 1932 by Camille Arambourg, who 35 years later found an australopithecine mandible, the first of many hominid specimens now known from Omo. F. Clark Howell and Yves Coppens continued to work until 1975 at Omo, where 238

Olduvai Gorge–a site in northern Tanzania, yielding remains of robust australopithecines and early *Homo*.

Laetoli–a site in northern Tanzania, south of Olduvai Gorge, where hominids were first found in the 1930s and again in the 1970s; dated to between 3.6 and 3.8 million years ago.

Omo–a site in southern Ethiopia along the lower Omo River, with numerous hominids dating from about 3.4 to 1.0 million years ago.

Lake Turkana–hominid sites on both the east and west sides of Lake Turkana (formerly Lake Rudolf), closely associated with Omo and dating to between 4.0 and 1.4 million years ago.

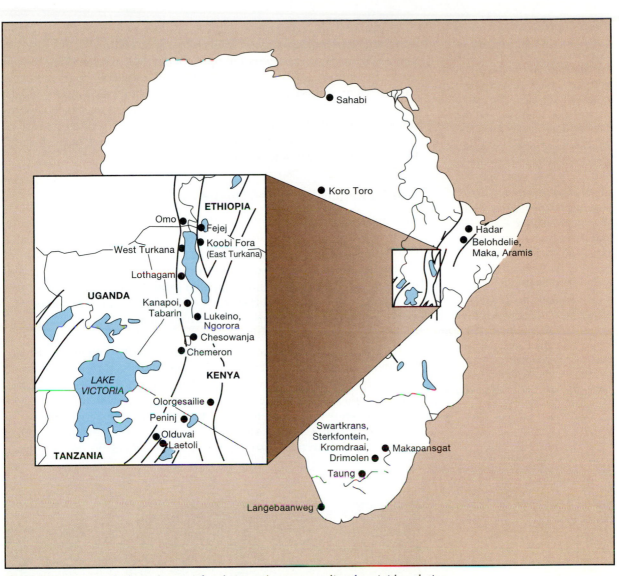

Figure 8–3 • Map of Africa showing fossil sites relevant to earliest hominid evolution.

fossil specimens have been discovered. Richard Leakey and Glynn Isaac began collecting fossils and stone artifacts east of Lake Turkana near Koobi Fora in Kenya. The Koobi Fora Research Project has recovered some of the best-preserved specimens of australopithecines and early *Homo* now known. Work on the western side of Lake Turkana by Richard Leakey, Alan Walker, and Frank Brown has resulted in the discovery of the australopithecine "Black Skull" (**A. aethiopicus**) as well as a nearly complete *Homo erectus* skeleton (see Chapter 9).

Australopithecus aethiopicus — earlier form of robust australo- pithecines in East Africa dated from 2.6 to 2.3 million years ago; most famous representative is the Black Skull discovered in 1986 at a site on the western shores of Lake Turkana.

Australopithecus afarensis—
gracile species of *Australopithe-cus* found at sites in East Africa and dated from 4.0 to 2.5 million years ago; most famous representatives of this taxon are "Lucy" from Hadar, Ethiopia, and the Laetoli footprints in Tanzania.

Hadar—hominid site in northern Ethiopia dating to between 3.0 and 3.4 million years ago.

Australopithecus robustus—robust australopithecines found in cave deposits from South Africa and dated from 2.0 to 1.0 million years ago; most famous representatives were found at the site of Swartkrans, South Africa.

Australopithecus boisei—
robust australopithecines found at site in East Africa and dated from 2.4 to 1.3 million years ago; most famous representatives were found at Olduvai Gorge (*Zinjanthropus*) and East Lake Turkana.

One of the most important eastern African sites for early australopithecines (***Australopithecus afarensis***) is at **Hadar,** in the Afar Triangle (Figure 8–4), northern Ethiopia. Hadar was explored by French geologist Maurice Taieb in the late 1960s, and fossil collecting and excavations were started there in 1973 by American paleoanthropologist Donald Johanson. Together with Laetoli, Hadar has given paleoanthropologists their best glimpse of the early australopithecines in eastern Africa at time periods earlier than at the South African sites of Sterkfontein, Makapansgat, and Taung.

The Subfamily Becomes Defined

After anatomical studies by William King Gregory and Sir Wilfrid Le Gros Clark in the 1940s, the Taung specimen and other South African australopithecines were generally considered to be *bona fide* members of the family Hominidae. These South African near-humans, however, were different and warranted some distinction from the genus *Homo*. For this reason they were placed in their own subfamily, the Australopithecinae, to be distinguished from the more advanced members of the family, placed in the subfamily Homininae.

Many paleoanthropologists consider there to be two types of australopithecines: a "gracile" species with a more lightly built skull, termed *Australopithecus africanus* (the earlier East African *A. afarensis* is sometimes included in this category), and a "robust" form with a more heavily built skull, known in South Africa as ***Australopithecus robustus,*** or in eastern Africa as ***A. boisei*** (Figure 8–5). Most of the anatomical differences between the two australopithecines are related to the very large

Figure 8–4 • View of the Hadar Formation.

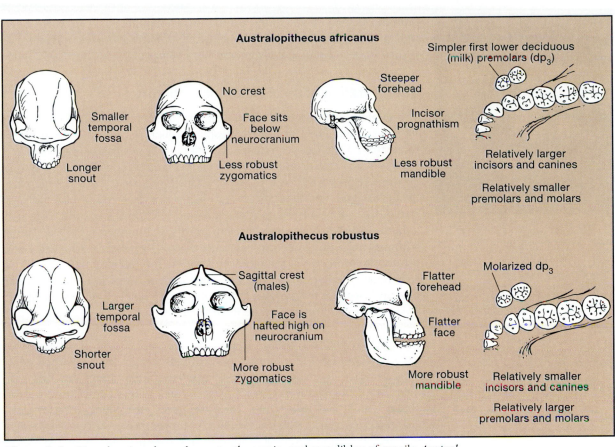

Figure 8–5 • Line drawing shows lower teeth, crania, and mandibles of gracile *Australopithecus africanus* compared to the robust *Australopithecus robustus*.

cheek teeth of the robust australopithecines and the chewing anatomy associated with this adaptation. The gracile forms, by most reckonings, occur earlier in time than the robusts and are considered by most paleoanthropologists to be ancestral, in a broad sense, to the genus *Homo*.

Stone tools have never been clearly associated with fossil remains of the gracile australopithecines. Artifacts are lacking at Laetoli, the early portions of the Omo sequence, and the early, hominid-bearing levels at Hadar, Makapansgat, Sterkfontein, and Taung. It thus appears unlikely that gracile australopithecines made and used stone tools.

Dart originally suggested that bone fragments found in Makapansgat were in fact tools that australopithecines had used to kill, dismember, and eat animal prey. Dart coined the term *osteodontokeratic* tool culture on the basis of this evidence, since the supposed tools consisted of bone (*osteo-*), tooth (*-donto-*), and horn (*-keratic*). Recent research has shown that much of the damage on fossil bones can be attributed to chewing by hyenas and other carnivores, but some wear and breakage on fossils from the cave of Swartkrans has been ascribed anew by C. K. Brain to

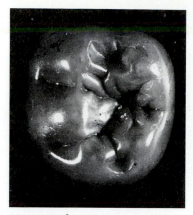

Figure 8–6 • The Lukeino specimen, a lower second molar, part of the scarce evidence currently available documenting hominid evolution from 5 to 8 million years ago.

hominid activity. It thus appears that australopithecines may have been tool makers, although their use of stone for this purpose remains improbable or at least unlikely on current evidence.

Interpretation of the Evolutionary History

The evolutionary origin of *Australopithecus* is a tantalizing question that has so far remained unsolved, despite recent discoveries dating up to more than 5 million years ago. Evolutionary relationships hypothesized between Miocene apes and *Australopithecus* cannot at the present time be demonstrated by fossil evidence. This is because there is a gap between 8.0 and 4.5 million years ago in the fossil record of hominids. In East Africa, only the fragmentary Lukeino (Figure 8–6), Lothagam, and Tabarin fossils have been recovered in this time range. At Sahabi, Libya, dating from 5 to 6 million years ago, a skull fragment and a leg bone (fibula) have been discovered. They are so fragmentary that even their identification as hominoid has not been generally acknowledged. These East and North African fossils constitute insufficient evidence to establish the evolutionary origins of the australopithecines.

Middle Awash, Ethiopia   The broad paleontological significance of the Afar region of Ethiopia was first brought to light by the French geologist Maurice Taieb in the 1960s. Further explorations in the 1970s by Taieb, Donald Johanson, Yves Coppens, and John Kalb focused on the Hadar locality in the central Afar, and, in 1981, a multidisciplinary team led by J. Desmond Clark undertook a comprehensive survey of the Middle Awash region south of Hadar. Tim White became project director, working alongside Berhane Asfaw and other researchers from the National Museum in Addis Ababa.

In 1981 the paleontological research team found at the site of Maka on the eastern side of the Awash River the first Pliocene-Age hominid fossil in the Middle Awash, that of an adolescent left proximal femur. This specimen, dated by associated faunal remains, is approximately 3.5 to 4.0 million years old. In the same year, at the nearby site of Belohdelie, a second hominid was recovered; this one consisted of seven skull fragments, three of which were from an adult frontal bone. Again on the basis of associated fauna, the Belohdelie fossils are dated at older than 4.0 million years. Structurally, the femur and skull fragments are similar to their counterparts recovered at Hadar and were attributed to *A. afarensis*.

Explorations of this area in the late 1980s moved to the paleontologically rich Aramis locality on the west bank of the Awash River. The sediments of this region are separated by several volcanic tuffs (ash layers), and initial dating provides a maximum age of 4.4 million years for the hominids. The fossil hominids, which total more than 90 specimens, represent most of the skeleton and include foot, leg, and pelvic remains. Initially named *Australopithecus ramidus* (*ramid* means "root" in the Afar language) by its discoverers (White et al., 1994), it was subsequently renamed as a distinct genus, **Ardipithecus ramidus** (*ardi* means "ground" or "floor" in the Afar language, thus, "ground ape") (White et al., 1995) on the basis that it is the most apelike hominid ancestor known (Figure 8–7).

While the *Ardipithecus* remains are the most primitive from this age found so far, White et al. (1994) insist that the diamond-shaped, blunt canine teeth (less projecting than those of other Miocene hominoids), the shortening of the cranial bone, and the shape of the elbow joint are all derived characteristics in the direction of later hominids. If the known remains of *Ardipithecus* are anatomically hominid, were members of this genus functionally hominid—bipedal—as well? Right now, indirect evidence points in that direction, but the question remains open.

Dental and paleoenvironmental data do give some provocative clues about how and where *Ardipithecus* lived. In contrast to any other known hominid, the enamel layer of the teeth was thin (Figure 7–15). If this isn't curious enough, the associated fauna, as well as seeds and fossilized wood, indicate that *Ardipithecus*'s habitat was forested, not the savanna-like setting where later hominids, such as Lucy, were found.

A forest environment for *Ardipithecus* is both confounding and illluminating (WoldeGabriel et al., 1994). It is confounding in the sense that, if *Ardipithecus* represents the earliest hominoid ancestor, and if it turns out also to be bipedal, then the selective agents for bipedalism, which have been thought to relate to an open, savanna-like setting, will have to

Ardipithecus ramidus—the most primitive species of hominid presently known, dating 4 to 4.2 million years ago from Aramis, Middle Awash, Ethiopia.

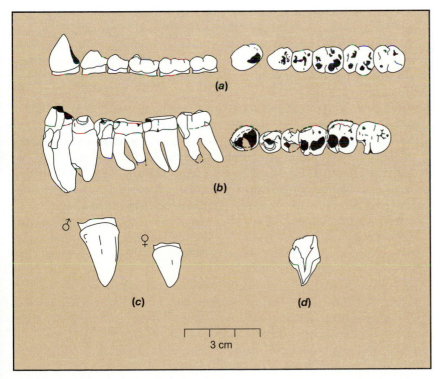

Figure 8–7 • (*a*) Side and occlusal (top) views of *P. troglodytes* (common chimp) lower dentition compared to (*b*) *A. ramidus;* (*c*) side views of upper canines, of *P. troglodytes* compared to (*d*) *A. ramidus.*

be rethought. It is illuminating in the sense that it explains why, so far, no hominoid remains older than 4 million years have been found in deposits representing savanna-like settings.

Kanapoi and Allia Bay, Kenya A new series of fossils was found by a team led by Meave Leakey and Alan Walker at two sites located near Lake Turkana: Kanapoi to the southwest of the lake, where nine dental, cranial, and postcranial pieces were found; and Allia Bay on the eastern rim of the lake, which yielded 12 additional specimens. These fossils fall between 3.9 and 4.2 million years, based on their stratigraphic position within dated tuff sequences. The Leakey team (1995) has named these specimens ***Australopithecus anamensis*** (*anam* means "lake" in the Turkana language of the region). The teeth are similar to those of *A. afarensis* except that the canine of *anamensis* is larger in size and usually more asymmetrical, possessing a long and robust root. The teeth have thicker enamel than *Ardipithecus*. The tibia that was recovered at Kanapoi comes from the same (upper) level as did an earlier discovered distal humerus, and it shows bipedal characteristics. Leakey and Walker believe that *A. anamensis* represents one of a number of early emerging, variable hominid species that all were based on the novel bipedal adaptation. Peter Andrews (1995) observes that while all of these so-called species may have been phylogenetically hominids, they seem, ecologically anyway, to be more similar to apes.

Laetoli, Tanzania The first major finds of australopithecines in eastern Africa are at Laetoli, in northern Tanzania (Figure 8–8). "Laetoli" is a Maasai word referring to a small flowering shrub that is abundant in the area. Following the discovery of some fragmentary hominid fossils, Mary Leakey started collecting there in 1974. Garniss Curtis used the **potassium-argon method** to date a sample of volcanic ash to 3.7 million years ago.

The hominid fossils from Laetoli were originally ascribed to the genus *Homo* by Mary Leakey. As such they represented the earliest known occurrence of this genus in the fossil record, fully 1.5 million years earlier than well-dated *Homo* fossils from other sites, such as Omo. The detailed description of the fossils by White, however, revealed that they possessed a number of primitive traits, not expected in specimens belonging to the genus *Homo*. Although the specimens were similar to South African *Australopithecus africanus,* a new species, *Australopithecus afarensis,* was named based on the combined fossil hominid sample from Laetoli and the Afar site in northern Ethiopia (Johanson, White, and Coppens, 1978; see Boaz, 1988).

In 1976 a remarkable discovery was made in a **tuff** at Laetoli. This volcanic deposit had preserved footprints of animals living when the ash was deposited 3.7 million years ago. Among these animal tracks were trails of two hominids walking side-by-side (Figure 8–8). These footprints of walking hominids constitute the earliest evidence of bipedalism

Australopithecus anamensis— new species of *Australopithecus* discovered at two sites around Lake Turkana, described in 1995 by Meave Leakey and Alan Walker, and dated to 4.0 million years ago.

potassium-argon method— dating technique pioneered by Garniss Curtis that measures the amount of radioactive potassium isotope (K^{40}) to its decay product, argongas (Ar^{40}), found in rocks of volcanic origin.

tuff—a geological deposit composed of volcanic ash.

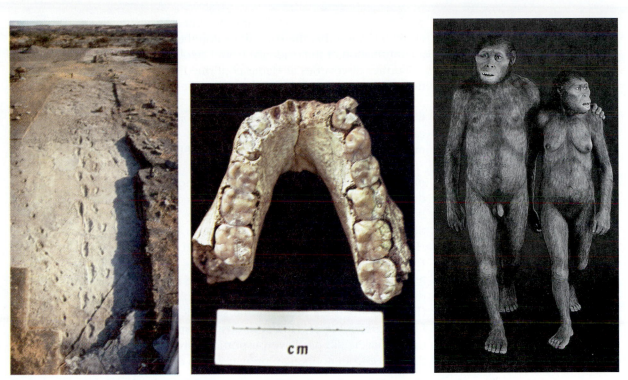

Figure 8–8 • Laetoli footprint trail (left), LH4 mandible of *A. afarensis* (center), and one possible behavioral reconstruction of the Laetoli hominids (right).

in the hominid fossil record. On the basis of the size of the feet, the height of the hominids was estimated to have been between 119 and 139 centimeters (3.9 to 4.6 feet). Other scientists used the estimated size of the hominids and the length of their stride to infer that they were walking at a slow rate of speed. Mary Leakey suggested that the footprints were probably those of a male and a female.

Hadar The most abundant fossil evidence for early australopithecines comes from Hadar, dated somewhat later in time than Laetoli. It is located some 1,600 kilometers to the north of Laetoli, in the Afar Depression of northern Ethiopia. These remains constitute the most complete evidence that anthropologists have so far of this period of hominid evolution and represent a group of hominids that may have been evolutionarily stable for almost a million years. Potassium-argon dates have bracketed the age of the Hadar hominids between 2.8 and 3.4 million years ago. The first hominid fossils to be discovered at Hadar were a distal thigh bone (femur) and the proximal shin bone (tibia), which fit together to form a knee joint (minus the knee cap). The angle at which the femur joined the tibia in the fossil from Hadar was like a hominid's and unlike an ape's. The femora in hominids slant downward to the knees, which are quite close together, whereas in apes the femora are aligned with the long axis of the tibia and the knees are widespread. This was a clear indication that the early australopithecines at Hadar were bipedal, a confirmation of the evidence from Laetoli.

Further discoveries at Hadar confirmed it as one of the most productive of hominid fossil sites. Since 1990, these deposits have yielded over 330 new specimens. Among the sample, consisting of between 35 and 65 individuals, were the largely complete skeleton from Hadar (Afar) Locality AL288, nicknamed "Lucy" (Figure 8–9), and a concentration of remains of some 13 individuals, nicknamed the "First Family."

In 1993, Yoel Rak found the first pieces of a skull that, when completely collected, turned out to be the most complete cranium thus far discovered in the *afarensis* group. Labeled AL 444-2, the skull is thick-boned, with large canine teeth and heavy cresting, all male characteristics (Figure 8–9). This skull, according to Bill Kimbel of the Institute of Human Origins, goes a long way toward showing that the Hadar and Laetoli remains represent a single species, with large males and smaller females, rather than two species, as some researchers contend. The size differences are best explained by sexual differences, or *dimorphism* (Figure 8–10). They represent the same degree of difference one would find in modern apes. However, australopithecine males, although larger than females, did not have proportionately larger canines, an important difference from nonhuman primates. This difference implies that canines

Figure 8–9 • Left: Fossil skull AL 444-2 from the site of Hadar, Awash Region, Ethiopia. This skull is the most complete find attributed to the *afarensis* species. Right: The partial skeleton of *A. afarensis* (AL 288-1, known as "Lucy") from Hadar.

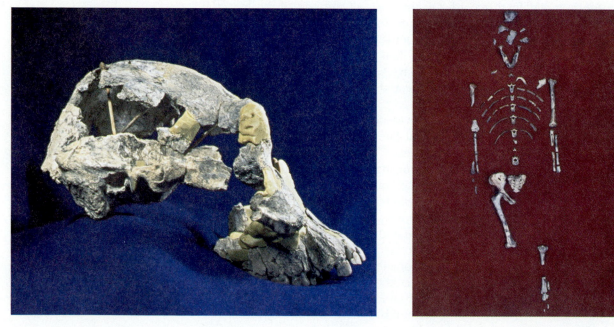

had ceased to be used in intraspecific display and in male–male aggressive competition. The Hadar hominid finds also confirmed estimates from the footprint evidence at Laetoli that the early australopithecines had been small. "Lucy," for example, was estimated to have been less than 4 feet tall, although males would have been taller and larger.

In 1994, researchers from the Institute of Human Origins announced the discovery at site 666 of pieces of an upper jaw belonging to the genus *Homo* dating to about 2.33 million years ago. Nearby were found stone tools of the same age, making this one of the oldest associations of fossils and tools thus far discovered.

Comparison of East and South African Early Australopithecines

Anthropologists have now carefully compared the East and South African samples of australopithecines. Dating at the South African cave sites has never been clear, because it has been based on relative ages, as ascertained by the evolutionary stages of the fossil vertebrates contained in the assemblages. Nevertheless, the ages of Sterkfontein and Makapansgat can be estimated to be between 2.5 and 3.0 million years old. Makapansgat appears to be somewhat earlier than Sterkfontein, and Taung may be somewhat later (Figure 8–11).

Recent work has shown that the two African groups of early australopithecines (*A. afarensis* and *A. africanus*) are similar. They both possess relatively large canines, a tendency for nonbicuspid premolars (like apes), a high degree of sexual dimorphism, and a face that is "dished" or depressed in the area around the nasal opening.

Skull morphology is the most important criterion for recognizing early, or gracile, *Australopithecus*, because most of the important anatomical and behavioral adaptations of the species are reflected in the skull. Three general adaptations account for cranial form: brain size, erect posture (bipedalism), and use of the teeth.

The relatively enlarged brain gives *A. afarensis* and *A. africanus* a somewhat globular head shape compared with modern apes. This shape is emphasized by the lack of the heavy ridges for muscular attachment, as seen in the ape, the exceptions being the presence of small crests on some specimens of *A. afarensis*. One of the muscles of mastication, *temporalis,* which can be felt in the "temple" region, is less developed, particularly in its front part, in *A. africanus* than in *A. afarensis.* This muscle attaches to a slight ridge, the temporal line, halfway up the side of the cranial vault in *A. africanus,* most *A. afarensis,* and *Homo.* In gorillas, male chimpanzees, some *A. afarensis,* and robust australopithecines, the *temporalis* muscles of both sides of the head meet in the midline at the top of the skull and a heavy ridge of bone is formed, known as the sagittal crest.

The face of *A. afarensis* protrudes less than in modern apes because the front teeth are smaller. *A. afarensis* and the australopithecines in general have a nose region that is depressed relative to the rest of the

Figure 8–10 • Sexual dimorphism in *Australopithecus afarensis* shown in a comparison of AL 333w-60 (top) and AL 333w-12 (bottom) mandibles.

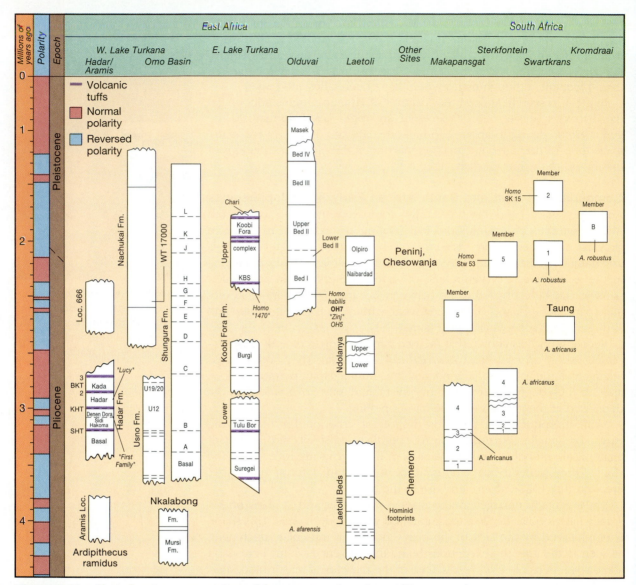

Figure 8–11 • Chart showing a comparison of the eastern and southern African australopithecine sites by age.

face. The functional significance of this "dished face" morphology is related to a relative increase in bone thickness of both sides of the nose and back along the cheekbones, which hold the large hominid molars (Rak, 1983). Erect posture in the australopithecines may also have placed a premium on facial reduction for head balance.

Overall, the gracile australopithecine face is orthognathous, pushed in under the braincase, in a form similar to that of later hominids. The facial skeleton has moved backward and downward, and the back of the braincase has rotated forward, a process known as **basicranial flexion.** Thus the opening through which the spinal cord enters the brain, the *foramen magnum* (Latin, meaning "great window"), is located halfway between the front and the back of the skull, so that the head is balanced on the vertebral column. In the knuckle-walking apes, the *foramen* is positioned more posteriorly and its opening is slanted more toward the back of the skull, characteristics related to horizontal posture. Heavy neck muscles hold up and move the head. In australopithecines a reduced face, basicranial flexion, a centrally placed foramen magnum, and a lack of heavy neck musculature reflect bipedality.

Pilbeam has applied the term **megadont,** meaning "large-toothed," to refer to the relatively large molar size of early hominids as compared with apes. Teeth are the most abundant remains of the gracile australopithecines. Their structure parallels that of later hominids of the genus *Homo:* generally large and wide incisors relative to canines, canines functionally similar to incisors, and lower third premolars that generally do not wear or hone against the back of the upper canines, as in apes. In certain aspects, however, australopithecines are more primitive. Their canines are generally larger than those in *Homo,* the lower third premolar is less "squared" in appearance, the molars are generally longer relative to their width, and they possess a complicated wrinkled ("crenulated") surface pattern. Australopithecines, like all hominids, possess thick enamel on the top surfaces of the molars, a characteristic also shared with some apes, such as the modern orangutan and *Sivapithecus.* Thick enamel increases the functional lifetime of the tooth, especially when the diet is abrasive.

Australopithecine Phylogeny

Most anthropologists now hypothesize *A. afarensis* as the ancestor of *A. africanus.* As will be discussed in Chapter 9, the earliest members of the genus *Homo* show a number of similarities to "gracile" australopithecines, specifically *A. africanus,* and this argues for an evolutionary sequence from *Australopithecus africanus* to *Homo.*

There are no certain occurrences of australopithecines outside Africa. G. H. R. von Koenigswald reported some single teeth from mainland China that he bought in Hong Kong and considered to be australopithecines. These specimens, however, are undated and are insufficient evidence to confirm the presence of *Australopithecus* in China. Three mandibles collected in Java were considered by J. T. Robinson, an expert on the South African australopithecines, to be robust australopithecines. But most other anthropologists consider these specimens to be large individuals of early *Homo.*

The temporal range of australopithecines, as determined by absolute and relative methods of dating, is circa 4.3 to 2.3 million years ago for early and gracile australopithecines (*Ardipithecus ramidus, Australopithecus afarensis,* and *Australopithecus africanus*).

basicranial flexion—the hinging of the base of the skull and the hard palate together to form a more acute angle; seen in both australopithecine lineages.

megadont—"large-toothed," referring to the relatively large molars of hominids; Boaz (1983) has suggested that "megamylic" ("large-molared") is a more accurate term.

FRONTIERS

The Earliest Australopithecines and Human Origins

by Alan Walker

Present-day Lake Turkana in northern Kenya is over 150 miles long and has an area of about 2,500 square miles. Because the lake dominates the local landscape, it is difficult to imagine that the lake was not always present, yet geological evidence clearly shows that for most of the last 4.5 million years, there was no lake. Instead, through most of this period there was only a huge, flat floodplain associated with the proto-Omo river that drained southwards from the Ethiopian highlands. The earliest of the several relatively brief lacustrine periods (when a lake was formed), just over 4.0 million years ago, was associated with sediments that contain the earliest known species of Australopithecus.

The first specimen of this species, a single distal humerus, was collected from the site of Kanapoi, south of Lake Turkana, by a Harvard expedition in the 1960s. Unfortunately, Kanapoi was at the time poorly dated and determining the fossil's affinities was difficult. Recent expeditions led by Meave Leakey have established new facts about both of these issues. The Kanapoi sediments were laid down by a river that built its delta out into the ancient lake between 4.2 and 4.0 million years ago, according to age determinations using the new and quite accurate method of single crystal laser fusion argon-argon analysis. Leakey's

expeditions have collected additional fossil teeth, jaws, cranial parts, and limb bones from Kanapoi, as well as similar fossils from slightly younger sediments (dated to between 3.9 and 4.0 million years ago) at Allia Bay, across the modern Lake Turkana from Kanapoi. Leakey and her colleagues named a new species based on the combined Kanapoi/Allia Bay sample. They call it Australopithecus anamensis, using the word for "lake" (anam) from the Turkana language.

To define a new species, biologists must differentiate between the new material and that of older similar species of comparable age. Leakey and her colleagues compared Australopithecus anamensis to other known early hominids, namely the more recent Australopithecus afarensis from between 3.6 and 2.9 million years ago and the slightly older Ardipithecus ramidus from about 4.4 million years ago.

This study showed that the new species belongs in the genus Australopithecus. First, the enamel on the teeth of the new specimens is thick, as is the enamel on all other australopithecines. Second, Australopithecus anamensis shows marked sexual dimorphism in body size, with males being considerably larger than females—another feature found in all species of Australopithecus. Finally, Australopithecus anamensis is clearly bipedal as is afarensis and other later species. A tibia from Kanapoi shows clear anatomical adaptations that make the knee stable in a bipedal position—adaptations that are lacking in quadrupedal apes. It has an ankle joint that places the foot at a right angle to the long axis of the shin, rather than being angled closer to the tibia, as in

apes. However, bipedalism is not the only locomotor adaptation of Australopithecus anamensis. A radius of this species, together with the original humerus from Kanapoi, shows that these animals had powerful forelimbs. These facts make it likely that, despite being bipedal, they could still climb effectively and may have spent substantial time in the trees. However, the new material could not be included in Australopithecus afarensis because anamensis has retained primitive features that are lacking in afarensis. Such features are today known only in African apes.

The new material also differs from Ardipithecus ramidus in a number of cranial and dental features, such as the thin enamel on all of the ramidus teeth, which contrasts with the thick enamel of anamensis. There is at present no published evidence about the locomotor pattern of ramidus, but it is found with many forest-dwelling species that suggests a closed habitat. Like ramidus, Australopithecus anamensis is found with animals that lived in an extensive gallery forest along the ancient rivers or their deltas. For example, there are six species of monkey found at Allia Bay. It is most likely that anamensis was also forest-dwelling.

Paleoanthropologist and anatomist Alan Walker is Professor of Anthropology at Pennsylvania State University. He has worked many years at fossil sites dating from the Miocene to the Pleistocene in East Africa, especially in Kenya.

HOMINID MORPHOLOGY AND BEHAVIOR

Although interest has been concentrated on hominid brain evolution since the first discoveries of fossil hominids, studies of fossil **endocasts** (casts of the inside of the cranial cavity) have yielded disappointing results. The external form of the brain is variable, making its study based on crania difficult. Additionally, too little is known regarding the function of the modern human brain for anthropologists to be confident in assessing the functional capabilities of early hominid brains.

The cranial capacity of *Australopithecus afarensis* is known to lie between approximately 375 and 425 cubic centimeters, and between 400 and 600 cubic centimeters for *A. africanus,* roughly equivalent to the brain sizes of modern apes. There is one important difference, however. Body size in gracile *Australopithecus* is smaller than in the modern gorilla or even chimpanzee. *Australopithecus* had a brain-to-body-size ratio that was larger than in modern African apes (Figure 8–12). A relatively

endocast—a three-dimensional replica of the inside of the brain case, revealing what the exterior of the brain would have looked like.

Figure 8–12 • Drawings showing cranial capacities of australopithecines compared with species of *Homo* and living African apes.

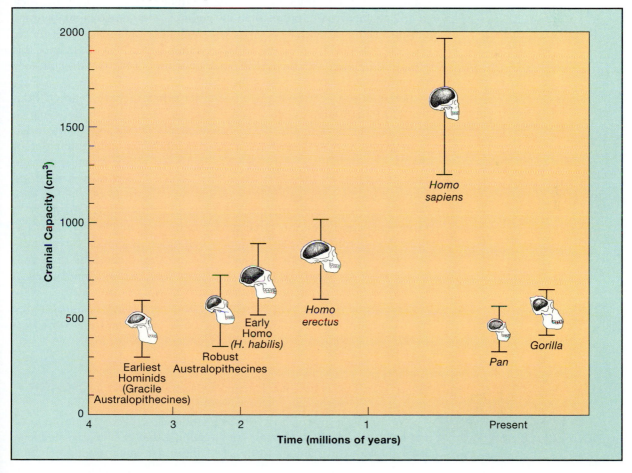

larger brain implies that reorganization of neurons had taken place and that australopithecine behavior had become in some respects more complex and elaborate than that of living apes. Gracile australopithecine endocasts suggest a greater degree of folding and a larger number of convolutions in comparison with living apes.

The pelvic, shoulder girdle, and limb bone remains that have now come to light confirm that the gracile australopithecines were bipeds. There is a difference of opinion on the degree to which they used their upper limbs in locomotion, if at all, and whether *A. afarensis* may have had significant foot and lower limb adaptations for climbing (Susman et al., 1984). Ron Clarke and Phillip Tobias (1995) report on four articulating hominid foot bones originally discovered in 1980 from Sterkfontein, South Africa. Labeled Stw 573 and nicknamed "little foot," these fossils are considerably older than the other Sterkfontein fossils. Consisting of a talus, navicular heel, medial cuneiform, and first metatarsal, which together make up part of the arch of a left foot, they show human features at the back of the foot, while displaying strikingly apelike traits at the front of the foot, the most remarkable being a great toe that was divergent, or opposable, and mobile. According to the discoverers, the Sterkfontein foot bones, possibly as old as 3.5 million years, support the idea of an "evolutionary experimentation" within a wide range of adaptations during the first few million years of hominid evolutionary divergence. However, Bruce Latimer (personal communication) has criticized this view and believes that the apelike characteristics of the Sterkfontein foot result from an inaccurate reconstruction.

Certainly the adaptation to bipedalism seems to have differed from that of modern humans. *Australopithecus* had a relatively wider distance from the hip joint to the muscle attachments at the top of the thigh (femur) and a wider flare of the upper crest of the hipbone (ilium, one of the three components of the pelvis) (Figure 8–9). This provided a wide base of support for the lower limbs in a bipedal stance, as well as strong leverage in lifting the lower limbs during walking. In *Homo* the hip joint has moved closer to the top of the femur and lateral edge of the ilium, in order to expand the birth canal for larger-brained infants. The australopithecine morphology is an efficient, albeit different, bipedal adaptation.

Overall body size can be estimated from the dimensions of certain fossil bones by comparing them to dimensions of the same bones in known samples of modern humans and living primates whose body weights are known. Recent estimates of body size for *A. afarensis* range approximately from 30 to 80 kilograms (66–176 lbs) and for *A. africanus* from 30 to 70 kilograms (66–154 lbs) (Jungers, 1988).

AUSTRALOPITHECINE PALEOECOLOGY AND BEHAVIOR

The arid habitat in which *A. africanus* must have lived at Taung would not have been habitable for an ape, assuming that extinct apes had similar ecological adaptations to those of the forest-living gorilla or chimpanzee of today. Further research has shown that *A. afarensis* and *A. africanus* lived in both arid and more well-watered environments in eastern and southern Africa. Even without the use of stone tools and fire, gracile australopithecines were able to adapt to a variety of environmental conditions, but apparently only in Africa.

The paleoecology of *Australopithecus* is reflected in the types of animals and plants and the geological conditions associated with these hominids in fossil deposits. It is important to determine how these remains came to be buried together in order to understand how they might have been associated in life. Such studies have shown that hominids in the South African cave sites were probably the remains of carnivore kills (Figure 8–13), while East African open-air sites contain hominids that had died under a variety of conditions.

In the early South African cave sites, *A. africanus* has been found in association with a high percentage of bush-adapted, as opposed to grassland-adapted, antelopes, indicating a more bush-covered habitat than the same area today. This paleoecological picture of South Africa is supported by similar reconstructions for the Omo and Hadar sites in Ethiopia. The fauna from Laetoli, on the other hand, indicates markedly dry, grassland conditions. However, surface water, in streams and water holes, was present. It is likely that early hominids were dependent on these because hominids, like many other mammals, need to drink water at least once a day.

On the basis of dental morphology, the diet of the gracile australopithecines was probably omnivorous. However, excavations at Omo indicate that australopithecines occur in similar numbers to large carnivores. If confirmed by further taphonomic analyses, this would indicate that these early hominids and carnivores occupied similar positions in the food chain.

Gracile australopithecines seem to have died quite young. It is possible to reconstruct age at death by the wear of the teeth. A study by Alan Mann (1975) on South African australopithecines showed the mean age at death to be a modern human equivalent age of 22 years. Mann suggested that australopithecines had a prolonged period of infant dependency, similar to that of modern humans. Recent work on the pattern of dental development and eruption (Bromage and Dean, 1985; Smith, 1986; Conroy and Vannier, 1987) has indicated that australopithecines may have had a more apelike, short, and rapid period of growth as infants.

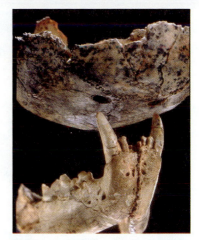

Figure 8–13 • Leopard mandible showing correspondence of canine with holes in robust australopithecine skull from Swartkrans.

ROBUST AUSTRALOPITHECINES

The robust australopithecines were a group of hominids that is known to have lived in eastern and southern Africa from 2.5 million years ago to about 1 million years ago (see Grine, 1988). Their presence has not yet been confirmed outside Africa. They were specialized para-human creatures (Figure 8–14), apparently not in modern humans' direct ancestry, but coexistent with early members of the genus *Homo*.

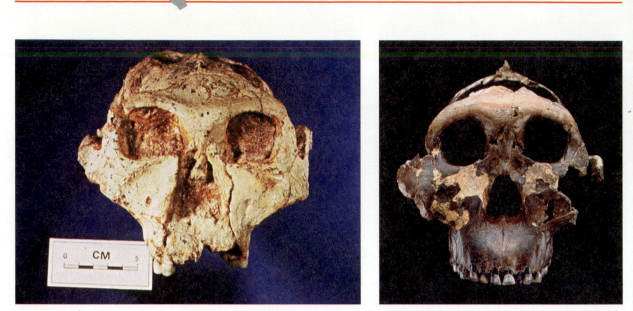

Figure 8–14 • The skulls of *Australopithecus robustus* (Swartkrans 48), left, and *Australopithecus boisei* (Olduvai Hominid 5), right.

Much of the characteristic robust australopithecine cranial morphology is related to a specialization for heavy mastication. One student of these hominids has termed them "chewing machines." Characteristic morphology includes a sagittal crest along the midline of the skull and heavy cheekbones (zygomatic arches) to support large muscles of mastication. The face is characteristically "dished" as in australopithecines generally, but is more heavily constructed than in the gracile species to withstand the forces generated in chewing. To lighten the weight of the head, large areas of the skull have developed internal air cells inside the bone. The East African species, *A. boisei,* and the South African *A. robustus,* both sometimes referred to as *Paranthropus,* seem similar in all these respects except that the former appears to be larger and more robust.

From the known cranial endocasts, robust australopithecines apparently possessed brains of an absolute size close to the earlier gracile australopithecines'. However, since the robust forms probably were of somewhat larger body size, they would have had a relatively smaller brain.

The teeth of these hominids are specialized for high-bite-force grinding. The chewing surfaces of the molars are expanded; premolars are larger and molarlike; and the incisors and canines, for cutting and tearing food, are reduced in size. Robinson put forth the so-called **dietary hypothesis** to account for this dental pattern. He proposed that the robust australopithecine was a vegetarian that ate large quantities of food to sustain its bulk. The dentition of the smaller gracile australopithecine, on the other hand, was adapted to a more varied diet that may have included meat.

The postcrania of robust australopithecines is poorly known. On the basis of extremity bones and pelvic fragments, the stature of these hominids has been estimated at between 145 and 165 centimeters (56

dietary hypothesis–hypothesis advanced by John T. Robinson that differences in the dentitions of the gracile and robust australopithecines were to be accounted for by differences in dietary adaptations, the former eating a more omnivorous diet and the latter eating a more herbivorous one.

in.–65 in.) with a weight range of 40 to 90 kilograms (88–198 lbs) (Jungers, 1988). The arm may also have been relatively longer. Although some foot bones in *A. robustus* suggest a divergent big toe, and, thus, an ape form of locomotion, the pelvis and lower limb bones, as well as the central placement of the foramen magnum, strongly suggest well-developed bipedalism.

A number of intriguing paleoanthropological problems still surround the robust australopithecines. According to the dietary hypothesis, one might expect these hominids in relatively large numbers in fossil deposits, because herbivores are generally more abundant than omnivores/carnivores in ecological food chains. In fact they occur in virtually the same percentages as the supposedly omnivorous gracile early hominids. The present best estimate of robust australopithecine adaptation is that of a bipedal, hard-object-feeding omnivorous dweller of either woodlands or grasslands within an overall savanna environment.

Another paleoanthropological dilemma associated with the robust australopithecine is ecological niche separation between this hominid and the contemporary *Homo habilis* (see Chapter 9). How could two such species live in the same environment without one eventually ecologically excluding the other? Perhaps tool use was exclusive to *Homo*. Robust australopithecines are found in sites in which **Oldowan** stone tools are also found, and, in some cases, where *Homo* is lacking. Despite the absence of *Homo* fossils from these sites, they may have left their stone tools there. General opinion seems to lean toward robust australopithecines' lacking the ability to fashion stone tools, but the question is still open.

The phylogenetic origin of the robust australopithecines is postulated by some to be from *A. africanus*. Discovery of the "Black Skull" (KNM WT 15000) at West Lake Turkana, Kenya, dated to 2.5 million years ago, has weakened this interpretation because there is now near overlap in dates for *A. africanus* and *A. boisei*, suggesting that *A. boisei* had an earlier origin.

Robust australopithecine species seem to persist in Africa until shortly after the appearance of the relatively advanced *Homo erectus* (see Chapter 9). Washburn has suggested that this *Homo* species was able to outcompete the robust australopithecine and thus drive the latter to extinction. As *Homo erectus* increased in size over time, groups required greater food resources and territory, and *H. erectus* were able to physically outcompete robust australopithecines. A second possibility is that ecological change to drier conditions did in the robust australopithecines.

SUMMARY

1. Hominids are those hominoids that are adapted to bipedalism, or walking on two legs. Australopithecines are the earliest known hominids in the fossil record, appearing at the boundary of the Miocene and Pliocene Epochs in Africa.

Oldowan—earliest recognized stone tool tradition associated with the first members of the genus *Homo*. Mode I tools.

2. A number of adaptations characterize australopithecines and set them apart from apes. In addition to adaptations related to bipedalism, these include larger brain-to-body size, larger molar teeth compared to body size, and relatively small canine teeth.

3. Hominids are rare in the fossil record and this may be because they occupied large home ranges and were rarely concentrated in one area where they might easily be fossilized.

4. There are two broad categories of australopithecines: "gracile" or early australopithecines, and "robust" australopithecines, which appear later in the fossil record. Robust australopithecines are characterized by very large molar and premolar teeth and relatively diminutive front teeth.

5. Australopithecines seem to be broadly adapted to savanna or woodland habitats.

6. One or the other of the early gracile australopithecines gave rise to the genus *Homo*. The robust australopithecines became extinct about 1 million years ago.

CRITICAL-THINKING QUESTIONS

1. What are the characteristics that define the family Hominidae?
2. Compare and contrast gracile and robust australopithecines.
3. Name two reasons that hominid fossils are relatively rare in the fossil record.
4. Why did Raymond Dart believe that the australopithecines possessed an osteodontokeratic tool culture?
5. Discuss australopithecine discoveries at Hadar and Laetoli.
6. Describe the probable australopithecine econiches.

SUGGESTED READINGS

Brain, C. K. 1981. *The Hunters or the Hunted? An Introduction to African Cave Taphonomy.* Chicago: University of Chicago Press. An important book on how bones become buried and fossilized and how we can reconstruct past ecology from fossilized remains.

Clark, Wilfrid Le Gros. 1967. *Man-Apes or Ape-Men?* New York: Holt, Rinehart & Winston. A discussion of the early controversies and debates over the position of the australopithecines in human ancestry. Excellent historical review of fossil discoveries from Taung onward.

Corruccini, R. S., and R. L. Ciochon (eds.). 1994. *Integrative Paths to the Past: Paleoanthropological Advances in Honor of F. Clark Howell.* Englewood Cliffs, N.J.: Prentice Hall. Essays in honor of one of the great paleoanthropologists. A book for the student who wishes to pursue some of the major paleoanthropological questions of the day.

Dart, Raymond. 1959. *Adventures with the Missing Link.* New York: Harper. The story of the discovery of the Taung child, its interpretation, and the follow-up research in South Africa by the discoverer of *Australopithecus africanus.*

Foley, R. 1997. *Humans Before Humanity.* Malden, Mass.: Blackwell. Re-creates the environmental setting and behavior of early hominids. Includes a guide to the intricacies of fossil discoveries and the reasons fossils were named the way they were.

Grine, F. E. (ed.). 1988. *Evolutionary History of the "Robust" Australopithecines.* New York: Aldine de Gruyter. The most comprehensive treatment of these fascinating "near-humans."

Johanson, Donald C., and Maitland Edey. 1981. *Lucy: The Beginnings of Humankind.* New York: Simon & Schuster. The story of the discovery and interpretation of *Australopithecus afarensis,* co-authored by the individual most responsible for bringing this new hominid species to light.

Johanson, D. C., and B. Edgar. 1996. *From Lucy to Language.* New York: Simon & Schuster. Discusses central issues in paleoanthropology and the human fossil record. Beautifully illustrated with photographs by David Brill.

Lewin, R. 1987. *Bones of Contention.* New York: Simon & Schuster. Controversies in the search for human origins. Russell Tuttle said it all when he described this exceptional work as "a lucid introduction to the old, the new, the borrowed, and the hullabaloo of paleoanthropology."

Reader, John. 1981. *Missing Links: The Hunt for Earliest Man.* Boston: Little, Brown. A beautifully illustrated volume about the discovery of early hominids, their interpretations, and the history of the field.

Tattersall, Ian. 1995. *The Fossil Trail: How We Know What We Think We Know about Human Evolution.* New York: Oxford University Press. A new book by American Museum of Natural History paleoanthropologist Ian Tattersall, stressing the importance of cladistic methodology in hominid evolutionary studies.

Tobias, Phillip V. (ed.). 1985. *Hominid Evolution: Past, Present, and Future.* New York: Liss. The proceedings of the Taung Jubilee International Symposium in 1985. A book edited by eminent paleoanthropologist Phillip Tobias in honor of the fiftieth anniversary of the discovery of Taung, discussing many of the themes and research directions that have characterized paleoanthropology in the last fifty years.

CHAPTER 9
The Genus Homo

Homo habilis—earliest generally recognized species of the genus *Homo.*

Homo erectus—primitive species of the genus *Homo,* generally considered to have evolved from *Homo habilis* and to be the ancestor of *Homo sapiens.*

Homo sapiens—species that includes modern humans as well as archaic *Homo sapiens.*

endocranial volume—synonymous with cranial capacity—the amount of space inside the skull, occupied in life by the brain and brain coverings.

There are three species of *Homo* generally recognized by experts: **Homo habilis, Homo erectus,** and our own species, **Homo sapiens.** Some paleoanthropologists now recognize two additional species, *Homo ergaster* and *Homo rudolfensis,* within what others consider *Homo habilis.* As a group the *Homo* species are distinguished from *Australopithecus* by a larger cranial capacity, indicating a larger brain, which is successively larger from *habilis* to *erectus* to *sapiens.* Members of the genus *Homo* also have shorter molars, smaller canine teeth, and more lightly constructed skulls generally lacking "dished faces" and cranial crests. Body size increased dramatically in the *Homo* lineage, especially with *Homo erectus.* Based on current evidence, members of the *Homo* lineage were stone-tool-making and culture-bearing hominids, in probable contrast to australopithecines.

MAJOR PHYSICAL CHANGES

The Brain

Perhaps the trait most widely believed characteristic of *Homo* is an enlarged brain in relation to body size. Brain size can be relatively accurately predicted from the **endocranial volume,** the space of the brain cavity inside the skull. But this determination is also somewhat larger than true brain size because of the thickness of the membranes that cover the brain (the *meninges*) and the *venous sinuses* that contain blood between the inside of the skull and the outside of the brain (see Appendix 1).

Body size and body weight of primates exist in a constant relationship to various dimensions of their skeletons. Using relationships with limb bones, anthropologists can compute the body weight and size of fossil hominids. With both brain size and body weight estimates, one can determine the degree of **encephalization**—the size of the brain in relation to body weight. *Homo* has an encephalization quotient higher than any australopithecine.

The human brain evolved to such a large size and to such complexity because of strong selective forces. Many hypotheses have been advanced to account for its phenomenal growth. Tool use and increasing cultural socio-behavioral complexity in the evolving *Homo* lineage have been important in the understanding of selection for an increase in brain size (Washburn, 1960). Cooperative hunting by males has also been implicated even though now it is realized that female social cooperation in food getting would have been of equivalent if not greater selective importance, because more of the daily caloric intake of modern hunter-gatherer groups derives from female-collected food sources (Lee and DeVore, 1968). Other ideas (see Falk, 1990; Foley, 1990) have implicated the selective importance of language, ecological parameters, diet, and, recently, the circulatory patterns in the head as a cooling mechanism for an enlarged brain.

encephalization—the process of extreme brain enlargement in the *Homo* lineage.

Teeth

The teeth as a whole, but particularly the back teeth, underwent reduction in size in *Homo* compared with the australopithecines (Figure 9–1). The molar teeth are more squared in outline, viewed from above, than they are in australopithecines. The canines are relatively smaller. The

Figure 9–1 • *Homo habilis* (OH 7) dentition, left, compared with that of *Australopithecus africanus* (Sts 52), right.

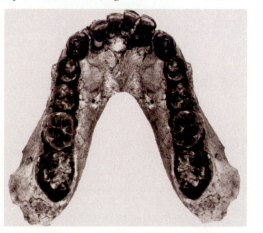
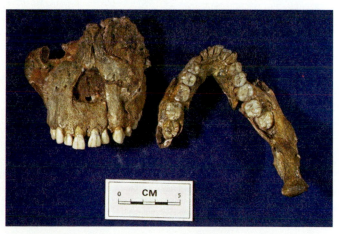

third premolar, which in australopithecines tends to be as large as, or larger than, the fourth premolar, is generally relatively smaller in *Homo*.

The grinding teeth, the molars and the premolars, have generally lost their complex enamel wrinkling ("crenulation") in *Homo* (Figure 9–1). The function of the crenulation in australopithecines was probably to increase surface area, particularly in younger individuals where jaw strength was less.

Skull and Jaws

The changes that we have seen in the size of the brain and in the teeth are reflected in the parts of the body skeleton that hold them. The increased size of the brain, around which the skull bones develop during embryonic growth, accounts for a higher skull vault in *Homo* than in *Australopithecus* (Figure 9–2). Anthropologists have developed several measurements that express this change, such as height of the skull above the ear opening and the curvature of the frontal bone (frontal angle).

In *Homo,* the parts of the skull that hold the teeth—the maxilla and the jaw or mandible—are decreased in size and bone thickness because the teeth are decreased in size. Because the dentition is not as large, the muscles that move the teeth are not as heavily developed. Thus, in *Homo* the

Figure 9–2 • Crania and faces of *A. africanus* (Sts 5), *H. habilis* (KNM ER 1470 and KNM ER 1813), and *H. erectus* (KNM ER 3733 and Choukoutien [Zhoukoudian]).

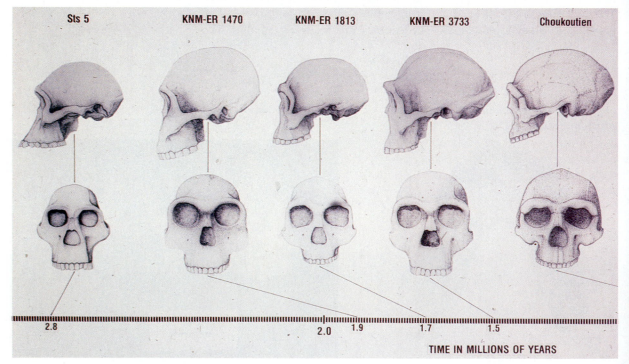

bony face protrudes less (is less prognathous and more orthognathous), the area medial to the cheekbone (zygomatic arch) is smaller, the mandible is lighter in construction, and the temporal lines are reduced in size.

Body Size and Limbs

Body size and weight have increased substantially during the evolution of the genus *Homo*. This increase over *Australopithecus africanus* is seen most dramatically in the near-six-foot reconstructed adult height of the 1.5-million-year-old *Homo erectus* skeleton (KNM WT 15000) from the site of Nariokotome in West Turkana, Kenya (Walker and Leakey, 1993). There was a change in relative lengths of limbs. *Homo* is characterized by longer lower limbs (thigh length and leg length) compared to trunk length, and perhaps relatively shorter upper limbs (arm length and forearm length) (Figure 9–3). Increase in lower limb length meant an

Figure 9–3 • Diagram showing intermembral indices (length of the forelimb divided by length of the hindlimb) of *Homo* and *Australopithecus*.

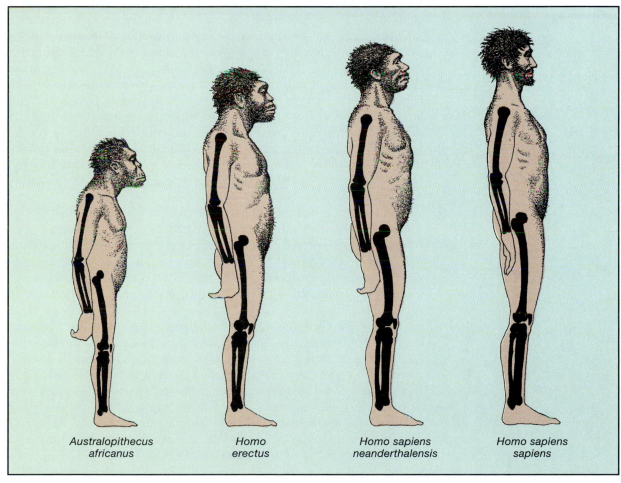

Australopithecus africanus   *Homo erectus*   *Homo sapiens neanderthalensis*   *Homo sapiens sapiens*

increased length in *Homo's* walking stride, allowing the attainment of greater speeds over greater distances. This may have been an important pre-adaptation for hunting of larger animals, which are characteristically "run down" over long distances by modern hunter-gatherers. Larger body size was of advantage in competition for food (in scavenging, hunting, or gathering) with other species, and in avoiding predation.

HOMO HABILIS

The earliest species of the genus *Homo* was discovered at Olduvai Gorge in l960. The species name had been suggested to Louis Leakey by Raymond Dart, and it means "dexterous" or "handy," on the assumption that this and not the contemporary *Australopithecus boisei* fashioned the stone tools at Olduvai Bed I.

Since 1964 other specimens of *Homo habilis* have been discovered in eastern Africa—at East Lake Turkana (Leakey and Leakey, 1978) and Omo (Boaz and Howell, 1977). Renewed work at Olduvai yielded a fragmentary skeleton of *Homo habilis,* Olduvai Hominid 62 (Johanson et al., 1987). Fossil discoveries dated to 2.33 million years from Hadar, Ethiopia, made in 1994 by teams from the Institute of Human Origins (Arizona State University), are possibly the oldest evidence for the genus *Homo* (Kimbel et al., 1996). The first find from a site (AL 666) high in the Hadar Formation is an upper jaw and partial dentition associated with Olduwan tools, making this the oldest combination of bones and artifacts so far discovered. The site is also important because the paleoenvironment was an open grassland. This reconstruction is based on the recovery of other fauna, primarily antelopes, that are commonly associated with savannas, rather than the more common forest-dwelling impala that is characteristic of the fauna found associated with the earlier *A. afarensis,* such as "Lucy."

This sampling, along with the earlier Olduvai finds, shows that *Homo habilis* probably had a relatively larger body size than gracile australopithecines, but apparently a more marked degree of sexual dimorphism than later *Homo*. The skeleton OH 62, for example, was a quite small individual, probably a female weighing between 30 and 39 kilograms (66–86 lbs), compared with the large, probably male members of the species, weighing between about 50 kilograms (110 lbs) and possibly up to over 90 kilograms (198 lbs) (see McHenry, 1988, however, who contests that *habilis* was larger than gracile australopithecines). All *Homo habilis* dentitions show decreased molar tooth size, in comparison with australopithecines. The facial skeleton of *Homo habilis* is also reduced in forward projection, a result of the generally smaller size of its teeth (Figure 9–2). The face shows the smoothly curved maxilla and parabolic-shaped mandible that differentiate it from the australopithecine dished face.

It is still a mystery whether *H. habilis* extended outside sub-Saharan Africa. A skull of a juvenile hominid found by G. H. R. von Koenigswald at Modjokerto, Java (Indonesia) prior to World War II served as the type specimen for a species named by him *Homo modjokertensis*. It was initially considered to be as old as 1.9 million years, and recent redating by Carl Swisher and colleagues (1994) at the Berkeley Geochronology Center has confirmed this date. Other hominid fossils in Java that have been considered of comparable age to the juvenile skull and that were thought to possibly represent the adult form of this species are equally suspect in terms of their age and provenance.

Evidence that suggests the presence of *H. habilis* in China was provided by Huang and his colleagues (1995) from the site of Longgupo Cave (Sichuan Province). Paleomagnetic studies and an archaic fauna suggest a date of earliest Pleistocene (~1.8 million years ago) for the assemblage. These researchers report that the discoveries from the cave—hominid dentition, jaw fragments, and stone tools—are comparable in age and morphology with early members of the genus *Homo* and the Oldowan technology of East Africa. These finds lend support to the claim that pre-*erectus* hominids entered Asia before two million years ago and provide the "most likely antecedents for the *in situ* evolution of *Homo erectus* in Asia" (page 278).

There is also evidence to suggest that although fossils of early *Homo* have not been found in Eurasia, their stone tools have been. Stone tool occurrences have been reported by Dennell (1989) from Pakistan in sediments with dates in excess of 1.6 million years old, and by Bonifay (1989) from France in sediments in excess of 2 million years old. Both claims will need to be bolstered by more supporting data and geological analysis if scientists are to use these dates, which are currently much earlier than accepted for most hominid fossils in Eurasia.

Age of *Homo habilis*

The dating of Olduvai Bed I was the first application of the new method of potassium-argon dating to an important paleoanthropological problem—the age of *Homo habilis* (and *Australopithecus boisei*). J. F. Evernden and Garniss Curtis of the University of California, Berkeley, reported in 1965 a date of 1.73 million years for a tuff, a potassium-rich layer of volcanic ash, in Olduvai Bed I. In time, the dating was confirmed by more analyses at Olduvai, by comparisons of fauna and potassium-argon dates from other sites, particularly Omo, and by **paleomagnetic dating.**

During the 1970s, teams led by Richard Leakey recovered many fossils of individuals belonging to the genus *Homo* from sites on the eastern shore of Lake Turkana. Perhaps the most famous, certainly the most controversial, was KNM ER 1470 (Figure 9–4). After a hot debate over the age of the associated KBS tuff, this important find was dated to about 1.8 million years ago, comparable to the dates earlier determined for fossils found at Olduvai Gorge. As mentioned earlier, new fossil evidence from sites such as Hadar, Ethiopia, has brought the age of the early species of *Homo* back to about 2.3 million years. General consensus

paleomagnetic dating–the matching of a sequence of strata with the dated pattern of changes in magnetic orientation through time, thereby dating the sediments.

Figure 9–4 • KNM ER 1470 skull from Koobi Fora, Kenya.

Table 9-1 • Major Fossil Specimens of *Homo*, Including Grades of *Homo sapiens*

Taxon	Locality	Specimen Number	Body Part	Geological Age
Homo habilis	Olduvai Gorge, Tanzania	OH (Olduvai Hominid) 7 ("Olduvai Hand")	Partial hand skeleton	1.8 million years
		OH 8 ("Olduvai Foot")	Partial foot skeleton	1.8 million years
		OH 13 ("Cinderella")	Partial skull	1.6 million years
		OH 24 ("Olduvai George")	Partial skull	1.9 million years
		OH 62 ("Son of Lucy")	Fragmentary skeleton	1.8 million years
	Omo, Ethiopia	L894-1	Fragmentary skull with teeth	1.9 million years
[also classified by some as *Homo rudolfensis*]	East Turkana, Kenya	KNM ER (Kenya National Museum, East Rudolf) 1470	Skull lacking teeth	1.9 million years
		KNM ER 1813	Complete skull with teeth	1.9 million years
Homo erectus	West Turkana, Kenya	KNM WT 15000 ("Turkana Boy")	Nearly complete skeleton, with skull and dentition	1.6 million years
[also classified by some as *Homo ergaster*]	East Turkana, Kenya	KNM ER 3733	Complete skull with dentition	1.5 million years
	Swartkrans, South Africa	SK 847	Partial skull with partial dentition	circa 1.5 million years
	Trinil, Indonesia	Trinil 1	Skull cap	circa 1.0 million years
	Modjokerto, Indonesia	Modjokerto 1 "Modjokerto Infant"	Partial skull	?1.9 million years
	Sangiran, Indonesia	Sangiran Skull IX	Complete skull and dentition	circa 1.5 million years
	Dmanisi, Georgia	Dmanisi 1	Mandible with teeth	circa 1.4–1.6 million years
Homo sapiens "Grade 1"	Bodo, Ethiopia	Bodo 1	Skull	circa 500,000 years
	Petralona, Greece	Petralona 1	Skull	over 230,000 years
	Dali, China	Dali 1	Skull	230,000–180,000 years
[also classified by some as *Homo heidelbergensis*]	Heidelberg	Mauer 1	Mandible with teeth	circa 300,000 years
Homo sapiens "Grade 2"	Steinheim, Germany	Steinheim 1	Skull lacking teeth	circa 150,000 years
Homo sapiens "Grade 3A"	Neandertal, Germany	Neandertal 1	Skull cap and partial skeleton	circa 50,000 years
	La Chapelle-aux-Saints, France	La Chapelle 1	Skull and mandible with teeth	circa 50,000 years
Homo sapiens "Grade 3B"	Omo, Ethiopia	Omo 1 and 2	Skulls lacking faces	120,000 years

Data from Wood (1992).

now holds that *Homo habilis* may have had its beginnings as early as 2.4 million years ago, and disappeared by about 1.5 million years ago, when *Homo erectus* came onto the scene (Table 9–1).

Homo habilis and Other Species of Early *Homo*

Some paleoanthropologists think that several species of early *Homo* co-existed. One of the species names that has been suggested is *Homo ergaster* (Groves and Mazek, 1975). Another is an earlier form, *Homo rudolfensis* (Alexeev, 1986). This splitting of the early *Homo* fossils into a number of separate species has received some mainstream paleoanthropological support. Wood (1992), for example, accepts *Homo ergaster* as a large-bodied, fully bipedal species distinct from the smaller and partially arboreal *Homo habilis*. He suggests that *Homo ergaster* is the early African version of *Homo erectus*. Other experts accept the single group *Homo habilis* as accommodating the variation that is seen in the fossils of early *Homo* (Tobias, 1991).

THE FIRST STONE TOOLS

It is likely that early australopithecines such as *A. africanus* had developed tool making to a high degree, at least by nonhuman primate standards. However, paleoanthropologists have found only hints of australopithecine bone tools at such sites as Swartkrans, South Africa, notwithstanding the possible "osteodontokeratic" tools from South Africa (see Chapter 8). **Stone artifacts**—pieces of rock that by their context or their pattern of breakage indicate hominid modification—have never been found in clear association with gracile australopithecines.

The advent of stone-tool-making is a major event in hominid evolution. It requires a knowledge of rock types (only hard, crystalline rocks make adequate stone tools), the ability to locate source areas for these rocks, an understanding of the properties of rock fracturing (Figure 9–5), and the ability to produce functional tool designs. These abilities are far beyond the interest or aptitudes of apes. The earliest evidence for stone tools comes from sites near the Gona River in central Ethiopia and is dated to 2.5 million years ago. The tools, now numbering over 3,000, were recovered over the past five years by Sileshi Semaw and Jack Harris of Rutgers University. These tools, consisting of Oldowan choppers and flaked cores, are remarkable in that they are at least 100,000 years older than known fossils belonging to the genus *Homo*. As yet there are no reports of fossil hominids found that might shed light on the mystery of who made the tools.

Why and how did early *Homo* start using stone tools? Other animals that use stone—apes, sea otters, and certain birds—do so in order to eat nuts, mussels, eggs, or some other food items not otherwise accessible to them. Early *Homo* discovered that flaked stone tools can cut—a principle that still underlies many of our food preparation techniques (grating,

stone artifacts—stones broken or flaked by hominids in order to be used as tools, or unmodified stones found in geological circumstances indicating that hominids carried them and placed them at a site.

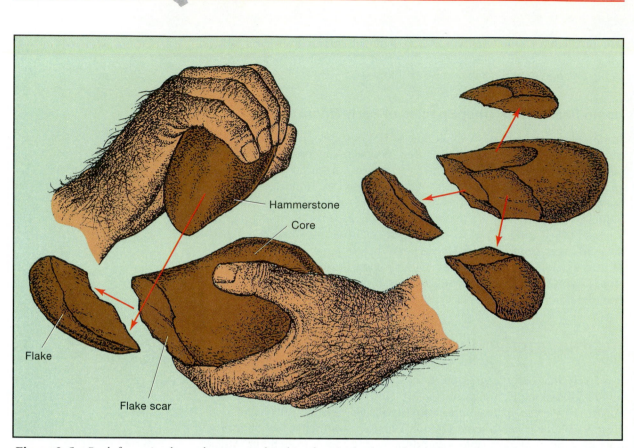

Figure 9–5 • Rock fracturing by early stone-tool-making hominids; the making of a core and flakes of early (Oldowan) stone tools.

slicing, paring, blending, chopping, etc.). With the increased cutting-edge surface of a stone flake tool and the force with which it could be used, early *Homo* was able to match the biting and chewing efficiency of much larger and stronger animals with much more impressive dentitions.

Another argument for the development of stone tools is that they were used as weapons for protection against predators and for aggressive purposes against other hominids.

The earliest stone tools that are more than merely battered pieces of quartzite are termed Oldowan, after Olduvai Gorge. Mary Leakey has categorized them into those tool types shown in Figure 9–5. Basically, there are two jobs for which these tools were used—cutting and bashing. Cutting tools were used primarily to dismember carcasses for meat. Recent research (Potts and Shipman, 1981) at Olduvai, Koobi Fora, and Senga (Congo, formerly Zaire) has revealed **cut marks** left on the animals' bones when the muscles were cut off. Bashing tools were used primarily to break open long bones for their fatty marrow. Fatty foods are a particularly valued commodity among modern hunter-gatherers,

cut marks—incisions left on bone as a byproduct of skinning or cutting muscle off the bone with stone tools; uniquely characteristic of hominids but sometimes difficult to distinguish from carnivore bite marks or scratch marks made by sand grains.

and the thousands of smashed bone fragments at Olduvai attest to the antiquity of this predilection (Potts, 1988).

Paleoecology and Behavior

Homo habilis lived in areas of sub-Saharan Africa not remarkably different from the savannas and savanna woodlands that one can still see today in places such as Serengeti, Maasai Mara, and Kruger National Parks. Trees, for fruit and shade, were generally scarcer than in *A. africanus* times. Early *Homo* groups were well-integrated into this environment, although they probably competed with robust australopithecines, wild dogs, hyenas, and other carnivores for meat, and with robust australopithecines, baboons, and perhaps some pig species for fruits, vegetables, nuts, and roots.

Archaeologists have found evidence of *H. habilis* having butchered and eaten hippopotamus as well as numerous small antelopes and other animals. A major question is whether early *Homo* hunted and killed these animals, or scavenged carcasses left by carnivores, drought, or disease. It seems likely that *H. habilis* individuals did not have the technical capabilities to kill animals much larger than themselves.

Because *H. habilis* had increased in body size and because trees were relatively sparse, individuals were not as free to climb into trees when danger threatened. Probably for these reasons *H. habilis* built shelters on the ground that served as a refuge from predators, provided shade in the day, and were warm at night. The earliest such structure has been found at Olduvai. It is a circle of large stones that probably served as the groundwork for a structure of sticks, branches, or skins.

Foley (1990) has suggested that as home range size increased, perhaps to take advantage of greater foraging or hunting opportunities, so did brain size in the *Homo* lineage. Excavations at Omo and ecological calculations based on body size have given us estimates of *H. habilis* population density, around 1.5 individuals per square kilometer (4.5 individuals per sq mile) (Boaz, 1979a). We can estimate early *Homo* home range size at about 10.5 square kilometers (~3.8 sq miles), and the average number of individuals in a group at about 16, values not unlike those of modern foraging peoples.

Other aspects of *H. habilis* behavior we must deduce from analogy to modern hunter-gatherers. The females likely gathered plant foods, while males cooperated in hunting for small game and scavenging for meat, an important source of protein. A nuclear family of a male, one or more females, and offspring was probably the basic economic unit. Kinship with others outside the family likely was recognized as a principle that organized the sharing of meat and of other valued food resources, and that regulated alliances both within the group and with other groups. *H. habilis* groups were seminomadic and moved in relation to availability of food and water. Some researchers have suggested that they had a "home base" to which all individuals returned after foraging or hunting, and where food was shared (Isaac, 1978).

HOMO ERECTUS COMES ONTO THE SCENE

The evolutionary trends toward relatively greater cranial capacity, orthognathy, dental reduction, and greater body size that had begun in _H. habilis_ continued in its descendants. The skull also began to change to a distinctive form—vault bones became very thick, the area over the eye sockets came to protrude markedly into brow (supraorbital) ridges, the back of the skull (occiput) developed a horizontal ridge known as the **occipital torus,** and the area along the sagittal suture became raised into a low "keel," called the **sagittal keel,** with flattened areas extending laterally from it (Figure 9–6). Hominids with this distinctive morphology began to appear in Africa at 1.5 to 1.6 million years ago. They are classified in the species _Homo erectus_ (Rightmire, 1990).

The biggest sample of _H. erectus_ fossils was discovered in China, at the cave site of **Zhoukoudian** near Beijing in the 1920s and 1930s. These fossils, of what was known popularly as "Peking Man," were described by Franz Weidenreich. After making casts of the specimens, Weidenreich arranged for the specimens to be sent to the United States for safekeeping at the outbreak of World War II. The Japanese invasion of China occurred after Weidenreich left China, and on the very day that the fossils were leaving with a detachment of U.S. marines, the marines were captured and the fossils were lost, never to be relocated.

occipital torus–a horizontal raised ridge of bone at the back of the _Homo erectus_ skull.

sagittal keel–a low rounded elevation of bone along the midline of the top of the _Homo erectus_ skull.

Zhoukoudian–Middle Pleistocene cave site of _Homo erectus_ near Beijing, China.

Figure 9–6 • Drawing of a reconstructed skull of an African _Homo erectus_ (KNM WT 15000) from West Lake Turkana (left), compared with an Asian _Homo erectus_ from Zhoukoudian (right). (After Alan Walker and Franz Weidenreich; art by Raymond Smith)

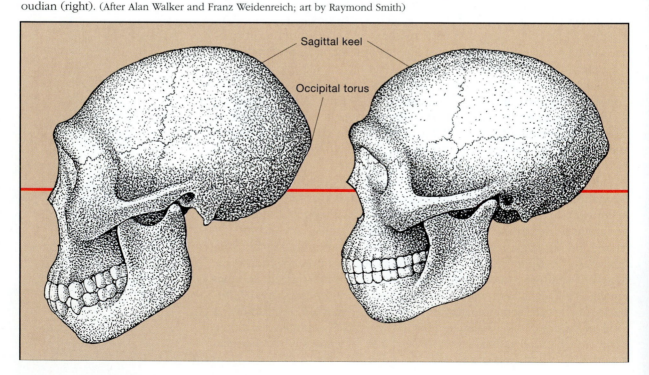

Sagittal keel

Occipital torus

Zhoukoudian is dated by both radiometric and paleomagnetic methods to between 230,000 and 500,000 years ago (Pope, 1988b). Despite recent critical review of the paleontological and archaeological data from the cave (Binford and Ho, 1985; Binford and Stone, 1986), the Zhoukoudian evidence seems secure in indicating the use of fire, the occupation of a single site for a long period of time, and the eating and probably hunting of large animals (Pope, 1988a, b).

Paleoecology and Behavior of *Homo Erectus*

Homo erectus was the first hominid species that we know extended its range outside Africa. In Asia, the earliest apparent evidence suggests an age of 1.9 million years for hominid fossils recovered in Java. In Europe, new fossil discoveries from Gran Dolino, in the Atapuerco Hills of northern Spain, date the presence of *Homo* there to 800,000 years, pushing back the date for the occupation of Europe by more than 300,000 years. Human fossil remains consist of a skull and dentition of a boy about 10 to 11 years old, and remains from five other individuals. Descriptions of the youth paint a picture of an individual who possessed both modern and primitive features. However, the young age of this boy no doubt contributed to some extent to his more modern appearance. It is too early at this point to conclude whether these finds represent yet another species of *Homo,* as claimed by their Spanish discoverers.

Elsewhere in Europe, fossil discoveries confirm the fact that humans had ventured into the region between 800,000 and 900,000 years ago. In 1994 near the Italian town of Ceprano, pieces of a skull that were found associated with chopper tools were dated to this period. According to the Italian paleontologists who discovered and reassembled the skull, its features resemble those of *Homo erectus,* with some distinctive characteristics.

In the same year that Ceprano Man was found, British scientists announced the discovery of a tibia, or lower leg bone, as well as hundreds of hand ax tools, from the site of Boxgrove. These belong to humans that arrived in Britain some 478,000 to 524,000 years ago. While both the human remains and the tools are more modern than those found at Gran Dolino and Ceprano, from 500,000 years onward Europe became continually occupied by one species of *Homo* after another. The fact that so little evidence exists for human presence in Europe should be no surprise, as the paleoenvironment was far from hospitable to tropically adapted early *Homo.* Major ice ages began around 900,000 years ago, and the fossil evidence of other fauna shows that very large carnivores, such as saber-toothed cats and hyenas, were roaming the landscape, factors that must have made it difficult for humans to survive. As groups pressed into more northern latitudes, they experienced greater seasonal temperature and climatic fluctuations. The colder temperatures likely were important in one of the biggest cultural developments in human history—*fire.*

The date that hominids first harnessed fire has recently come into question. Evidence of fire—charred bones, pieces of charcoal, and fire-cracked rocks—were long ago found with *H. erectus* at Zhoukoudian.

Figure 9–7 • Acheulean hand ax.

Recent excavations at the sites of Chesowanja and Koobi Fora in Kenya, dated at 1.4 million years ago—that is, about 1 million years earlier than Zhoukoudian—have revealed fire-hardened clay. If this early date for the discovery of fire by humans is upheld by further investigation, early and not latest *Homo erectus* would have been responsible.

Homo erectus was perhaps the first hominid to adapt culturally to forest habitats (Pope, 1988a), making use of bamboo and other nonstone materials. This emphasis on nonstone tools may explain the archaeological record associated with *Homo erectus* in Asia—that of relatively unsophisticated "chopper/chopping tool" assemblages largely lacking the hand axes that are found during this period in Africa and Europe. This gives what is perhaps a skewed view of the true cultural capabilities of Asian *Homo erectus*.

The stone tools that *H. erectus* did make were more sophisticated than those of *H. habilis*. Beginning archaeology students with practice can generally make Oldowan choppers, but few attain the skill to make a hand ax (Figure 9–7), the bifacial stone tools with greatly increased cutting edges frequently found associated with *H. erectus*. The assemblages of stone artifacts that include hand axes are referred to by most archaeologists as **Acheulean,** after the site of Saint Acheul in France. The Acheulean first appears in Africa during Bed II times (1.5 to 1.2 million years ago) at Olduvai, and probably evolved from the "Developed Oldowan," an advanced type of chopper tradition. "Scrapers," flat-edged flaked stone tools, became important during *H. erectus* times, possibly for preparing animal skins for use as clothing.

Using Acheulean tools, *Homo erectus* hunted large animals. The best evidence is at the sites of Torralba and Ambrona in Spain, where hominids apparently killed and butchered several elephants 500,000 years ago. Hunting large animals has important implications for human behavior. One animal could provide enough meat for a large group, and because it had to be eaten all at once (there was no way to store it), more complicated systems of sharing based on kinship and reciprocity must have developed. Since hunting large animals was also more dangerous and difficult than catching and killing smaller animals, more complex hunting strategies evolved.

One possibly gruesome aspect of the behavior of *H. erectus* has been the discovery at Zhoukoudian that the brains of individuals found in the cave had been removed after death, through the foramen magnum that had been broken to provide access to the brain. This sort of damage is not characteristic of hyena or other carnivore damage. Cannibalism is still a reasonable interpretation for the hominid skulls found at the site (Weidenreich, 1939).

Acheulean–stone tool culture characterized by "hand axes" flaked on two sides, thus termed "bifaces."

THE APPEARANCE OF *HOMO SAPIENS*

In the several decades following Darwin's publication in 1859 of the theory of natural selection, scientific and popular interest in human origins burgeoned in Europe and America. There was extremely little fossil evidence, so most research concentrated on comparative studies of the living primates and human beings. Emphasis has been placed on the importance in human evolution of human locomotion (bipedalism), the opposable thumb of the grasping human hand, the very large human brain, and other attributes (Bowler, 1989). Mainstream conceptions centered on the primacy of the enlarged human brain in differentiating humans from their closest primate relatives in the slowly growing fossil record. A large cranial capacity came to be accepted as the hallmark for human status.

The time of appearance of the earliest members of the species *Homo sapiens* is still an unsolved question. Several recent discoveries indicate that *Homo sapiens* was on the scene earlier than many paleoanthropologists previously thought (Figure 9–8). General opinion has held that 250,000 years ago was a reasonable estimate for the appearance of *Homo sapiens*. The discoveries of skulls from Petralona, Greece, dated at over 230,000 years old, and from Bodo, Ethiopia (Figure 9–9), that could be as old as 500,000 years, have demonstrated the presence of the earliest *Homo sapiens*. These specimens have retained so many primitive features in their morphology that some authorities have included them within the species *Homo erectus*. But a number of characteristics seem to indicate that these and other later specimens from Africa and Asia fit into a framework of worldwide appearance of *Homo sapiens* at about 500,000 years ago. The major specimens now attributed to earliest *Homo sapiens* are listed in Table 9–1.

Molecular studies have thrown some light on the timing and place of origin of anatomically modern *Homo sapiens,* although consensus on the significance of these findings has not yet been reached (Eckhardt, 1989). Studies of mitochondrial DNA (Cann et al., 1987; Vigilant et al., 1989), popularly known as the **"African Eve" Hypothesis,** have shown that the basic division in human populations is between sub-Saharan African populations and the rest of the world, and that the greatest genetic differences in the human species occur in Africa, with the Khoisan (Bushman) being the most divergent population. Despite a dissenting opinion (Templeton, 1993), these results indicate that Africa is the most likely home of most of the mt-DNA genetic diversity of the human species. By analyzing the data for mt-DNA evolution among human populations it has been proposed that all living human populations derive from ancestors who came from Africa between about 140,000 and 290,000 years ago.

Evolutionary Origins of *Homo sapiens*

As we have seen, *Homo erectus* managed to colonize virtually all of the Old World. Although we are reasonably certain that the earliest *Homo sapiens* superseded *Homo erectus,* the timing, geography, ecological settings, and evolutionary contexts for this replacement are still areas of active research. Did *Homo sapiens* evolve from *Homo erectus* across a broad front worldwide, or did the former evolve from one localized population of *H. erectus* and spread out to populate the rest of the

"African Eve" Hypothesis—the hypothesis, based on studies of mitochondrial DNA, that all modern humans descended from one closely related population, or even from one woman, living in Africa approximately 100,000 to 200,000 years ago.

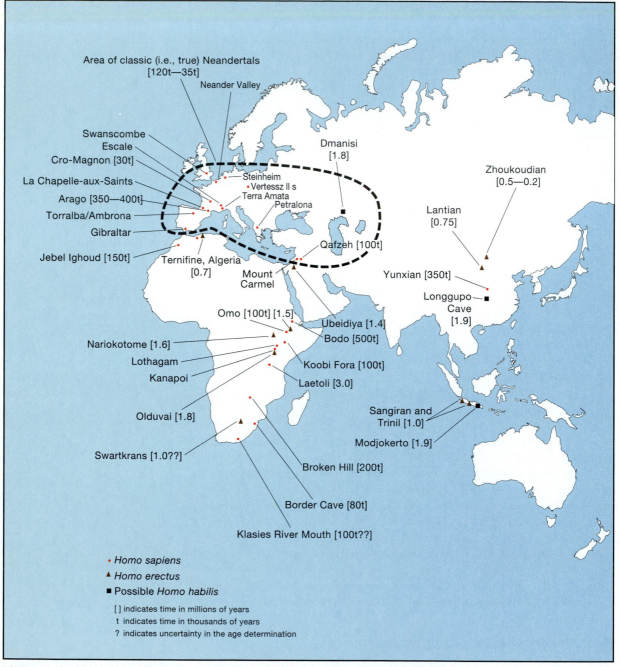

Area of classic (i.e., true) Neandertals
[120t—35t]

Neander Valley

Swanscombe
Escale
Cro-Magnon [30t]
La Chapelle-aux-Saints
Arago [350—400t]
Torralba/Ambrona
Gibraltar
Jebel Ighoud [150t]
Ternifine, Algeria [0.7]

Steinheim
Vertessz II s
Terra Amata
Petralona

Dmanisi
[1.8]

Zhoukoudian
[0.5—0.2]

Lantian
[0.75]

Yunxian [350t]

Longgupo
Cave
[1.9]

Qafzeh [100t]

Mount
Carmel

Omo [100t] [1.5]
Nariokotome [1.6]
Lothagam
Kanapoi

Ubeidiya [1.4]
Bodo [500t]
Koobi Fora [100t]
Laetoli [3.0]

Olduvai [1.8]

Sangiran and
Trinil [1.0]

Swartkrans [1.0??]

Modjokerto [1.9]

Broken Hill [200t]

Border Cave [80t]

Klasies River Mouth [100t??]

• *Homo sapiens*
▲ *Homo erectus*
■ Possible *Homo habilis*

[ ] indicates time in millions of years
 t indicates time in thousands of years
 ? indicates uncertainty in the age determination

Figure 9–8 • Map of localities and ages for fossil *H. erectus* and *H. sapiens*. Estimated ages for each site are provided in brackets. Decimal numbers are in millions of years; numbers followed by a "t" are in thousands of years. The ages for each site are derived from the use of different radiometric techniques and biostratigraphic comparisons.

Figure 9–9 • Grade 1 archaic *Homo sapiens* skulls from (left to right) Petralona, Greece; Bodo, Ethiopia; and Dali, China.

world, as the molecular interpretations now indicate? Was there inter-breeding between the immigrants and the resident populations, or were the latter totally replaced?

The fossil evidence of *Homo sapiens* is much more extensive than the bones and teeth of early *Homo* or australopithecines. *Homo sapiens* has also been a more geographically widespread species, even in comparison with *Homo erectus*. The taxonomy of *H. sapiens* is also historically complex. We adopt here a **grade** system for evolutionary stages of *H. sapiens,* presented in Table 9–1, with the major specimens at each grade. The geological ages of specimens are important for piecing together the sequence of events in their evolutionary history, and it is important to recognize that fossil specimens in the same grade may be of substantially different ages in different parts of the world. Figure 9–10 shows the evolutionary relationships of the known species of *Homo.*

The most primitive representatives of *Homo sapiens* (Grade 1) appear between 400,000 and 500,000 years ago. They are characterized by a rounded skull vault, lacking the sagittal keel and pronounced occipital bun of *H. erectus* (Figure 9–9). The brow ridges are still prominent, but unlike in *H. erectus,* the ridges are thickest over the medial part of the orbit and they blend smoothly into the frontal bone behind. The cranial capacity of Grade 1 *Homo sapiens* is expanded compared with *Homo erectus,* although both are substantially lower than modern human values. The changes in the teeth from *H. erectus* to *H. sapiens* are limited to slight reduction in overall size.

Grade 1 *H. sapiens* occurred throughout the Old World, except probably in the northernmost latitudes. Broken Hill or Kabwe (Zambia), Bodo (Ethiopia), and Salé (Morocco) have provided ample evidence of earliest *Homo sapiens* in Africa. Petralona (Greece), a mandible from Mauer near Heidelberg (Germany), and skull fragments from Bilzingsleben (Germany) are among the earliest evidences for *Homo sapiens* in Europe. Numerous fossil remains from Ngangdong (Java) and a skull from Dali (China) attest to earliest *Homo sapiens* in Asia. Some of these

grade–a level of organization or morphological complexity in an evolving lineage of organisms.

Figure 9–10 • The human family tree showing known fossil types and their possible relationship to each other from 4.3 million years ago to present day.

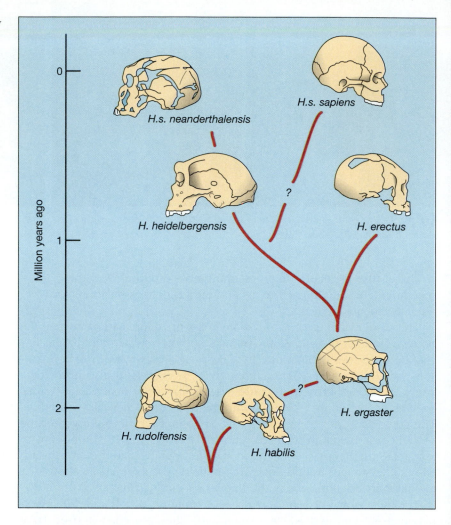

fossils, particularly Mauer, Bilzingsleben, and Ngangdong, have also been referred to as the species *H. erectus*. The morphology of these specimens makes a good case for the evolution of *Homo sapiens* from *Homo erectus*.

What do the anatomical changes seen in earliest *H. sapiens* connote in terms of changes in behavior or adaptation, and what selective forces caused them to evolve? There is no clear answer to these questions, because anthropologists have yet to explain the major anatomical peculiarities of *H. erectus*. We do not know why the sagittal keel or the occipital torus disappeared, because we do not know what forces accounted for their presence in the first place. One trend is clear, however, and that is increasing cranial capacity. Selection in earliest *Homo sapiens* strongly favored greater brain size and presumably greater cerebral ability.

Archaic *Homo sapiens*

Homo sapiens Grade 2 probably ranges in time from approximately 300,000 to somewhat less than 100,000 years ago, although the ages of the fossils in many cases are unclear. The skulls of this grade have lost the *erectus*-like characteristics and their vaults are higher.

The evidence for these hominids in Europe and Africa is good (Figure 9–8). The Saccopastore (Italy), Arago (France), and Ndutu (Tanzania) specimens are the best representatives. Two partial skulls from Swanscombe (England) and Steinheim (Germany) have been intensively studied, and they occupy important positions in hominid evolutionary studies. Asia so far has yielded few if any *H. sapiens* fossils of Grade 2. *H. sapiens* Grade 2 provides a good evolutionary source for both Grade 3A (Neandertal) and Grade 3B (anatomically modern *Homo sapiens*).

Homo sapiens sapiens

Anatomically modern humans (*Homo sapiens* Grade 3B or *Homo sapiens sapiens*) appear around 100,000 years ago in the Old World. Major specimens documenting this apparently gradual evolutionary step from *H. sapiens* Grade 2 are found at several localities in both Africa and Asia. In Europe and the Middle East the Neandertals were replaced approximately 34,000 years ago in Western Europe and about 40,000 years ago in the eastern Mediterranean. New dates from Israel indicate that the anatomically modern Qafzeh cranium is 100,000 years old, indicating that both anatomically modern and Neandertal lineages may have existed side by side in the Middle East (Stringer, 1990). *H. sapiens sapiens* lacks the very heavy brow ridge development, the midfacial prognathism, and the forward positioning of the teeth characteristic of Neandertals. The postcranial skeleton shows that *H. sapiens sapiens* individuals were in general taller than Neandertals.

Geographic expansion of modern humans continued as environments changed. Glaciation caused sea levels to drop 350 feet, exposing land masses previously under water. While land bridges never completely connected Australia to the Southeast Asian mainland, the exposure of much of the bottom of the shallow seas that surround neighboring islands would have increased the area of these land features and made short sea voyages feasible. It appears that early modern humans made their way into Australia by about 50,000 years ago, as evidenced by the presence of stone tools that date to 55,000 years from the site of Malakunanja (Arnhem Land, Northern Territory). The Bering Sea between Siberia and Alaska did become a land bridge during these times of spreading ice sheets. This allowed people to spread into the New World at different times between 30,000 and 9,000 years ago through ice-free corridors from Alaska and northern Canada down to the more temperate areas of North America.

There is evidence that big-game hunters were living in Siberia by 30,000 years ago. It is evident that groups of these hunters began crossing into the Americas soon after this. They followed herds of now extinct animals into an area devoid of other humans apparently much earlier than the first recognized Clovis cultural tradition of 11,000 years ago. Archeologists previously thought that the fluted stone projectile points that characterize the Clovis culture, first found at a site in Clovis, New Mexico, were evidence of these first immigrants. However, in recent years a number of well-dated and researched sites have been excavated that are clearly earlier than the Clovis sites. Tools and the remains of mastodons dating to 13,000 years ago were found in Taima-Taima, Venezuela. An entire village, later covered by a peat bog that preserved stone and wood tools, huts, and mastodon meat, was excavated at Monte Verde, Chile. This important site, located nearly at the tip of South America, was also dated to 13,000 years ago. A final example of pre-Clovis sites is at Meadowcroft, Pennsylvania, which was studied by archeologists from the University of Pittsburgh and determined to be between 19,000 and 16,000 years old. It is clear from this evidence that human occupation of the New World occurred much earlier than previously believed. How much earlier will await the results of work on other sites on both continents.

Homo sapiens neanderthalensis

By a strange linguistic coincidence, "**Neandertal**" means "valley of the new man," an appropriate name for the site that provided the first generally recognized human fossil. It was named for Joachim Neumann, a Dusseldorf clergyman and hymn writer of the mid-seventeenth century who wrote under the name of "Neander," meaning "new man" in Greek. "Thal" (later "tal") is German for "valley."

Limestone quarrymen found remains of a skeleton, which they thought might be a bear, at a cave in the Neandertal in 1856. They shoveled the bones out of the cave, losing many pieces in the process, and informed the local schoolmaster, Johannes Fuhlrott, that they were there if he chose to collect them. Fuhlrott and an anthropologist from Bonn, Herman Schaafhausen, recognized and described for the first time an extinct human (Figure 9–11), which, in 1864, the British anatomist W. B. R. King named *Homo neanderthalensis*. It is now recognized as a subspecies of *Homo sapiens* by most workers.

The Neandertal discovery sparked a scientific controversy unrivaled in length in a field known for controversy. One side maintained that the fossils documented an extinct species intermediate in morphology between humans and the apes, and the other maintained that they represented an aberrant, perhaps pathological, modern human. As with most longstanding scientific debates, both sides were partially right and partially wrong. We now know from increased fossil samples that the Neandertals are very similar to modern *H. sapiens* and do not in any meaningful way resemble apes. They are, nevertheless, morphologically distinct and represent an extinct race of *H. sapiens* restricted to Europe and Southwest Asia. Neandertals date to the period of about 100,000 to 34,000 years ago.

Neandertal—a hominid-fossil-bearing cave site in Germany. Fossils representing a late Pleistocene human population in Europe and parts of the Middle East were first used to define the taxon *Homo sapiens neanderthalensis*.

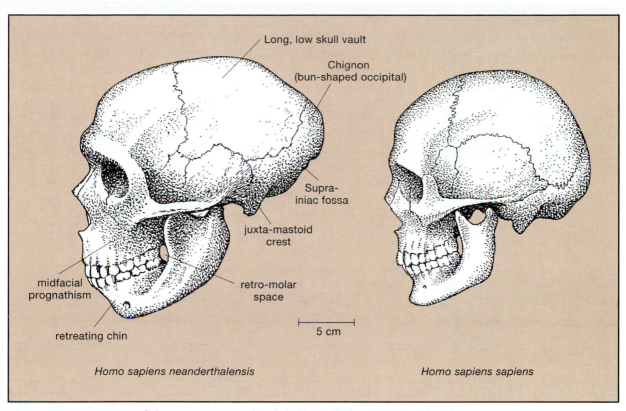

Figure 9–11 • Drawing of characteristic Neandertal skull morphology, compared with *Homo sapiens sapiens*.

The best-known anatomical trait of Neandertals is their heavy brow ridge. The middle portion of the face, around the nasal opening, protrudes greatly in Neandertals, and the teeth as a whole are moved forward relative to the skull vault. Because of this anatomical change, there is a gap, called the **retromolar space,** to be seen in lateral view behind the last molar (Figure 9–11). The forward projection of the face and teeth and the pointed occiput, retained from early *H. sapiens,* give to the Neandertal skull a low, flat appearance, even though its known range of cranial capacities is greater than the mean in modern humans. The facial skeleton and cheek-bones are less strongly constructed and massive than in early *H. sapiens.*

Why the teeth in Neandertals are positioned so far forward is still a question, but their **midfacial prognathism** and brow ridge formation are almost certainly related to it. The bone forming the brow ridges transfers the forces from the face generated by the anterior teeth. C. Loring Brace has argued that the unique rounded wear on the incisors of Neandertals suggests that they used their teeth to process skins or to hold objects. Although this hypothesis helps to explain the heavy brow ridges and tooth wear in Neandertals, it does not account for the anterior position of the teeth.

Most parts of the Neandertal skeleton are known. Overall body size had increased, certainly in comparison with average *H. erectus* and

retromolar space—a gap to be seen between the last upper molar and the ascending ramus of the mandible when articulated with the skull.

midfacial prognathism—forward projection of the bony nose region of the skull; characteristic of Neandertals.

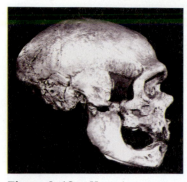

Figure 9–12 • *H. sapiens nean-derthalensis*—Edentulous (lacking teeth), old individual, from the cave site at La Chapelle-aux-Saints, France.

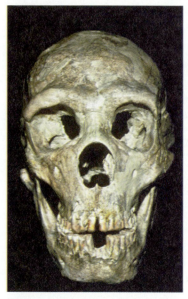

Figure 9–13 • Neanderthal specimen from Shanidar (Shanidar I, showing evidence of cranial fracture in the left eye orbit).

Mousterian—a middle Paleolithic stone tool culture characterized by prepared flakes struck off a core; ca. 250,000–40,000 years ago.

Cro-magnon—a cave site in southern France where late Pleistocene anatomically modern humans were first found.

probably also relative to earlier *H. sapiens*. This body size increase may likely have been effected by an adaptation to cold climatic conditions. A general principle known as Bergmann's Principle states that animals in a related group tend to be larger in colder climates (see Chapter 12).

The limb bones of Neandertals show them to have been powerfully built, stocky individuals. Otherwise, with two major exceptions, the anatomy of the limbs and axial skeleton of Neandertals was similar to ours. The Neandertal scapula shows a deep groove for attachment of the *teres minor* muscle. This muscle contracts to counteract the medial rotational force of very strong arm flexors, thus refining flexing movements used in throwing or pounding. Neandertals also show a thin and elongated pubic arch in the pelvis. This increases the diameter of the birth canal and may be related to a relatively large head size in Neandertal newborns.

Behavior of Early *Homo sapiens*

Early *Homo sapiens* of Grades 1 and 2 used stone tools classified as within the Lower Paleolithic or Old Stone Age. Acheulean hand axes remained a distinguishing component of these cultures, except in Asia, where modified chopping tools or nonlithic tools apparently served similar purposes.

Neandertals, whose primarily **Mousterian** flake tools are considered Middle Paleolithic, show the first indications of many cultural aspects that we recognize as "human." Burial of the dead (even with flowers, as indicated by pollen analysis at Shanidar Cave, Iraq) implies a belief in life after death. The discovery of fossils of old, physically handicapped or virtually toothless Neandertal individuals (Figure 9–12) means that groups to which they belonged cared for and helped to feed them. Special arrangements of bear skulls and deer bones suggest magical hunting rites. A few pieces of crude polished bones and ivory with scratches indicate the beginnings of artistry. A single tooth with a hole drilled in it, possibly worn as a necklace, and intentional cranial deformation show early ideas of personal esthetics and perhaps group identity. There are clear indications that some Neandertals were wounded or killed with spears or by blows to the head (Figure 9–13).

Discoveries in the European late Pleistocene demonstrated the existence of anatomically modern large-framed people ("**Cro-magnon**" after the cave site in which some of the original fossils were found). When these *H. sapiens sapiens* appear in Europe, so do stone tools made from "blades," elongated pieces of stone deftly struck off a core (Figure 9–14). These tools signal the beginning of the **Upper Paleolithic.** There is significant regional variation in these tool traditions, suggesting cultural differences between groups. *H. sapiens sapiens* controlled fire more adeptly than earlier species, constructing stone-lined hearths that generated more heat and in which fires could be banked. Impressive cave art in the form of paintings (Figure 9–15) and figurines occur. Materials from distant sources, such as marine shells and flint, indicate long-distance trading contacts or individual movements. People

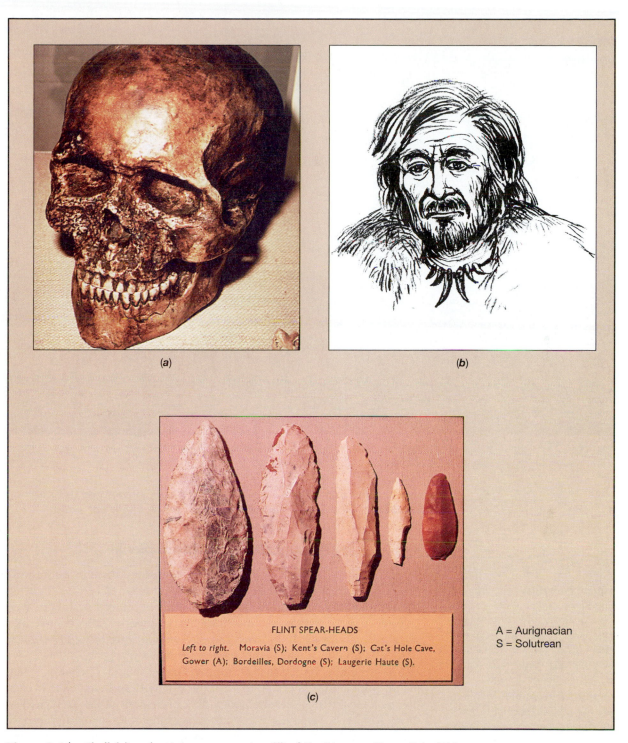

(a)

(b)

FLINT SPEAR-HEADS

Left to right. Moravia (S); Kent's Cavern (S); Cat's Hole Cave, Gower (A); Bordeilles, Dordogne (S); Laugerie Haute (S).

A = Aurignacian
S = Solutrean

(c)

Figure 9–14 • Skull (*a*) and artistic reconstruction (*b*) of Cro-Magnon; Upper Paleolithic stone tools commonly associated with anatomically modern *Homo sapiens* in Europe (*c*).

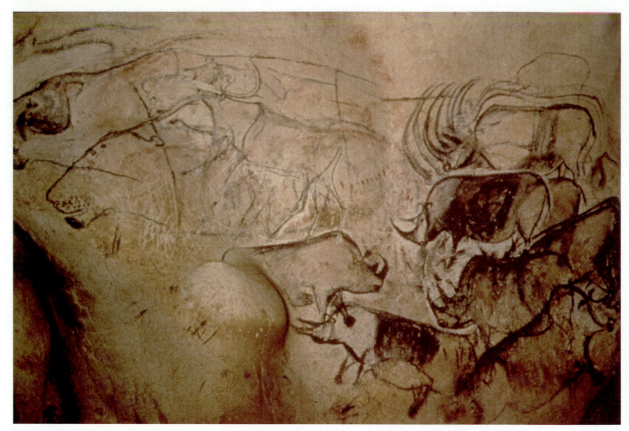

Figure 9–15 • Painting on wall of a prehistoric cave discovered in 1995 in the Vallon Pont d'Arc region of France dating to the Solutrean, circa 20,000 years ago.

congregated in relatively large groups (perhaps in response to local food abundance) for part of the year, as indicated by larger site sizes.

Evolutionary Relationships in *Homo sapiens*

Upper Paleolithic—a series of late Pleistocene cultures typified by a diversification of traditions and stone tools made from blades struck from cores; associated with anatomically modern humans; *ca.* 40,000–10,000 years ago.

Out-of-Africa Model—evolutionary hypothesis that holds that modern humans evolved first in Africa and then spread out over the rest of the world, displacing or driving to extinction other populations.

As discussed earlier in this chapter, the accumulated fossil evidence indicates to most scholars that *H. sapiens* evolved from *H. erectus*. This hypothesis has been seriously questioned only recently by authors who consider that *H. erectus* was too "specialized" anatomically to serve as a possible ancestor for *H. sapiens*. The discovery of *erectus*-like *H. sapiens* (Grade 1) hominids makes this suggestion unlikely.

It is generally agreed that *H. sapiens* Grades 1 and 2 are representative of populations ancestral to anatomically modern humans. However, the geological dating and the geographic placement of the sites yielding these fossils, as well as the constraints on evolutionary hypotheses placed by the emerging molecular data, have led to three major hypotheses on the origins of modern humans (Stringer, 1990).

The **Out-of-Africa Model** (Figure 9–16), which is consistent with the "African Eve" Hypothesis discussed earlier, holds that an African

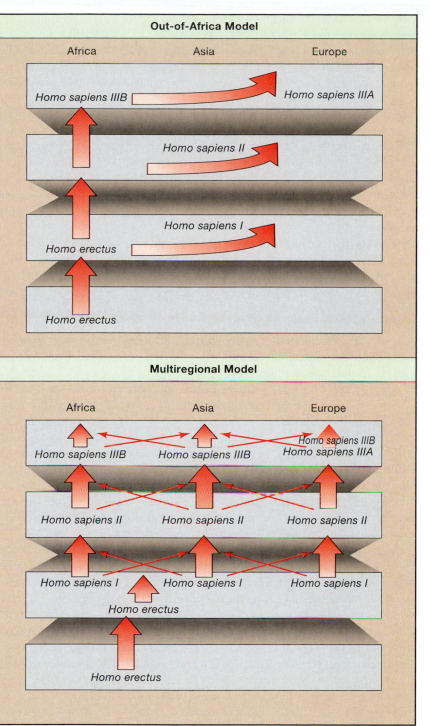

Figure 9–16 • Two models of *Homo sapiens sapiens* phylogeny.

population of anatomically modern *Homo sapiens,* as exemplified by fossils such as those from the Klasies River site in South Africa, left Africa about 100,000 years ago. This population spread over the entire Old World and accounts for all the racial differences seen in the fossil record and in modern populations. This model considers *all* the pre-*Homo sapiens sapiens* fossils in Eurasia extinct side branches, unrelated to the lineal ancestors of modern human beings. This model fits the genetic data best but fails to account for some of the apparent morphological continuities that are seen from earlier fossil populations in the same areas. For example, Asian populations today have a high proportion of shovel-shaped incisors, as do Asian *Homo erectus* and archaic *Homo sapiens* in the same region, and modern Europeans have projecting mid-facial regions and relatively heavy brows, just as do the archaic *Homo sapiens* in that area.

The **Hybridization Model** accounts for these morphological continuities by suggesting that the human populations migrating out of Africa did replace the older populations in the same areas, but there was gene flow as the immigrants interbred with the resident populations. The resulting genetic intermixture could account for the mixture of anatomical traits seen in anatomically modern populations. This model is less consistent with the molecular interpretation, which maintains that there is no evidence for genetic intermixture after the divergence from the ancestral *Homo sapiens* population in Africa.

The third model, the **Multiregional Model,** rejects the one-region (African Eden) origin and molecular interpretation of Cann (1988). It instead regards regional ancestral populations of *Homo sapiens* as the major genetic evolutionary pathways to anatomically modern humans. There must have been some genetic interbreeding between regional populations of *Homo sapiens* to have maintained the biological unity of the species and its ability to interbreed, but this model holds that this interbreeding was of little importance. The support for the third model comes primarily from one interpretation of the paleontological record, and its accommodation of the available molecular data is poor.

Where then do Neandertals fit in human evolution? One school, termed "pre-*sapiens,*" analogous in this case to the Out-of-Africa model, has considered populations of *H. sapiens* Grade 2, represented by Steinheim and Swanscombe, as uniquely ancestral to *H. sapiens sapiens,* with Neandertals, therefore, an evolutionary dead end, supplanted or perhaps wiped out by Cro-Magnon populations. The school promoting the "Neandertal Phase" hypothesis, analogous here to the multiregional model, holds that Neandertals were directly ancestral to *H. sapiens sapiens.* There are some cogent anatomical arguments supporting the latter interpretation, at least in Europe, but the rapidity of the transition from *H. s. neanderthalensis* to *H. s. sapiens* and the localized nature of Neandertals argue against their being ancestral to *H. s. sapiens* on a species-wide, global scale.

Hybridization Model—evolutionary hypothesis that suggests interbreeding between emigrant African populations and resident human populations in other parts of the world.

Multiregional Model—evolutionary hypothesis that suggests primary continuity from earlier to later human populations in each area of the world, with some gene exchange between populations.

Neandertals were most likely a geographic variant, a race of *H. sapiens,* which differentiated in Europe and Western Asia because of at least partial geographic isolation. Expanded glaciers in northern and mountainous regions and extensive bodies of water formed by glacial melt waters reduced gene flow during the last two Pleistocene glaciations. Neandertals disappeared when very arid conditions, which affected southern Asia and northern Africa, forced populations we now recognize as *H. s. sapiens* into Europe, as the coldest period of the last glaciation approached. There may have been at least some interbreeding, explaining transitional morphology in a few specimens, and cultural exchange, explaining some continuities observed in the archaeological record. But because Neandertals occupied a relatively restricted area and their population densities were probably low, they likely were genetically swamped and thus became extinct as a distinct population. Nevertheless, certain Neandertal characteristics, such as heavy brow ridges and facial prognathism, persist in some modern populations.

Studies of mitochondrial DNA show only small differences in sequences between different modern human populations, especially among Europeans. These data suggest to many researchers that modern *Homo sapiens* is of recent origin, without significant genetic contributions from earlier forms of *Homo.* Recent work by Krings et al. (1997) investigating mt-DNA from a sequence of 378 base pairs in a sample of bone belonging to the original Neander Valley hominid has shown that it differs considerably from sequences in modern *Homo sapiens.* Modern sequences differ from each other by an average about 8 substitutions for the same mt-DNA region studied. Chimpanzees and humans differ by an average of 55 substitutions, supporting the notion of a split from a common ancestor about 4–5 million years ago. The sequence differences between humans and the Neander Valley hominid numbered 27, indicating a separation between European Neandertals and modern *Homo sapiens* about 600,000 years in the past. This new work on the mt-DNA certainly lends support to the Out-of-Africa model. Does this mean that the Neandertals were in fact a different species in the true meaning of the term incapable of interbreeding with modern *Homo sapiens?* Probably not. Whether Neandertals and early *Homo sapiens* did interbreed remains an open question. However, the mt-DNA data does suggest that if they did, Neandertal's contribution to the modern gene pool was modest at best.

Phylogenetic interpretation of the fossil record of *Homo sapiens* has now been significantly augmented by the data and perspectives that molecular studies have contributed to this question. Research into modern human origins can now draw from paleontological, genetic, and paleoecological data bases to formulate more sophisticated and more defensible hypotheses for this best-known period of hominid evolution.

SUMMARY

1. The evolutionary history of the genus *Homo* is a story of expansion of a series of species out of Africa, not once but several times.
2. The earliest members of *Homo* had brains even larger than did australopithecines, and this trend of increasing brain size has been sustained through to our own species, *Homo sapiens*. Other evolutionary trends are decreases in the size of the dentition, face, and jaws.
3. The first species of *Homo* seen in the fossil record is *Homo habilis,* which appeared at about 2.4 million years ago in sub-Saharan Africa. There is a strong presumption that *Homo habilis* was a maker of stone tools, even though robust australopithecines were also present.
4. *Homo erectus* succeeded *Homo habilis* and spread out of Africa and into Eurasia. It is typified by a larger brain, thick cranial bones, heavy brow ridges, and other identifying cranial traits.
5. By about 500,000 years ago archaic *Homo sapiens* fossils are known from Africa and Europe. These show a number of similarities to the earlier *Homo erectus* and are likely lineal descendants.
6. Anatomically modern *Homo sapiens* appears by 100,000 years ago in Africa, by 50,000 years ago has spread to Australia, and by 12,000 years ago has extended to the Americas.
7. Neandertals were a race of *Homo sapiens* that lived in Europe during the late Pleistocene and were extinct by 32,000 years ago.
8. There is lively debate concerning the exact evolutionary relationships of species of the genus *Homo* and a developing interaction between paleoanthropological and biomolecular research approaches.

CRITICAL-THINKING QUESTIONS

1. What criteria are used to distinguish the genus *Homo* from the genus *Australopithecus?*
2. Who found and named *Homo habilis*? Why was this find so important?
3. Draw a hominid phylogeny including a probable time frame for each member. Include the corresponding type specimen.
4. Discuss Neandertals and their placement in the hominid lineage.
5. Who was "Mitochondrial Eve"?

SUGGESTED READINGS

Aiken, M. J., C. B. Stringer, and P. A. Mellars (eds.). 1993. *The Origin of Modern Humans and the Impact of Chronometric Dating: A Discussion*. Princeton, N.J.: Princeton University Press. A volume discussing the important new methods of accurately dating fossil sites in the period of time covering the evolution of anatomically modern humans.

Bowler, Peter. 1986. *Theories of Human Evolution: A Century of Debate, 1844–1944*. Baltimore: Johns Hopkins University Press. A detailed and fascinating book on the history of the ideas and hypotheses of human origins.

Ciochon, Russell, and John G. Fleagle (eds.). 1993. *The Human Evolution Source Book*. Englewood Cliffs, N.J.: Prentice Hall. A collected book of readings of major recent papers in human evolution.

Falk, Dean. 1992. *Braindance*. New York: Henry Holt. A book on the evolution of the human brain as understood by a study of fossil brain endocasts.

Isaac, G. L., and Elizabeth McCown (eds.). 1976. *Human Origins: Louis Leakey and the East African Evidence*. Menlo Park, Calif.: W.A. Benjamin. A series of chapters covering both fossil and archaeological reviews of the Early Pleistocene record of African early *Homo*.

Jones, Steve, Robert Martin, and David Pilbeam (eds.). 1992. *The Cambridge Encyclopedia of Human Evolution*. Cambridge, England: Cambridge University Press. A useful compendium and reference volume.

Klein, Richard. 1989. *The Human Career: Human Biological and Cultural Origins*. Chicago: University of Chicago Press. A general treatment of the archaeological, ecological, and paleoanthropological changes that characterize human evolution.

Leakey, Richard, and Roger Lewin. 1992. *Origins Reconsidered: In Search of What Makes Us Human*. New York: Doubleday. A review of the theories of human behavioral and morphological evolution from the starting point of Richard Leakey's discoveries of early *Homo* in Kenya.

Rightmire, G. Philip. 1990. *The Evolution of Homo Erectus: Comparative Anatomical Studies of an Extinct Human Species*. Cambridge, England: Cambridge University Press. A review of the anatomy and evolutionary relationships of this fossil human species intermediate between early *Homo* and *Homo sapiens*.

Smith, Fred, and Frank Spencer (eds.). 1984. *The Origins of Modern Humans: A World Survey of the Fossil Evidence*. A good review of the major finds of anatomically modern *Homo sapiens* and a sampling of the hypotheses explaining their evolution.

Trinkaus, Erik (ed.). 1989. *The Emergence of Modern Humans: Biocultural Adaptations in the Later Pleistocene*. Cambridge, England: Cambridge University Press. An up-to-date account by some of the major workers in the field on new dating, new archaeological discoveries, and new morphological analyses relating to the evolutionary transition to anatomically modern humans.

Trinkhaus, E., and P. Shipman. 1992. *The Neandertals: Of Skeletons, Scientists and Scandals*. New York: Vintage Books. A nicely written history of the discoveries of Neandertal fossils and of the people involved in their discovery and interpretation.

CHAPTER 10
Evolution of Hominoid and Human Behavior

Genetically the living apes are our closest relatives. Studies in the field and laboratory have shown that this is true behaviorally as well. This makes studies of the social behavior of apes important in terms both of increasing our knowledge of the genetic basis of behavior and of developing models for understanding human evolution. This chapter will review ape social behavior and show how a behavioral continuum model is useful to an understanding of human behavior. The chapter concludes with a discussion of the genetic and physical underpinnings of human behavior within the context of human culture.

There is no single pattern of social organization among the hominoids (Figure 10–1). Field observations have shown that patterns of behavior among the apes are considerably more complex than those observed in the monkeys, and in some cases they are also unpredictable. Long-term field studies on the best known of the apes, the chimpanzees, have shown how complex this behavior can become as patterns emerge and change with varying environmental or social conditions.

THE GREAT APES

The Orangutan

In 1967, David Horr initiated the first long-term study of the orangs in Borneo. Later MacKinnon, Rodman, Galdikas, and Mitani also worked in the same general study areas. Additionally Rijksen and Schurmann

Social Organization Among Various Primates

Bonobo

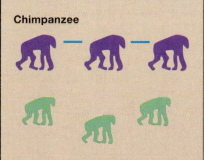

Bonobo communities are peace-loving and generally egalitarian. The strongest social bonds (blue) are those among females (green), although females also bond with males. The status of a male (purple) depends on the position of his mother, to whom he remains closely bonded for her entire life.

Chimpanzee

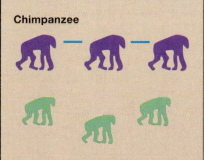

In chimpanzee groups, the strongest bonds are established among the males in order to hunt and protect their shared territory. The females live in overlapping home ranges within this territory but are not strongly bonded to other females or to any one male.

Gibbon

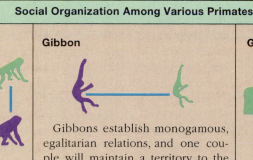

Gibbons establish monogamous, egalitarian relations, and one couple will maintain a territory to the exclusion of other pairs.

Human

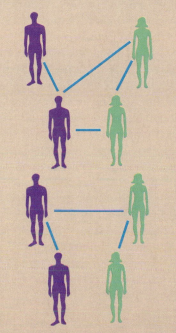

Human society is the most diverse among the primates. Males unite for cooperative ventures, whereas females also bond with those of their own sex. Monogamy, polygamy, and polyandry are all in evidence.

Gorilla

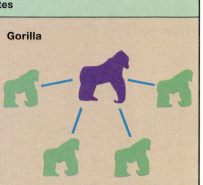

The social organization of gorillas provides a clear example of polygamy. Usually a single male maintains a range for his family unit, which contains several females. The strongest bonds are those between the male and his females.

Orangutan

Orangutans live solitary lives with little bonding in evidence. Male orangutans are intolerant of one another. In his prime, a single male establishes a large territory, within which live several females. Each female has her own, separate, home range.

Figure 10–1 • Studies of the behavioral organization of the living apes and humans have provided a good deal of insight about traits that our ancestors may have possessed. This information has enabled us to develop different hypotheses that we can test about behavioral evolution.

laryngeal sacs—outpocketings at the sides of the voice box (larynx) used as resonating chambers in certain primates; remnants of the laryngeal sacs can be seen in human individuals who, like trumpet players and glassblowers, create high air pressure in their throats.

sternal glands—glands located near the sternum or breast bone.

observed orangs at the site of Ketambe in Western Sumatra. Orangutans are the largest living arboreal mammals, with males weighing as much as 83 kilograms (183 lbs). Females weigh about half the males' weight, approximately 37 kilograms (81 lbs) on the average.

The extreme differences in body form between adult male and female orangs is comparable to that seen in gorillas and baboons (Figure 10–2). At full maturity one striking characteristic of the male is the large cheek pads of subcutaneous (Latin, meaning "under the skin") tissue located between the eyes and the ears. The exact function of the cheek pads is unknown but appears to be related in some fashion to full maturity and dominance rank. The appearance and development of these pads may be retarded in younger males if older and more dominant adult males are present. Adult males also possess large **laryngeal sacs** that are inflatable, producing their characteristic "long call," the function of which is probably to keep groups spaced apart. Orangs also possess a unique set of **sternal glands** on their chest that may function in territorial marking. In postcranial structure orangs have a very mobile hip joint and a more fully opposable big toe than is found in the African apes.

Field studies have shown that adult female orangs travel nearly exclusively through the middle layers of the forest canopy. Adult males, on the other hand, while also arboreal, are known to come down to the ground when they travel over long distances. Both modes of locomotion, arboreal and terrestrial, are slow going. The orang's selection of habitat use may in part depend upon avoidance of danger from predators. On Borneo, where tigers are absent, orangs are much more terrestrial than in Sumatra, where tigers have been observed in orang home ranges (Galdikas, 1979).

Orangs are the least gregarious of all the diurnal primates studied so far. The primary units consist of solitary males, solitary subadults, and adult females with their young offspring. Larger units occasionally occur

Figure 10–2 • Male and female orangutans.

when two or more primary units aggregate at a common food source, engage in social play (usually involving subadults), or form consort units for reproductive purposes. Social interactions in orangutans tend to increase as preferred fruit trees come into season and produce a temporary abundance of concentrated food.

Despite a temporary concentration of many orangutans in a single area, social interaction in the form of play takes place almost exclusively between immature individuals and infants. Encounters between adult males are usually aggressive, and chases and physical fights are common. Physical confrontation between the males, however, may be mediated by natural avoidance, the result of the long call given exclusively by full-grown adults. On the other hand, with the exception of a subadult attempting to copulate with an adult female, adult males tolerate subadult males, and subadult males are rarely aggressive toward each other.

Interactions among adult female orangs are also relatively rare but generally amicable. Adolescent females are the most sociable of all of the age-sex classes and they remain so until the birth of their first offspring. The home range of adult females is between 1.5 to 6 square kilometers (0.5–2.1 sq miles). Adult females occupy overlapping ranges located within the larger adult male ranges. Male residency is generally not permanent because regularly observed males often leave particular areas when resident females give birth. Males often stay away for up to several years, returning only when the particular female begins her sexual cycling.

Unlike chimpanzees, female orangs show no external signs of ovulation, but they do develop pale labial swelling during their pregnancy. Orangutans in mating tend to be promiscuous, even though one dominant male's home range tends to overlap that of several females. The relatively large size of each female's home range, in combination with the generally slow locomotion of adults, make it difficult for a single male to defend his entire range and maintain exclusive access to "his" females (Rodman, 1984). When the females are cycling, they prefer the company of adult males and often seek them out. Unescorted females are prone to being raped by subadult males until a larger adult male drives them away. Females who are sexually receptive avoid subadult males and resist mating attempts if they come in contact with them.

The interbirth intervals in orangutans seem to be among the longest of any primate species. The minimum interval has been reported by Galdikas to be about five years, with an average span of between six and seven years (Table 10–1).

Mothers and their infants remain together for a number of years. The dispersal of the young away from their mothers begins when the juveniles start to travel and forage independently. Occasionally, older juveniles rejoin their mothers for variable periods of time. Young females probably settle in a home range near their mothers, whereas males disperse over larger distances, competing with other males for home ranges.

Table 10–1 • Gestation and Interbirth Intervals in Hominoids		
Taxon	Gestation Length	Interbirth Interval
Gibbon	210 days[1]	2 years[1]
Orangutan	275 days[1]	6–7 years
Chimpanzee	225 days[1]	4.5–7.5 years[2]
Gorilla	251–289 days[1]	4 years[2]
Homo sapiens		
!Kung (Botswana)	266[2]	4–5 years[2]
Hutterites (North America)	266[2]	2 years[2]

[1]Data from Napier and Napier (1967).
[2]Data from Jolly (1985).

The areas where orangs live today have been substantially modified by humans, and because of this, present-day orang ecology may be greatly different from what it was when orangs roamed most of Asia. In Borneo, where most field studies have been undertaken, the lack of nonhuman predators may also be a contributing factor to orangutan behavior. MacKinnon (1979) astutely noted that in Sumatra, where tigers still roam the home range of the orangs, adult males spend a great deal more time with females and their offspring. This behavior no doubt serves to mitigate the tigers' potential threat as a predator.

The Gorilla

The gorilla is distributed discontinuously in Central and West Africa into three subspecies: the western lowland gorilla (*Gorilla gorilla gorilla*), the eastern lowland gorilla (*Gorilla gorilla graueri*), and the mountain gorilla (*Gorilla gorilla beringei).*

The gorillas are the largest of all the wild species of primates: The males weigh over 180 kilograms (426 lbs) in the wild and up to 300 kilograms (660 lbs) in captivity, and the females weigh 70–115 kilograms (154–253 lbs) (Figure 10–3). The gorilla shares with the other apes the brachiating anatomy of the upper torso, but because of its large size, arm-swinging is not an efficient form of locomotion. Adult gorillas spend most of their time on the ground and, like the chimpanzee, knuckle walk. Gorillas often assume a bipedal stance while displaying, chest beating, or charging. The display is initiated by the male, who begins to vocalize with a low "hoot" that gets louder and faster as the display continues. The male may stand bipedally, running about, throwing vegetation, and slapping his chest, making a violent noise with cupped hands. The sequence may end with the male thumping the ground with one or both palms. However, the gorilla is basically an extremely shy, unobtrusive vegetarian. For obvious reasons of size, gorillas consume on a daily basis large quantities of leaves, shoots, and the pith of trees, which they break apart with their hands and canine teeth.

Figure 10–3 • Male and female mountain gorillas in the Virunga mountains, Rwanda.

Gorillas live in relatively stable units of up to 30 animals consisting of one or more "silverback" males (those whose hair along the upper back on fully adult males turns a silver or white color), black-backed younger males, females, and their immature young. Recent reports show that gorillas may also form all-male units that last for at least three years. Younger males who have typically emigrated from their natal groups travel alone for long periods of time, eventually forming their own bisexual troops by taking one or more young females from other groups (Fossey, 1983). Only in rare cases do adult males migrate between established troops. After the formation of a social unit, females generally remain in that unit, probably because of mutual attraction to the dominant male. Fossey reported that in groups that lose their male—usually, presumably, by death—females do not remain together but rapidly disperse into other groups.

Gorillas occupy an average home range of up to 4,000 hectares (10,000 acres) that may overlap with the range of a neighboring group. Even with extreme overlapping of range and the consequent frequent intergroup contact, gorillas do not appear to be territorial. The daily routine of slow feeding, play, and resting is usually accomplished over an average distance of only 1 kilometer. The abundance of food makes for a leisurely pace, and social encounters are conducted in the same relaxed fashion. Fossey reports infrequent dominance behavior among the group's linearly ranked members. The dominant silverback appears to lead the group in its daily activities without quarrel. Play and grooming behavior among the juveniles and subadults appear to be relatively infrequent.

Gorillas apparently have no breeding season. Reproductive behavior in the wild, though infrequent, is varied, with observations of not only dorso-ventral mounting but also ventro-ventral (face to face) mounting

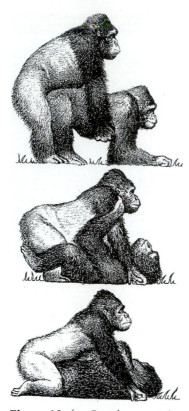

Figure 10–4 • Copulatory positions assumed by gorillas. (Based on Schaller, 1963; and Dixon, 1981)

as well (Figure 10–4). In all-male groups, extensive male–male interactions resembling the courtship and mating patterns of the heterosexual troops are common.

The end of the day for a gorilla group finds individuals searching out a suitable spot for retiring for the night. Like chimpanzees, gorillas construct nests of branches and leaves. However, most nests are built low in the forest canopy or, not uncommonly, on the ground. Gorillas usually find different sites to sleep in each night.

The Chimpanzee

Chimpanzees are anatomically similar to gorillas in form but are less massive. The average weight of a male chimpanzee is about 40 kilograms (88 lbs), and that of the female is less than 30 kilograms (66 lbs) (Figure 10–5). Sexual dimorphism between male and female chimpanzees is less than in the gorilla. In terms of overall body size differences, chimpanzees show less prognathic (Greek, meaning "forward face") jaws, less massive cheek and temporal muscles, and, consequently, in males, a less pronounced sagittal cresting on the top of the skull.

In postcranial anatomy, the limb proportions are much the same as the gorilla's. The morphology of the limbs, however, is much less robust, and the digits of the hand and feet are more slender and curved. These differences bear witness to the fact that even adult chimpanzees are generally more active arborealists than gorillas.

Chimpanzees inhabit a broad range across Central and West Africa and they occupy more diverse habitats than gorillas, ranging from tropical rain forests to open dry savanna. Behavior of the chimpanzee largely depends upon the specific ecological niche that it inhabits. The diet of chimpanzees is opportunistic, though fruit (60%) and leaves (20%) consti-

Figure 10–5 • Male and female chimpanzees.

tute the majority of the food types. Movement from food source to food source on the ground is generally achieved by quadrupedal knuckle walking. Arboreal locomotion is accomplished either quadrupedally or by arm-swinging (Figure 10–6).

Chimpanzees exhibit a **fusion-fission social organization** first described by Badrian and Badrian in 1984, in which groups are flexible in size and composition. Within many wild groups, small, very temporary subgroups form on the basis of mutual attraction, friendship, and inclination. They forage over a loosely defined but familiar home range.

Females tend to show little affection toward each other and spend much of their time alone or with their offspring in extensively overlapping home ranges. Males, in contrast, are much more gregarious and at times cooperate in defending communal territory that includes the feeding areas of several females. The social structure of the community depends upon male–male bonding, and males often show affiliative behavior toward one another, such as in grooming. Male–male grooming may account for almost 50% of all adult interactions. On the other hand, female cooperative aggression, as well as grooming among adult females, accounts for only 10% of those interactions. Grooming between adult males and females appears to be directly correlated with mating. Female chimpanzees tend to mate with males who spend substantial amounts of time near them grooming or sharing food. Grooming between mothers and sons becomes more reciprocal with age, but sons tend to groom their mothers more than the reverse. Grooming is also used by all individuals as an exchange for access to infants, for assistance in alliance formation, and in aggressive behavior.

No male chimpanzees, except for a few immatures, have been observed to transfer from one community to another. On the other hand, female chimpanzees at puberty frequently leave their natal group and transfer to other groups (Goodall, 1986). Consequently, the males in a group tend to be more closely genetically related than the females, who may come from many different backgrounds (Tutin and McGinnis, 1981). Females who do transfer typically do so only when they exhibit genital swelling.

Female chimpanzees exhibit genital swelling during their normal menstrual cycle and also during the early phases of pregnancy. Swelling during pregnancy is accompanied by typical sexually receptive behavior. When in estrus, females are usually seen moving with one or more adult males. When more than one cycling female is present in a subgroup, their periods of genital swelling often become synchronized. At primatologist Jane Goodall's study site (Gombe Stream Reserve) one mother and daughter pair traveled and cycled together and later gave birth within days of each other.

More than 70% of the copulations seen in the wild are opportunistic, involving virtually no competition and allowing free choice for either sex. **Consort relationships** lasting from 3 hours to 50 days, during which a male monopolizes an estrous female, constituted under 25% of recorded copulations (Tutin and McGinnis, 1981).

Figure 10–6 • A chimpanzee foraging and feeding.

fusion-fission social organization—social organization based on formation and dissolution of groups.

consort relationships—pairing off of a female and male for the purposes of mating.

For females transferring between groups, sexual receptivity may help to establish bonds with resident males and to reduce the immediate danger of aggression. Establishing bonds with resident males increases male protection of the female and her offspring, reduces aggressive encounters that might adversely affect females' pregnancies, and later may reduce the chance of neonatal infanticide by the males. Male chimpanzees may use a recent history of social–sexual interactions with females as determinants of whether to attack or to tolerate females and offspring (Hrdy, 1979). It is noteworthy that all of the victims of male-instigated infanticide at a study site in Tanzania (Mahale) were male infants. In the one reported incident from Gombe, an attack on a female newborn, the individual was rescued and not eaten (Goodall, 1977). So it appears that male infants are at greater risk than females.

Foraging subgroups offer another common pattern of social interaction. Subgroups that find an ample food source will pass this information on by hooting and drumming on trees. In nonterritorial groups, any individual, whether of the callers' group or not, may respond to these calls and join this temporary gathering. This congregation, described by Reynolds and Reynolds (1965) as a "carnival," has all the earmarks of a large party. Different individuals dash about in highly excited nonaggressive displays, then finally settle down for a period of intense social interactions, including copulations and grooming.

Other unique social behaviors recorded for chimpanzees include cooperative hunting of small animals by adult males. They often share the kill among themselves and occasionally with other bystanders, who may beg, often gesturing with upturned palms (Figure 10–7).

Perhaps the most exciting observations of chimpanzee social behavior are those of tool use. The most common tool described by Goodall is the termite tunnel probe, which is a stick or blade of grass sufficient in

Figure 10–7 • Chimpanzee hunting and food sharing in Gombe, Tanzania.

Figure 10–8 • Chimpanzee tool use.

size and length to penetrate a termite mound, inviting the resident termites to attack it (Figure 10–8). The probe is then carefully drawn outward by the chimpanzee and the termites consumed as a tasty dish. Other tools fashioned by chimpanzees include stone and wood hammers used to crack open hard seeds or nuts, and munched-up leaves that act as sponges to retrieve water from caches in trees or otherwise inaccessible small pools.

In the area of communication, chimpanzees are the most outspoken of all the apes. The remarkable behavior of the chimpanzee led some observers to believe that, with sufficient training, chimpanzees could be taught to use human language and directly communicate their thoughts to us.

These efforts at teaching chimpanzees to speak ultimately failed, primarily because chimpanzees as well as all other nonhuman primates lack the specialized language centers unique to the human neocortex. Efforts were then directed towards teaching chimpanzees some form of hand sign or visual cue language (Figure 10–9). The success of the captive ape nonverbal language studies is partially based on the fact that apes have a large preexisting inventory of signs and gestures, with the capability of learning new ones.

The supposed success of the ape language studies was not without criticism. In a paper published in 1979, Herbert Terrace et al. jolted the entire field of ape language research by reporting work from his own project with a chimpanzee he named Nim. Terrace maintained that neither Nim nor the other signing chimpanzees were talking. Rather, they were doing tricks or simple mimicking in order to get what they wanted, usually a food reward. Terrace claimed that there was no meaning behind their signs. The Lana project, founded by Duane Rumbaugh and Sue Savage-Rumbaugh at the Yerkes Primate Center, however, provided

FRONTIERS

Chimpanzee Hunting Behavior and Human Evolution

by Craig B. Stanford

In a forest in Tanzania in East Africa, a group of a dozen chimpanzees is travelling along the forest floor, stopping occasionally to scan the trees overhead for ripe fruit. The group is composed of five adult males, plus several females and their offspring. They come upon a tree holding a group of red colobus monkeys. The male chimpanzees scan the colobus group looking for immature animals or mothers carrying small babies. The colobus, meanwhile, have heard the pant-hoot calls of the chimpanzees approaching and have gathered up their offspring and positioned themselves against a possible attack.

The chimpanzees do indeed attack, the five males—Frodo, Goblin, Freud, Prof, and Wilkie—climbing the larger limbs of the tree. They meet the male colobus, who have descended to counter-attack. Just in front of me a young colobus attempted to flee the chimpanzees by leaping onto a branch that unfortunately held a male chimpanzee named Atlas. Atlas quickly grabbed the young colobus and dispatched it with a bite to the skull.

Within seconds, an estrous female chimpanzee named Trezia ran up to Atlas and begged for meat. Atlas held the colobus carcass away from her; she then turned and presented her sexual swelling to him, they copulated, and only then did she receive a share of the meat. An hour later, the last strands of colobus meat, bone, and skin are still being consumed amid occasional outbursts of aggression by individuals who have not received meat.

Two of the most important and intriguing questions in human evolution are when and why meat became an important part of the diet of our ancestors. The presence of primitive stone tools in the fossil record tells us that 2.5 million years ago, early hominids were using stone implements to cut the flesh off the bones of large animals that they had either hunted or whose carcasses they had scavenged.[1] The pattern of obtaining and processing meat by more recent people has been studied by examining archaeological sites[2] and also by studying the hunting and meat-eating behavior of modern foraging people, the so-called hunter-gatherers.[3]

Modern people and chimpanzees share an estimated 98.5 percent of the DNA sequence, making them more closely related to each other than either is to any other animal species.[4] Therefore, understanding chimpanzee hunting behavior and ecology may tell us a great deal about the behavior and ecology of those earliest hominids.

After three decades of research on the hunting behavior of chimpanzees at Gombe and elsewhere, we already know a great deal about their predatory patterns. Adult and adolescent males do most of the hunting, making about 90 percent of the kills recorded at Gombe over the past decade. Females also hunt, though more often they receive a share of meat from the male who either captured the meat or stole it from the captor.

Chimpanzees are largely fruit eaters, and meat-eating comprises only about 3 percent of the time they spend eating overall. I estimate that in some years the forty-five chimpanzees of the main study community at Gombe kill and consume more than 1,500 pounds of prey animals of all species. During the peak dry season months, the estimated per capita meat intake is about sixty-five grams of meat per day for each adult chimpanzee. This approaches the meat intake by the members of some human foraging societies in the lean months of the year. Chimpanzee dietary strategies may thus approximate those of human hunter-gatherers to a greater degree than we had imagined.

Whether or not chimpanzee hunters cooperate is a question that has been debated, and the degree of cooperative hunting may differ from one forest to another.[5] In the Taï forest in the Ivory Coast, Christophe Boesch has documented highly cooperative hunting behavior and meat-sharing behavior after

results that contradicted Terrace's position. Rumbaugh designed experiments that utilized a keyboard with over 100 symbols with which the chimp could respond, and these tests seemed to show that the chimp could formulate some basic rules for grammatical ordering of responses. Chimpanzees, it seems, can learn words spontaneously, and they can

a kill that rewards those chimpanzees who participated in the hunt.[6] The highly integrated action by Taï hunters has never been seen at Gombe. In both Gombe and Taï, however, there is a strong positive relationship between the number of hunters and the odds of a successful hunt.[7] This points out the difficulty of interpreting cooperative behavior; even though Gombe hunters do not seem to cooperate, the greater success rate when more hunters are present suggests that some cooperation is occurring.

Did early hominids hunt and eat small and medium-sized animals in numbers as large as these? It is quite possible that they did. We know that these earliest hominids were different from chimpanzees in two prominent anatomical features: they had much smaller canine teeth, and they had a lower body adapted for walking on the ground rather than swinging through trees. In spite of lacking the weaponry such as large canine teeth and tree-climbing adaptations that chimpanzees possess, early hominids probably ate a large number of small and medium-sized animals, including monkeys. Chimpanzees do not use their canine teeth to capture adult colobus; rather, they grab the prey and flail it to death on the ground or a tree limb. And once the prey is cornered in an isolated tree crown, group cooperation at driving the monkeys from one hunter to another would have been a quite efficient killing technique.

In addition to the availability of prey in the trees, there were of course small animals and the young of larger animals to catch opportunistically on the ground. Many researchers now believe that the carcasses of dead animals were an important source of meat for early hominids once they had stone tools to use for removing the flesh from the carcass.[8] Wild chimpanzees show little interest in dead animals as a food source, so scavenging may have evolved as an important mode of getting food when hominids began to make and use tools for getting at meat. Before this time, it seems likely that earlier hominids were hunting small mammals as chimpanzee do today, and that the role that hunting played in the early hominids' social lives was probably as complex and political as it is in the social lives of chimpanzees. When we ask when meat became an important part of the human diet, we therefore must look well before the evolutionary split between apes and humans in our own family tree.

Notes

1. Richard Potts, Early Hominid Activities in Olduvai Gorge (New York: Aldine de Gruyter, 1988).

2. Mary C. Stiner and Steven L. Kuhn, "Subsistence, Technology, and Adaptive Variation in Middle Paleolithic Italy," American Anthropologist 94 (1992): 306–39.

3. Hillard Kaplan and Kim R. Hill, "The Evolutionary Ecology of Food Acquisition," in Eric Alden Smith and Bruce Winterhalder, eds., Evolutionary Ecology and Human Behavior (New York: Aldine de Gruyter, 1992), pp. 167–202.

4. Maryann Ruvolo, Todd R. Disotell, Michael W. Allard, W.M. Brown, and R.L. Honeycutt, "Resolution of the African Hominoid Trichotomy by Use of a Mitochondrial Gene Sequence," Proceedings of the National Academy of Science 88 (1991): 1570–74.

5. Curt Busse, "Do Chimpanzees Hunt Cooperatively?" American Naturalist 112 (1978): 767–70.

6. Christophe Boesch, "Hunting Strategies of Gombe and Taï Chimpanzees," in William C. McGrew, Frans B.M. de Waal, Richard W. Wrangham, and Paul Heltne, eds., Chimpanzee Cultures (Cambridge, MA: Harvard University Press, 1994), pp. 77–92.

7. Craig B. Stanford, Janette Wallis, Eslom Mpongo, and Jane Goodall, "Hunting Decisions in Wild Chimpanzees," Animal Behaviour 131 (1994): 1–20.

8. Henry T. Bunn and Ellen M. Kroll, "Systematic Butchery by Plio/Pleistocene Hominids at Olduvai Gorge, Tanzania," Current Anthropology 27 (1986): 431–52.

Craig B. Stanford is Associate Professor of Anthropology at University of Southern California.

use them to refer to things that are not present, an ability known as "displacement." Rumbaugh claims that they can learn words from one another and talk to one another about things that the listener does not know about. As Rumbaugh (1985) describes it, "apes are in the language domain, a behavioral domain that is a continuum, not a dichotomy."

Figure 10–9 • Chimpanzee sign language.

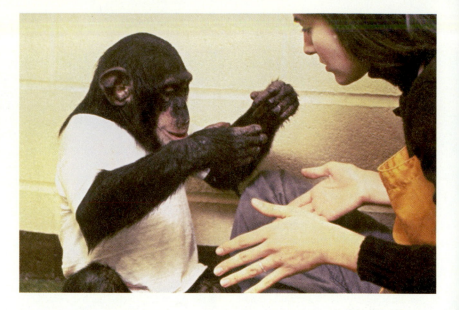

The Bonobo

There is only one species of pygmy chimpanzee—the bonobo, *Pan paniscus* (Figure 10–10), which is limited in its distribution to the forests of central Congo (formerly Zaire). Its anatomy, possibly because of its smaller size, is at first glance more similar to humans' than it is to the common chimpanzee's.

Pan paniscus is not in fact much smaller than *Pan troglodytes,* and when skeletal size differences between the two are compensated for, very few traits are significantly different (McHenry, 1984). The bonobos, like the other African apes, are sexually dimorphic in body size; females weigh only about 75% of what males weigh. In their cranial anatomy, bonobos have smaller brow ridges, show less prognathism in jaw size, and are more *pedomorphic* ("childlike") in overall form than is the common chimpanzee.

Like *Gorilla* and *Pan troglodytes,* pygmy chimpanzees knuckle walk as a general mode of locomotion while on the ground and in the trees. In arboreal locomotion the pygmy chimpanzee appears to be more agile than the common chimpanzee at both arm swinging and climbing, again due no doubt to its lighter body build.

In many ways the overall social structure of the pygmy chimpanzee reflects an adaptation to feeding in large, predictably abundant food patches. Mixed parties of pygmy chimpanzees, consisting of between 2 and 15 individuals, and containing individuals of both sexes and all age classes, are generally larger than those of the common chimpanzee. In any party of pygmy chimpanzees one can always find females who are both reproductively active or nursing offspring. Groups of the common chimpanzee seldom contain both kinds of females. During the frequent

Figure 10–10 • Male and female bonobos.

intragroup interactions, various behavioral patterns may be seen, such as branch-dragging displays by adult males, female-to-female genital rubbing, which appears to be unique among chimpanzees, male homosexual mountings, and heterosexual copulations initiated by either males or females that include both the dorso-ventral and ventro-ventral positions.

Pan paniscus social units revolve around a stable core of females who regularly associate with one another, and are characterized by high levels of affiliation (Kuroda, 1980). Friendship bonds between individual males and females appear to be quite strong at times, as demonstrated by two individuals cooperating in obtaining food and even sleeping together in the same nest at night. The more frequently observed sexual behavior of the females apparently has resulted in a strong tie forming between female and male, with the resulting inclination to form stable mixed groups. Although male *Pan paniscus* show little affection toward one another, and all-male groups are almost totally absent, the males show little interest in aggressive interactions outside of intergroup interactions or dominance rivalry among themselves.

Figure 10–11 • Kanzi, a pygmy chimpanzee, making a stone tool.

One unusual characteristic of the reproductive behavior of the female pygmy chimpanzee is the greater length of time she is receptive within her menstrual cycle. Furthermore, studies demonstrate that the adult female is fully or partially swollen almost all of the time, and this genital swelling continues through much of her pregnancy. Apparently only when the adult female has reached advanced age does she show complete detumescence, perhaps related to menopause.

Pygmy chimpanzees also show some unique features in their communicative skills. As Savage-Rumbaugh et al. (1985) report, some pygmy chimpanzees who were used in the Yerkes ape language studies spontaneously began to use symbols to communicate with people. They apparently acquired these symbols by observation.

The observation powers of the bonobos are exceptional, as demonstrated in recent attempts to teach one of them, Kanzi, to make stone tools. Stone-tool-making has been thought to be an exclusively human ability. However, experiments have shown that, while the judgment necessary to calibrate the correct angle and force of impact required to create early human stone tools may be beyond bonobo intellectual capacity, Kanzi, at least, has learned to flake stones and to produce a usable tool (Figure 10–11).

HUMAN SOCIAL BEHAVIOR

Although this section of the chapter concerns the biological and evolutionary basis of human behavior, we must temper our remarks and observations. In our search for the evolutionary origins of human social behavior we are reminded of a unique influence on that behavior: culture. Culture is part of the modern human environment; it molds behavior and makes an indelible imprint on each one of us. One can argue persuasively that it is the cultural variables that have a much more immediate influence on behavior than do biological variables. For humans, as in any other species, however, biology forms the template upon which behavior is acted out.

Throughout this book we have attempted to show humans as part of the natural world, confronting the view that we are a species set apart from it and able to exploit it at whim with little consequence. With this in mind, our review of the biological basis of human behavior returns to an earlier discussion of the concept of the fixed action pattern and the ethological approach to the study of behavior (Chapter 3). We will start with examples of genetically controlled human behaviors and advance to a discussion of more complex behaviors.

Fixed Action Patterns

Many of the clearest human examples of fixed action patterns (FAPs) come from infants, because learning, culture, and language can be discounted as factors influencing their behavior and because certain behaviors occur only at certain developmental stages after birth.

Certainly mothers and midwives were able to describe many "instinctual" patterns of behavior in newborns long before these were recognized by behavioral scientists. These neonatal behaviors might include rhythmic searching movements for the mother's nipple, grasping reflexes of the hands and feet (Figure 10–12), and paddling reactions if the infant is set into water. Newborn infants show FAPs in the first few days of life when their lips are touched, a stimulus that evokes a rhythmic side-to-side movement of the head. The movement stops when the infant begins to suckle. This is a programmed "search for the nipple" that disappears between six and ten days after birth, when it is replaced by a visually oriented search. Programmed crying, homologous to the "lost

Figure 10–12 • Hand- and foot-grasping reflexes in response to touch in human infants, examples of fixed action patterns.

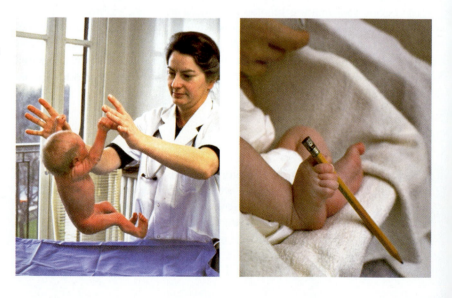

call" of other mammals, occurs in human infants. When the infant is "found," that is, is picked up, the behavior stops.

As time goes on, infants continue to react innately to certain other stimuli. For example, until the onset of the second month, eye-sized spots painted on a square or round two-dimensional surface invariably evoke smiling in the infant. Up to a point, in fact, this cardboard schematic representation of the human face does a better job eliciting smiling than a completely painted and lifelike face. More recent experiments have shown that it makes no difference whether the pair of dots is parallel or vertical or whether in fact there are three dots instead of two. Only one dot by itself fails to evoke infant smiling. In addition to smiling, laughing also appears to arise innately. Infants at this stage are not attempting to imitate adult behavior. In fact, laughing by adults often startles an infant, causing distress. As a further example, at an initial stage of language development deaf-born children begin to babble.

No doubt the reason for many of these behaviors can be found by examining the reactions they evoke in the mothers. Experiments show that mothers, as well as surrogates, react very strongly and positively to infants as the infants start to look at them and as their vision focuses at about four to five weeks. Similarly, laughing reinforces an already very strong mother–infant bond as the child matures.

Some FAPs seen in infants exemplify "evolutionary baggage." They are left over from earlier stages of evolution when they were important for survival. For example, when human infants close their fingers and curl their toes around any object that touches their palms or soles, they are probably exhibiting a relic adaptation from clinging onto a hairy mother, especially while nursing.

Adult human fixed action patterns are more difficult to define. Evidence suggests, however, that adult behavior has a stronger biological component than many social scientists might admit. Acoustical signals, such as crying, sobbing, or calls for help, have the effect of alarming us, eliciting negative or fearful responses that can be measured by heart rate increases and irregularity in breathing. Olfactory signals, too, can bring very subtle responses. Women often can distinguish odors, such as musk, that are imperceptible by adult males. Women who have lived together in dormitories show a tendency for synchronic menstruation. It appears, however, that ovulation rather than menstruation is the cause of synchronization and that the cause is the hormonal content of urine, perspiration, and saliva passed directly from one individual to another during grooming or through the exchange of clothing (Russel et al., 1980).

Cross-cultural comparisons provide one indication of shared behavior patterns (Table 10–2). Cultures around the world share characteristics, and individuals within cultures also show consistent forms of behavior. These similarities do not seem to derive from contact between cultures, but result from a common biological and psychological substrate. Some examples of these possible adult human FAPs are flirting behavior (Figure 10–13) and greeting behavior (including a very brief upward "flash" of the eyebrows).

imprinting—the fixation in an individual of a specific stimulus or set of stimuli during a particular period of sensitivity to learning that stimulus.

innate releasing mechanism—a sensory cue that triggers a certain behavior or set of behaviors in an animal.

Table 10–2 • Universal Cross-Cultural Human Behavioral Characteristics

Age-grading	Sports	Vengeance
Cosmology	Divination	Community organization
Food taboos	Hospitality	Ethics
Law	Magic	Kin groups
Ritual	Sexual restrictions	Status differentiation
Symbolization	Incest taboos	Dominance-subordination
Altruism	Defense and/or	Ethnocentrism
Self-sacrifice for	attachment to territory	Warfare
others	Reification and personification	

From Lopreato (1984).

Other "Innate" Behaviors

In addition to FAPs, ethologists have discovered other sorts of "innate" behaviors. The first of these is **imprinting,** the formation of a lasting impression during a period of heightened sensitivity to a certain stimulus. Konrad Lorenz became the "mother" on which a group of goslings became imprinted, because he was the sole mature being around them after their hatching. He became the **innate releasing mechanism** that initiated the goslings to follow him as their mother. Human imprinting is much less clear-cut and more subject to interpretation.

Figure 10–13 • Flirting—the prolonged look, looking away and down, reestablishing brief eye contact, and the slight smile—provides an example of an adult human FAP. (Eibl-Eibesfeldt, 1989)

Mammals in general and humans especially have an added level of complexity in their behavior: "logical," or reasoning, ability residing in the large cerebral hemispheres. This part of the brain often overrides the innate releasing mechanisms of the more primitive brain. This override should not obscure the fact that some part of our brains may be reacting to the world in a different manner than our "thinking" brain. The study of human ethology concentrates on important areas in understanding human behavior—including whatever FAPs, innate dispositions to learn, and innate releasing mechanisms we may have inherited from our ancestors, as well as how our brains are affected by this inheritance.

We have good evidence that certain visual and olfactory cues in humans are innate releasing mechanisms for sexual behavior. Bare legs, buttocks, and torsos, especially in poses suggestive of copulatory positions, arouse sexual interest in both males and females. These cues are a mainstay of the advertising and entertainment industries. In regard to olfactory cues, women can identify musk odors at lower concentrations than can men, and this threshold varies with the menstrual cycle, being at its lowest point during ovulation. Recently a substance (androstenol) that smells like musk was isolated from human male axillary perspiration. Musk-dominated perfumes that mimic normal human scent are also widely used by both males and females as sexual attractants.

Human Sociobiology

A growing number of biologists accept *sociobiology* as an important new discipline within which scientists can effectively study the evolution of social behavior in animal species. In comparison with human beings, however, no animal has a spoken language with unlimited possible constructions, nor other aspects of "culture," nor as highly developed and large a cerebral cortex.

How do we relate, then, the findings of sociobiology to human behavior, considering that so much of what we do is apparently learned, affected by personal choice, and subject to change from one situation to the next? Wilson (1996) has suggested three possibilities:

1. Genes merely prescribe the capacity for culture because during hominid evolution natural selection needed an adaptive mechanism which provided additional variability to social behavior—more than was available through genetically programmed behaviors (such as FAPs). Therefore, all human behavior is determined by culture; or
2. Genetic variability affecting behavior has been exhausted, as in (1), but the genotype predisposes humans toward development of certain genetically controlled species-specific behaviors; or
3. Genetic variability still exists, and . . . at least some human behavioral traits have a genetic foundation.

Many sociocultural anthropologists would opt for possibility 1. A detailed consideration of human ethology (e.g., Eibl-Eibesfeldt, 1989), however, argues for at least the possibility of point 2 insofar as it suggests that there are human species-specific behaviors. Even point 3 goes only so far to maintain that *some* human behaviors have a genetic foundation. Sociobiologists generally do not maintain the extreme position, sometimes imputed to them, that all human behavior is under direct genetic control. It obviously is not.

As we have learned, sociobiologists have discovered that the degree of relatedness between individuals, thus the percentage of shared genes, can affect certain behaviors. This realization explains both the existence of apparently selfless or altruistic behaviors on the one hand and selfishness and interpersonal competition on the other. Humans throughout the world tend to favor their relatives; furthermore, the higher the degree of relationship is, the greater the number of social interactions tends to be. If the common substructure of kinship is rooted in biology, then sociobiological theory could predict behaviors that are based on this linkage. Napoleon Chagnon (1983) of the University of California, Santa Barbara, for example, demonstrated that genetic relatedness does play a role in a South American Yanomamö's life, often explaining the basis on which villages fission and fights between village hosts and guests occur.

Human Behavioral Ecology

The field of behavioral ecology has borrowed tools from many disciplines, such as economics and engineering. Thus, decision making under risk and uncertainty, tradeoffs, and **game theory,** to name a few, have become a part of behavioral ecological analysis.

In terms of human behavioral analysis Smith (1992a) lists the following topical areas of interest: subsistence strategies, mating ecology, spatial organization, and the ecological determinants of variation in patterns of competition and cooperation. The earliest applications to humans of this theory researched certain hunter-gatherer groups and their spatial organization. These studies looked at the incidence of territoriality in light of projected benefits of exclusive use versus the costs of monitoring and defending that territory (Dyson-Hudson and Smith, 1978). More recent analysis involving subsistence strategies through optimal foraging theory has demonstrated that foragers will make choices that yield the highest feasible rate of return (in energy) from their foraging efforts (in time). Studies of the Ache Indians of Paraguay have shown, for example, that changes in technology to hunting with shotguns from hunting with bows and arrows predictably altered the expected return rates for certain prey species (Hill et al., 1987). This simplified picture is complicated by the fact that in humans, unlike other species of animals, prey choice may be ranked in multiple dimensions beyond simple nutritional values. Human cultural values may rank certain prey higher in accordance with their material value (ivory, pelts, etc.) and social value (i.e., prestige). Also, gender differences in foraging strategies must be taken into account.

game theory—the analysis of win-loss combinations in any competitive relationship in order to determine strategy or to predict outcomes of the competition.

In terms of reproductive strategies, behavioral ecological analysts look at such topics as maturation rates, age at first and last reproduction and at senescence, birth spacing, offspring sex ratios, and those ecological determinants of variation in mating systems involving monogamy, polygyny, and polyandry. It is in this area that human behavioral ecology most clearly overlaps with sociobiological interests. Early research efforts involved investigations of South African Kalahari !Kung San birth spacing and the idea of self-regulation of fertility. The average birth interval of !Kung mothers is about four years. Lee (1980), who studied these people, argued that the wide birth spacing among foraging !Kung was an adaptation that benefited the mothers by reducing their work effort in terms of transporting and feeding children. Later Blurton-Jones (1987) showed that offspring survival was maximized by 48-month inter-birth intervals. However, another foraging population, the Hadza, living on the East African savanna, provided quite different data from that of the !Kung. Hadza mothers carry their infants less, allow them to forage independently for their own food, and show a significantly higher fertility. These differences seem to stem from the fact that the !Kung live in an area where the relatively flat land surface provides for poor distance visibility and a lowered concentration of plant foods for collection. Both of these factors contribute to the !Kung's greater parental vigilance and care per child and, consequently, the increased spacing between births.

Thus far human behavioral ecologists have designed their research efforts to ask and answer simple questions, only to discover that this research involves complex social interactions. A simple matter of prey choice turns out to be connected with gender roles and mating strategies as well as with a decision as to who hunts and who stays in camp to reap the benefits brought back by the hunters; optimal birth spacing is interconnected with divisions of labor, parent–offspring relations, and perceived investment. It will be difficult to look at ecological adaptations in any social species, especially humans, without considering social processes and cultural transmission.

Culture and Biology

It is apparent from studies on the learning process that the kinds of things that humans do are learned easily. If a genetic basis exists for behavior and culture, it must lie somewhere within the area of ease of learning those adaptive behaviors. This may explain why humans find it so difficult to live within large groups in urban environments where, for example, kinship usually does not guide social interaction and economic exchange.

Some aspects of our behavior have been looked upon by social scientists as inappropriate and undesirable. Aggression, **ethnocentrism,** territoriality, and dominance might join the list of human behavior patterns that may appear to be dysfunctional. However, as aggression appears to be a fundamental characteristic of nearly all animal life, especially in social species, it must have a substantial heritable component. In the nonhuman primates, aggressive behavior often leads to the

ethnocentrism—the pervasive belief present in all cultures that tends to lead individuals within a culture to view their own culture as superior to all others.

Figure 10–14 • A World Cup soccer game. Lorenz (1965) suggested that national sports might be a harmless substitute for war.

establishment of rank or dominance, which, in turn, provides societal stability to the relationships between individuals. Aggressive behavior is limited, because high-ranking individuals assume a leadership function and are not frequently challenged.

Human aggression probably functioned much the same in the past. Organized group aggression served a valuable function for defense and territorial spacing in early hominid societies. Organized national sports may be one harmless way for modern-day humans to release these phylogenetically ancient behaviors (Figure 10–14). In recent years, however, the violence that has accompanied many sports, such as soccer, has removed even these events from the category of "harmless."

Humans are not unlike other animals in exhibiting distinct territorial behavior. Territoriality and the maintenance of individual space are similar phenomena. Although the exact parameters are culturally defined, we do maintain specific distances between one another. Children develop an awareness of culturally determined appropriate individual distance at about the same time they develop an understanding of property (Ploog, 1964).

Some work has shown that there is a correlation between low levels of the hormone (neurotransmitter) serotonin and individuals who are prone to violence. As with the nonhuman primates, aggression, or the threat of it, often leads to higher status, and, predictably, in many cases to increased reproductive success. Human males compete for status through whatever means are available to them. Urban street gang members often use violence, or a credible threat, to maintain their reputations. Research on nonhuman primates demonstrates that serotonin levels can be raised or lowered by environmental stimuli.

Michael McGuire of the University of California, Los Angeles, in his study of vervet monkeys has shown that the highest-ranking males in a troop have the highest serotonin levels. Low-ranking males show the lowest levels, and also tend to be more impulsively aggressive. These studies suggest that serotonin levels increase with an increase in individual dominance rank, and that once high rank is achieved, high levels of serotonin function to maintain, in the case of monkeys, self-confidence, or, in the case of humans, high self-esteem. In the view of some researchers, serotonin levels function to regulate self-confidence depending upon feedback from others. High levels of serotonin assist in the maintenance of high social status; low levels are likely to discourage an individual from conspicuously challenging others for fear of punishment. The hypothesis explains observed behavior in low-ranking monkeys whose rage centers in the brain were stimulated through implanted electrodes. These monkeys, rather than attacking other monkeys as higher-ranking males under the same circumstances would do, would cower by themselves in a remote corner of their laboratory cage.

On the other hand, what is the significance of the correlation between low levels of serotonin and impulsive behavior? For low-ranking individuals who find themselves in a situation where the existing social system is not providing adequate rewards, it may pay to circumvent the rules.

Low-dominance monkeys often attempt to mate surreptitiously, hiding from the view of dominant males. In the absence of legitimate ways to achieve status, individuals use illegitimate means, and risk-taking increases. It seems, therefore, that low serotonin levels are adaptive in the sense that they prepare individuals to take risks and evade the rules. In humans, this evolutionary explanation suggests that the way to reduce urban violence would be to develop nonviolent means for young men to achieve social status.

Future Prospects

No matter what the sequence of events that brought together the behaviors of modern humans, anthropology has offered many useful perspectives towards an understanding of human nature. As we have seen, the behaviors that were thought to make humans unique from the rest of the animal world, such as tool use, cognitive thought, and language, are, at least in part, shared with other primates. Anthropology has brought us, thus far, towards the realization that we humans with all our advanced technological skill still bear the stamp of our earlier history. As we learn more about ourselves, this fact becomes even more obvious. Distinctions created between ourselves and the rest of the animal world continue to fall as research progresses. In the final section of this chapter, we will attempt to reconstruct what we now know about the behavior of our earliest human ancestors. We will see that within us lies a heritage that is still mostly unexplored, mostly misunderstood, and, until quite recently, mostly ignored as a matter of scientific investigation. The promise of anthropology has begun to change all that.

RECONSTRUCTING EARLY HUMAN BEHAVIOR

Historical Overview

Three characteristics, historically, have been used to emphasize the differences between human and nonhuman primates: *bipedalism;* our *large brain;* and our ability to *communicate symbolically* with language. Using these three characteristics a number of models of early human behavior emerged to sort out what came first and why these adaptations developed.

In *Descent of Man and Selection in Relation to Sex,* Darwin (1871) held that the human brain was the primary feature that initially separated humans from their closest relatives, the African apes. Darwin viewed increased brain size as important in terms of the technological behavior that developed from it. He believed our ancestors became skillful toolmakers, producing weapons that allowed the males to become efficient hunters. Darwin did not ignore bipedalism in his model of human evolution, but it was held to be of secondary importance. Darwin believed that bipedalism arose when the ancestral hominid came "to live somewhat less in the trees and more on the ground" as a response to "a change in its manner of procuring subsistence or to a change in the conditions of its native country" (Darwin, 1871:135). Darwin also helped to develop the idea of sexually dimorphic behavior. Men were courageous, inventive, and sexually competitive. Females, in his view, leaned more towards the nurturing, housemaking, and reclusive aspects of behavior. Darwin saw selection as operating almost exclusively on the males, producing larger, more colorful, and stronger individuals than the smaller, more drably ornamented females (as in birds).

New Behavioral Models Emerge: Bipedalism

By the turn of the century as the number of fossil finds increased, anthropologists created new models of human evolution. These models differed from those of Darwin. The fossil discoveries showed that our earliest ancestors possessed brains similar in size to those of living apes, but differed from the apes primarily in their bipedal mode of locomotion. Bipedalism, it seemed, was an ancient form of locomotion and, perhaps, the most ancient of all of the hominid anatomical specializations. After the discovery of the Laetoli footprints, there could no longer be any doubt about the matter.

Why did bipedalism become the predominant form of hominid locomotion? Bipedalism certainly was not without costs, because it placed early humans at a disadvantage, should they find themselves in the midst of predators they could not outrun. Some argued that hominids could outdistance potential predators, if they had a head start.

Bipedalism provides a selective advantage in other behaviors, such as carrying objects (Hewes, 1964), displaying threat behavior (Wescott, 1967), or foraging for widely dispersed food sources (Sigmon, 1971). However, the most pervasive explanation revolves around the question of tool use, as stated by Washburn (1960) in his article entitled "Tools and Human Evolution":

> Substantial, adaptively important use of objects goes back millions of years before [tool-use] can be proved from the archaeological record. The nature of the evidence leads to underestimating the importance of tools in the early part of human evolution and to over-estimating the intelligence of humans before *Homo sapiens.*

S. L. Washburn and Chet Lancaster's (1968) article entitled the "Evolution of Hunting" depicted men as the active and aggressive procurers of food, defending their families and supplying food through hunting. Women were viewed as dependent, staying close to a home camp and trading sex for protection and provisioning.

During the 1970s a shift in emphasis away from hunting as the major means of obtaining food was prompted by studies of many nonhuman primates, especially the chimpanzees, and by studies of modern-day hunters and gatherers. Lee, who studied the South African !Kung people, concluded that on the average, hunting produced only about 35% of the total food supply, while women's gathering activities contributed the rest. These data showed that in most modern hunter-gatherer societies women are not economically dependent on men for provisioning and most often produce more than men do. Women were also not sedentary. Lee's studies showed that women were away from their base camps for at least as many hours and covered as many miles as the men. At the same time they often carried infants and other heavy objects (Figure 10–15).

The matrifocal, matrilineal nature of most nonhuman primate societies also altered ideas about the male role and male associations with females. From this information, new models of early hominid behavior were developed to incorporate female gathering, carrying, and sharing foods with their young, emphasizing the mother–infant bond and kin relationships. In 1971 the first of these revisions appeared in an article entitled "Woman the Gatherer" by Sally Linton. Reciprocal sharing, she believed, occurred first among members of a kin group and was not based on the establishment of sexual bonds or sexual exchange. Where hunting did occur, the first hunters shared food not with sexual partners, but with mothers and siblings who had shared food with them. Adrienne Zihlman (1981) stressed that obtaining plant foods with tools was the important event that promoted the development of bipedalism, as well as the invention of ways to carry food and/or infants while walking long distances.

Parker and Gibson (1979:373) developed the concept of *tool-aided extractive foraging* that focused on behaviors that were designed to benefit offspring, such as maternal food sharing and maternal assistance in obtaining hard-to-get-at or hard-to-process foods, such as nuts, ants, termites, and honey. It was hypothesized that mothers, using tools, extracted and processed foods and then shared this food with young offspring who had not yet developed tool-using behaviors. Gibson

Figure 10–15 • !Kung San women foraging.

(1993) continues by saying that "such food sharing may have selected for communication capacities similar to those of children just learning to talk." These practices favored the elaboration of sensorimotor and symbolic abilities similar to those of two-year-old children. This analysis based on the supposed information-processing abilities of the earliest hominids suggests that they had diverged from apes by increasing their tool-using, linguistic, and social capabilities. The growing dependence on tool-aided extracting foraging practices, Parker and Gibson believe, was the primary basis for the ape–human split.

Building on these ideas, King (1994) developed a **diachronic** model that viewed tool-aided extractive foraging as important not only in terms of obtaining difficult-to-get-at foods, but also in terms of the donation of information from the adults to the immatures. Her hypothesis is that the more primates are dependent on tool-aided extractive foraging, the more donated information is required to accomplish difficult tasks. This situation selected for greater cognitive abilities that, in turn, resulted in the ape–human split.

Whether or not tool-aided extractive foraging was the important variable in the split of the hominids from the apes, as King (1994:101) remarks, it "is consistent with the suggestion that hominids donated more information than did other primates, and that information donation increased during human evolution." This observation is important for the discussion in Chapter 12 on the evolution of childhood as a stage in the human life cycle.

Parker (1987) claimed that females were "courted" by males with gifts of especially nutritious and/or hard-to-get foods. Bipedal behavior would have had a selective advantage in allowing the females to accurately assess the size of the male, the size of his gift, and the size and tumescence of his genitals. According to Parker, bipedal locomotion arose through sexual selection; it was a part of the male reproductive strategy of "nuptial," or courtship, feeding of estrous females. The model is consistent with some primate field data on pygmy chimpanzees that show males and females sharing food during copulations (Kuroda, 1984).

The possibility that environmental change had something to do with the emergence of bipedalism has been promoted by several authors. There is good evidence to suggest that about 5.5 million years ago at the close of the Miocene and, later, about 2.5 million years ago, a shift to cooler world climates resulted in major forests giving way to grasslands. During the earlier shift, bipedalism may have arisen as an adaptive response to covering the distances required by larger home ranges in the relatively treeless grasslands (Vrba, 1988). This model states that a shift to open savanna environments stimulated greater reliance on a bipedal form of locomotion that in turn may have been related to increased tool use and ultimately the origins of family Hominidae. However, recent studies of forest-living chimpanzees contradict this notion. Boesch-Ackermann and Boesch (1994:10–11) compared the behavior of chimpanzees in the Tai Forest with that of chimpanzee populations living in more open environments and have shown that "the forest chimpanzees

diachronic—historical; extending through time.

use more tools, make them in more different ways, hunt more frequently and more often in groups, and show more frequent cooperation and food sharing." These authors believe that the environment no doubt plays an important role in the evolution of behavior, but disagree that the open savanna had much to do with the behaviors that we have come to believe characterize the early hominids. In addition, they cite new paleoecological studies that suggest our earliest ancestors, in fact, lived in tropical rain forests (Bailey et al., 1989; Rayner et al., 1993).

The questions of where, when, and why bipedal locomotion arose among primates still remain open. As we saw in Chapter 8, if *Ardipithecus ramidus*, a forest-dwelling early hominid, proves to be a biped, our current notions of the selective advantage of this form of locomotion in the open savanna environment will have to be revised (Shreeve, 1996).

Brain Size

The advance of paleoanthropological knowledge of human behavior depends not only on new discoveries of fossil crania and brain endocasts, but also on the advancement in knowledge about the workings of the modern human brain. The large size and complexity of the human brain form the most important components of the anatomical and phylogenetic definition of the genus *Homo*. Our knowledge of the evolution of the brain is derived from neurophysiological and anatomical studies of living species and comparative studies of endocasts of fossil species.

From about 2 million years onward some selective advantage resulted in larger brain size, leading to greater intellectual and symbolic abilities. The expansion of the brain was, no doubt, related to a number of factors that might have included a shift in the way humans procured food, for example, towards a greater reliance on hunting or more effective scavenging of larger game, aided by an increasingly sophisticated technology that produced stone tools.

The evolution of large brains, however, was not without its drawbacks. First, larger brain size in the adult human meant larger brain size in the newborn, creating more complications in the birth process, exacerbated by a pelvis designed for bipedal locomotion (Figure 10–16). The smaller-brained *Australopithecus* probably had no more problems with birth than chimpanzee mothers (Leutenegger, 1987), because newborn head size was most likely smaller than the opening of the birth canal. As the brain enlarged (Figure 10–17), however, several new factors compensated for a small human birth canal. First, infants were born at increasingly less mature states, which minimized head size, and second, the female pelvis changed in shape to maximize the area of the birth canal. Although these solutions alleviated some obstetrical problems, they caused others. At some point human infants lost their ability to cling to the bodies of their mothers and possessed at birth such poorly developed locomotor skills that much greater effort and care was required from the mother. At this point a sexual division of labor may have developed, causing males and females to join together in more stable

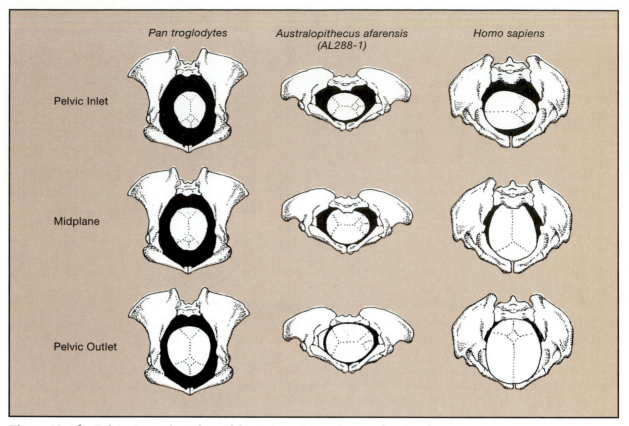

Pan troglodytes   *Australopithecus afarensis (AL288-1)*   *Homo sapiens*

Pelvic Inlet

Midplane

Pelvic Outlet

Figure 10–16 • Pelvic size and newborn delivery in various primates, showing the very large head size of the human neonate. (From Tague and Lovejoy, 1986)

and longer-term bonds. Modifications of the pelvis involving expansion of the birth canal may also have placed certain limitations on female locomotion, especially on running.

Cerebral Laterality: Two Brains in One

The human neocortex is divided into two cerebral hemispheres (Figure 10–18). Each has somewhat different functions. But what functions do the two hemispheres divide up and to what degree? Between the hemispheres lies a large tract of fibers, called the ***corpus callosum*** (Latin, meaning "hard body"), that connects the two halves. Early investigations into the functions of the right and left hemispheres were conducted by Roger Sperry and his colleagues at the California Institute of Technology, who began a series of unique tests on individuals who had "split brains." These patients had histories of "grand mal" epilepsy, a neuroelectrical storm in the brain that disrupts all activity, and had undergone surgical cutting of the corpus callosum. The operation was quite successful not only in reducing the severity of the attacks, but also in reducing their fre-

***corpus callosum*—**the fiber tract connecting the two halves of the brain across the midline.

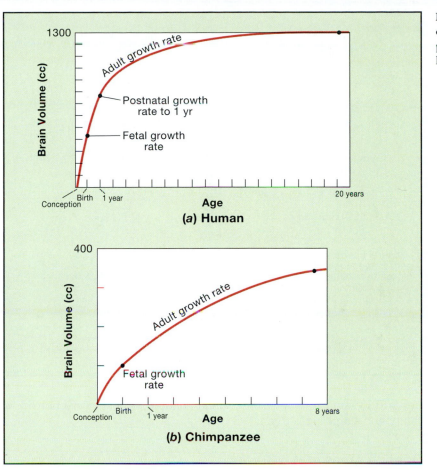

quency in both hemispheres. Even more surprising, the patients seemed to have no mental impairment whatsoever. What was a major structure like the *corpus callosum* for if cutting it produced no obvious defects?

Sperry received the Nobel Prize in 1981 for his work in demonstrating that speech, writing, and calculation are centered in the left hemisphere. The right hemisphere has a number of capabilities that the left does not have. It can copy three-dimensional diagrams whereas the left cannot. The right hemisphere can understand speech, can think abstractly, and may be important in the appreciation of music.

Why did evolution produce this unusual specialization of the two sides of the cerebrum? One suggestion is that only one hemisphere is needed to control a midline structure, such as the tongue. Similarly, handedness may have evolved because greater hand skill, whether the right or the left, was needed in early hominid tool-making. Another suggestion is that as the hominid brain expanded, the left side assumed the computer-like capability of calculation and the right became specialized for memory storage. (However, current popular thinking that people are either "right-brained" or "left-brained," and that "right-brained" people

Figure 10–18 • The "split brain," showing the cerebral hemispheres and the corpus callosum.

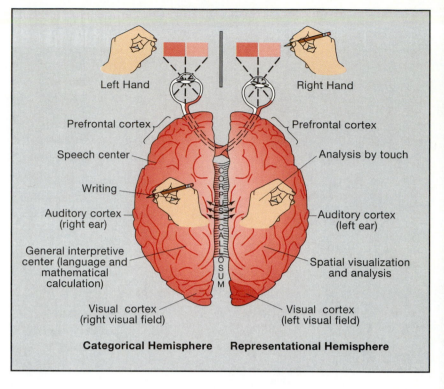

are artistic–intuitive while "left-brained" people are practical–analytic, is faulty and simplistic.)

Speech Areas of the Cortex

In 1863 the French physical anthropologist and physician Pierre-Paul Broca announced a discovery based on autopsies of brains of individuals who had lost the ability to speak coherently prior to death. In all instances he found that the brain had sustained an injury to the "posterior third of the third frontal convolution." He correctly inferred from this observation that speech ability was localized in this particular part of the brain, now known as **Broca's Area.** Individuals with brain damage to this area can utter only short, disjointed fragments of sentences, if they can speak at all. The most surprising aspect of Broca's findings was that the brain injuries were all only in the left hemisphere. Broca was one of the first researchers to discover that the cerebral hemispheres have different functions.

In 1874 the German physiologist Karl Wernicke located an area of the temporal lobe that is the center for understanding speech, now known as **Wernicke's Area.** Damage to Wernicke's Area results in lack of comprehension of both spoken and written language, although the patient can still speak. This area of the brain lies just above the auditory cortex, the part of the temporal lobe that analyzes sound. Like Broca's Area, Wernicke's Area is bigger on the left side. Interestingly, Wernicke's Area is also larger on the left than on the right side in the chimpanzee, which lacks verbal language (Figure 10–19).

Broca's Area–portion of the cerebral cortex (posterior part of the inferior frontal gyrus, usually on the left side) that is essential for the motor control of speech.

Wernicke's Area–portion of the cerebral cortex (parts of the parietal and temporal lobes near the lateral sulcus, usually on the left) that is responsible for understanding and formulating coherent speech.

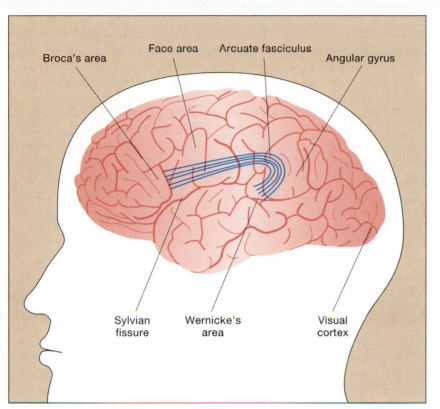

Figure 10–19 • Language centers of the brain.

Language and Tool Use

The debate involving the first appearance of spoken language focuses on whether it played a role in the evolution of modern *Homo sapiens* (Conkey, 1980). Language may have emerged earlier in human evolution, perhaps as far back as the earliest members of the genus *Homo,* but at what point and to what extent is unclear. King (1994:131) believes that human communicative behavior, including social information transfer and language, should be studied as a continuum with that of other primates. Human language can best be understood when compared and contrasted with other forms of information transfer, such as calls and gestures.

In 1957, Noam Chomsky of MIT challenged the idea that language is an exclusively cultural phenomenon. He argued that the way in which language develops makes it more likely that linguistic ability is innate or instinctual: The brain must have a built-in program that can put together an inexhaustible array of sentences from a limited number of words. Because sentences that individuals produce often consist of novel combinations of words, it would be difficult to explain such creations solely on the basis of past experiences. He further observes that children before the age of two learn grammatical structure rapidly without any formal training. More recently, Stephen Pinker (1994), also of MIT, has reaffirmed the Chomskian position, but disagrees with Chomsky's belief that language abilities emerged as a result of an increase in brain size, passing a cultural threshold with the emergence of modern *Homo sapiens*. Pinker believes that spoken language, in some primitive form, emerged as the result of natural selection early in prehistory. He asserts that the human brain enlarged as a result of the gradual elaboration of language structures and that language provided a survival advantage for early hominids as they developed a hunting and gathering mode of subsistence.

Lynn Schepartz (1993) of the University of Michigan provides us with some useful definitions of language. First, she notes that language has both internal (cerebral) and external (vocal tract) components. The internal components involve conscious thought that includes "complex mapping and simulation of the world" around us. The external components are basically behavioral expressions that include gestures, vocalizations, and articulate speech. **Speech** is defined as "a coordination of activity of both the brain and the vocal apparatus." Spoken language is unique to humans.

In determining the origin of language, some believe that it is important to know when humans first gained the ability to name objects. Washburn (1960) believed that the situation that originally led to naming was tool-making of a kind more complicated than that performed by chimpanzees. Others believe that some early form of language may have arisen as a more sophisticated system for communicating the location and type of dispersed food, or of important individuals such as close kin. Such vocal communication may also have become more elaborate as a response to the requirements of coordinating individuals in cooperative hunting (Parker, 1985; Parker and Gibson, 1979).

Aiello and Dunbar's (1993) hypothesis, that the size of the brain is the key to understanding cognitive ability and language, is based on a close relationship between relative neocortex size, group size, and the amount of time needed to devote to "social grooming." They believe that group size is limited by the number of relationships that an individual can successfully monitor and this, in turn, is limited by the relative size of the neocortex. They theorize that hominid group size would have been too great to be sustained by methods of social grooming such as those used by nonhuman primates, and conclude that language evolved as a binding mechanism for large groups.

Certainly as time went on language would have played a more important role in encoding complex cultural rules involving ritual, the control and regulation of reproduction and resource distribution, and other rules that ritually transform people's reproductive status through important rites of passage (Hockett and Asher, 1964).

Humans use about the same number of sounds as do chimpanzees; however, in human language it is not the sounds that have meaning but the combination of sounds put together as words. About the evolution of language, Calvin (1994) ponders the question of how and at what point our ancestors replaced the ape system of "one sound, one meaning" with the human system that uses individually meaningless sounds in meaningful combinations.

speech—the set of verbal sounds that is used by humans in language.

Attempts to answer this question use interpretations based on the archaeological record. In terms of language, to what extent can technological ability be correlated with neurological complexity? Toth and Schick (1993) caution that technological change occurs according to need and to demand. Unlike anatomical change that often occurs quite slowly, technological development usually proceeds independently at a much faster rate. As Toth and Schick point out, "the challenge is to identify what patterns of material culture in the prehistoric record have implications for intelligence and language."

The earliest Oldowan or Mode I stone tools are technologically quite simple, consisting mainly of discarded cores used for flake production. Toth and Schick believe there is little evidence that early hominid toolmakers might have had a "mental template" for constructing Oldowan tools. The final shape of the "tool" was probably more determined by a matter of size, shape, and raw material of the rock being flaked. Wynn (1988) agrees, and believes that the construction of Oldowan tools involved only rote learning of a sequence of specific actions that could be transmitted visually (see Figure 10–20).

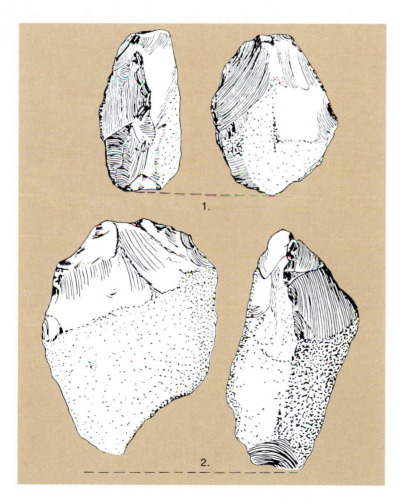

Figure 10–20 • Oldowan-type choppers (Mode I stone tools) c. 2 million years. (Drawings courtesy of Mrs. J. Desmond Clark)

Mode II, or the Acheulean, tool tradition presents a different picture. The skills required to make these artifacts are much more sophisticated. Acheulean tool-makers had the ability to conceive of a predetermined shape and to construct it. They had the ability to flake and produce a straight cutting edge and, apparently, with cultural standardization, they could produce consistently shaped tools (see Figure 10–21). If the Acheulean tool-makers had limited or no language skills, their geo-

Figure 10–21 • (Top) Acheulean-type hand ax and cleaver (Mode II stone tools) c. 1.0 million years. (Drawings courtesy of Mrs. J. Desmond Clark)

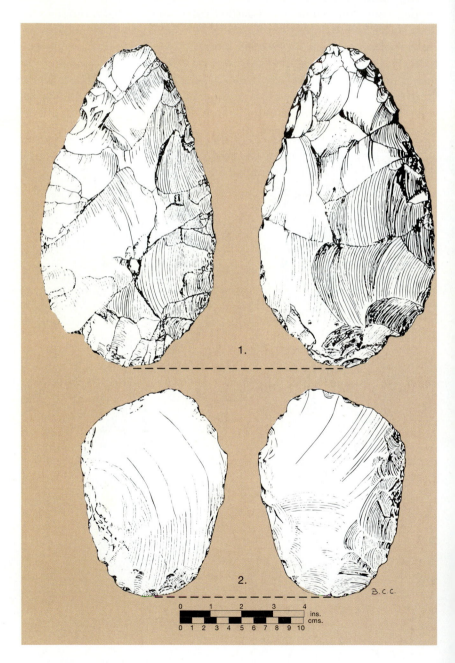

graphic dispersion would have made cultural uniformity difficult. This could account for the lack of Acheulean tools in the Far East.

Paleoenvironmental evidence suggests that few differences existed between Middle and Upper Paleolithic mammalian faunas in Europe. In both periods, game drives and selective ambush hunting indicate extensive cognitive capacities for earlier, as well as later, forms of *Homo sapiens* (Chase, 1989). As a consequence, archaic *sapiens* populations, including Neandertal, were probably capable of a wide variety of procurement strategies that show cognitive ability equal to that of modern *Homo sapiens*. The recent excavations at Kebara Cave, Israel, reveal specialized uses of the living area by Neandertals that suggest substantial cognitive ability. For example, hearths and a thick accumulation of bone characterized by cut-marks and relatively little carnivore gnawing were found in the central area of the cave. There was also evidence of the removal of bone and larger lithic refuse from the central area, perhaps an indication of cleanliness (Bar-Yosef and Vandermeersch, 1993).

Art, Symbolism, and Speech

Most examples of artwork are unquestionably associated with modern *Homo sapiens*, and they are found relatively late in the record, well after 35,000 years ago. Although it is rare, the evidence for Lower and Middle Paleolithic art, not associated with modern humans, is perhaps more to the point of understanding the origin of language. Although earlier archaic *Homo sapiens* may have lacked the modern ability to verbalize, their conceptual ability, as witnessed in their artwork, supports the notion that they possessed speech to some extent. The oldest example of artwork of this age thus far discovered is a figurine of exaggerated female human form dated to about 230,000 years ago that was excavated from the Acheulean site of Berekhat Ram, Israel (Figure 10–22) (Goren-Inbar, 1986). The earliest Mousterian burials themselves should also be considered as evidence for symbolic behavior, as the human body becomes a symbol once it is provided a burial (Schepartz, 1993).

Contemporary with these art forms are examples of objects that were, presumably, used as body ornamentation. This evidence provides additional insight into the evolution of symbolic behavior and speech. Ornamentation is one form of communication (Wobst, 1977). Ornaments name individuals, either their owner or their maker, and the use of shared ornamentation can be used to identify a member of a group (Wiessner, 1990). Alexander Marshack (1989) has offered evidence for body ornamentation beginning with the Lower Paleolithic, believing that as early as 110,000 years ago pierced animal teeth and bone were used as beads or pendants.

Anatomical Evidence for Speech

Interest in the evolution of cognition, such as sequential thinking and planning, has been revived by Binford (1989). Although most recognize the possibility that hominid behavior in the past may not have been

Figure 10–22 • Acheulean figure from Berekhat Ram.

cognitively structured as it is now, paleoneurologists are in complete agreement that the brains of archaic *Homo sapiens*, especially the Neandertal's, are morphologically similar to modern human brains.

In the early 1970s, Lieberman and Crelin (1971) began pioneering research on vocal tract reconstruction, comparing the shape and position of the tract in modern humans and infants, nonhuman primates, and fossil hominids. They described the supralaryngeal vocal tract of the Neandertal male from La Chapelle and compared it with that of a modern human newborn. In both they found lacking the elongation and bending of the tract that develops later in young juveniles of modern *Homo sapiens*. These authors concluded that the La Chapelle male, like the modern newborn, was limited in his ability to produce some vowels and consonants. They conceded, however, that the brain itself might have been "sufficiently well developed for him to have established a language based on the speech signals at his command" (1971:217).

Following this work were a number of critical studies of other specimens of archaic *Homo sapiens* indicating, contrary to Lieberman and Crelin, that many of them might have been capable of human speech. Other criticisms were leveled on the basis that the La Chapelle fossil is too pathologically altered to justify any conclusions on speech capabilities (Frayer, 1992) and that errors may have been made in the original reconstruction (Houghton, 1993). Kathleen Gibson of the University of Texas (1994) showed that the range of variation in the shape of modern human vocal tracts is not as limited as previously thought. Certainly, more comparative anatomical work on vocal tracts and the exact relationship of speech to individual variations of shape and position is needed.

Additional insights into the language origins problem have come from an entirely different corner of research, that of linguistic analysis. Johanna Nichols recently proposed that the common ancestor of modern languages must be at least 100,000 years old. In a paper presented at the annual meeting of the American Association for the Advancement of Science (1994), she described her analysis of grammatical features. She assigned an average age of 5,000 years for each language family and a branching rate of 1.6 languages per family. She concluded that, if there were a single common language, it would take about 100,000 years for it to differentiate into the number of different languages that presently exist.

The varied lines of evidence presented in this section show that a relationship exists between language and technology that preceded the late arrival of modern *Homo sapiens*. From the evidence at hand, the exact links between them remain insufficiently clear to allow a completely satisfactory reconstruction of the evolution of language and cognition. Certainly, more information is necessary from many fields such as neurology in order to shed further light on ape and human cognitive abilities.

SUMMARY

1. The great apes exhibit various degrees of sexual dimorphism. The larger orangutan adult males defend extensive home ranges that overlap with the smaller ranges of a number of adult females. Female orangutan social organization is usually limited to interactions with close female kin, a mother's younger offspring, and, when a female is sexually receptive, an adult male.

2. Gorillas form stable groups consisting of one or more older "silverback" males, some younger "black-backed" males, females, and their young. Groups consisting of adult males only and solitary males are also observed. Heterosexual groups apparently remain together because of the attraction to the adult "silverback" and often dissolve upon the death of that individual.

3. Chimpanzees display a fusion-fission pattern of social organization in which members of a community interact with others on an on-demand basis. Although female kinship relations are an important component in understanding social interactions, female chimpanzees usually emigrate from their birth group. Chimpanzees have been observed in unique behavior patterns of tool use and cooperative hunting.

4. Pygmy chimpanzees, or bonobos, exhibit a higher degree of female affiliation and lower levels of male intratroop display and aggression among members of the social group. Sexual behavior is frequent, and this may account for the appearance of stronger, longer-lasting bonds established between males and females, and, consequently, much more stable mixed groups.

5. Nonverbal language skill studies with the great apes show all species capable of learning and using symbols, signs, and gestures. Some chimpanzees have even learned signs from other chimpanzees, and have then used them to communicate among themselves.

6. Studies of the apes hold promise in increasing our understanding of early human behavior patterns and the evolution of those patterns towards the modern human condition. Tool use, hunting and gathering practices, and bipedal locomotion are homologous behaviors shared with the apes.

7. The most clearly recognizable human behaviors that bear a genetic stamp are fixed action patterns of infants. Whereas culture provides the framework for almost all human interactions, biology forms the template that, in many ways, limits human behavioral plasticity. Human sociobiology and human behavioral ecology have the potential to be two useful tools in looking at the interface of biology and culture.

8. Apes do not speak as we do because they lack the neurological structures for human language. More complicated language may have arisen early in our evolutionary history, certainly before the emergence of

modern *Homo sapiens,* but at what point in time and to what extent speech began still eludes us.

CRITICAL-THINKING QUESTIONS

1. Is the study of the nonhuman primates a valid way to learn about human behavior? Why or why not?
2. Explain how sociobiology has been used to explain deviant behavior; give an example.
3. How does aggression function as an adaptive strategy?
4. List and describe the costs and advantages of bipedalism in the evolution of early human behavior.
5. Outline the experiments conducted by Roger Sperry and give their significance in understanding brain functioning.
6. Discuss the anatomical evidence for language and speech, both in terms of the vocal tract and in terms of the brain.

SUGGESTED READINGS

de Waal, F. 1982. *Chimpanzee Politics: Power and Sex Among Apes.* Baltimore: Johns Hopkins University Press. A detailed account of daily life in a chimpanzee community, showing recognizably human actions and reactions. Traces the roots of human power politics in a primate community.

de Waal, F. 1996. *Good Natured: The Origins of Right and Wrong in Humans and Other Animals.* Cambridge, Mass.: Harvard University Press. This noted primatologist argues that the basis of human morality is in our genes. He makes recent knowledge of genetics accessible to general readers.

de Waal, F., and F. Lanting. 1997. *Bonobo: The Forgotten Ape.* Berkeley and Los Angeles: University of California Press. Beautiful photographs and the first extensive profile of the bonobo for the general reader. A fascinating view of the little-known fourth great ape.

Dunbar, R. 1996. *Grooming, Gossip, and the Evolution of Language.* Cambridge, Mass.: Harvard University Press. Dunbar, a psychology professor, traces the roots of human social organization to primate social and grooming behavior. He suggests that language evolved as a necessary way of holding together large human social groups.

Eibl-Eibesfeldt, I. 1989. *Human Ethology.* Hawthorne, N.Y.: Aldine de Gruyter. Text discusses the basic concepts and methodology of ethological studies as they apply to humans. Provides specific examples and offers ethological contributions to the understanding of such topics as aesthetics and ethics.

Gibson, K. R., and T. Ingold (eds.). 1993. *Tools, Language and Cognition in Human Evolution.* New York: Cambridge University Press. Interdisciplinary study of the question of how humans evolved as creatures who can make and use complex tools, communicate in complex ways, and engage in complex forms of social life. Questions the idea that the evolution of tool-making and language are interrelated phenomena.

Goldsmith, T. H. 1991. *The Biological Roots of Human Nature: Forging Links Between Evolution and Behavior*. New York: Oxford University Press. Chapters in this lively text discuss coevolution of biology and culture and sociobiology and cultural materialism.

Goodall, J. 1986. *The Chimpanzees of Gombe*. Cambridge, Mass.: Harvard University Press. In-depth study recounting 25 years of research among the wild chimpanzees of the Gombe Stream Reserve, Tanzania. Descriptions of various aspects of chimpanzee behavior, including tool use and warfare.

Iaccino, J. F. 1993. *Left Brain–Right Brain Differences: Inquiries, Evidence, and New Approaches*. Hillsdale, N.J.: Lawrence Erlbaum. Addresses the issue of cerebral asymmetries as it encompasses perceptual, physiological, comparative, and cognitive fields as these contribute to the question of human nature.

King, B. J. 1994. *The Information Continuum*. Santa Fe, N.M.: School of American Research Press. Describes the ability of primates to obtain, use, and transfer information that is critical to their survival and reproduction.

Pinker, S. 1994. *The Language Instinct*. New York: William Morrow. Argues that spoken language, in some primitive form, emerged early in human prehistory and is instinctual. Pinker asserts that the human brain enlarged as a result of the gradual elaboration of structures that underlie language, a result of natural selection.

Pinker, S. 1997. *How the Mind Works*. New York: W. W. Norton. Pinker, a cognitive linguist, describes how the human mind works by describing what, in evolutionary terms, it was designed to do. He argues, forcibly and intriguingly, for the formative influence of natural selection in shaping human nature.

Savage-Rumbaugh, E. S., J. Murphy, R. A. Sevcik, K. E. Brakke, S. L. Williams, and D. Rumbaugh. 1993. *Language Comprehension in Ape and Child*. Chicago: University of Chicago Press. Discusses research into the linguistic capacities of apes and their ability to produce words and comprehend them.

Wright, R. 1994. *The Moral Animal: Evolutionary Psychology and Everyday Life*. New York: Vintage. An evolutionary view of human sexual and social relations that views human behavior as expressing our biological heritage. Wright uses Charles Darwin's biography to illustrate how evolutionary forces shape human life.

CHAPTER 11

Human Biology and Variation

The Nature of Human Genetic Variation
How Variation Is Measured
The Process of Geographic Isolation
Early Studies of Human Variation
What is "Race"?
Inadequacy of Traditional Racial Classifications
Using Genetic Markers to Trace Population Relatedness
How Natural Selection Causes Human Variation
Blood Group Polymorphisms
Skin Pigmentation
Genetic Influence on Behavioral Variation
Twin Studies
Race, IQ, and Social Class
Summary
Critical-Thinking Questions
Suggested Readings

A cross-section of human individuals shows the extent to which we vary (Figure 11–1). Humans are one of the most morphologically variable species of living animals, and part of the reason this variation exists is because members of our species occupy many diverse habitats. Yet the exact genetic basis of this variation must be quite small. Biochemical evidence shows that humans and chimpanzees differ genetically by only 1–2% and that this amount of difference was accumulated over a period of approximately 7 million years. The human gene pool has apparently

Figure 11–1 • College-aged individuals showing physical features that are found in some of the world's population. Based solely on the criteria of physical appearance, biological diversity in humans is substantial.

changed very little since the widespread appearance of anatomically modern humans about 35,000 years ago. Humans today remain genetically nearly identical to our Upper Paleolithic pre-agricultural hunter-gatherer ancestors (Eaton, Shostak, and Konner, 1989).

Given these facts, why do modern humans appear to vary so much from one another and what are the factors responsible for this inherited variation? In this chapter we will review what we know about human variation, attempt to explain this variability at the genetic level, and discuss the evolutionary framework in which these characteristics have come to exist.

THE NATURE OF HUMAN GENETIC VARIATION

Inherited characteristics are variable at all levels of our biology, down to the genes. These characteristics include features of our external appearance—hair and skin color, facial features, and stature, among others—and of our internal characteristics—our blood types and our abilities to digest or metabolize certain substances. Inherited variation results from the reshuffling of genes within populations from one generation to the next. As we saw in Chapters 2 and 3, inherited variation is a critical component in the action of evolution by natural selection. We study inherited variation to understand how evolutionary forces have acted and continue to act to produce modern human populations.

There are important patterns to human biological variation. All individuals within a species do not vary equally from one another. Individuals within one family share significant genetic, anatomical, and even behavioral similarities due to their close genetic bonds. There is also a geographic component to variation—individuals drawn from indigenous populations at the far north of Greenland and at the tip of southern Africa will show a great degree of difference, although they are still clearly within the same zoological species, *Homo sapiens*. As a rule, the amount of variation between individuals increases with distance: The farther away individuals' populations are, the more they tend to differ. Conversely, individuals who live close together within a population tend to resemble one another both genetically and morphologically. However, overall the level of heterozygosity (between 10 and 15%) at loci among individuals in a population is only slightly lower than the difference seen between populations. These patterns are the result of and are maintained by the forces of evolution: selection, migration, and genetic drift.

However, a population must pay a price for its variability; it is called **genetic load.** A definition provided by the geneticist J. F. Crow in 1958 describes the genetic load of a population as the proportional decrease in fitness relative to the fitness of an optimum genotype. These unfavorable genotypes act to lower the reproductive potential of those individuals who possess them by causing disease, and, in some cases, death. Genetic loads may be calculated for all loci, or sites on the

genetic load—the deleterious or lethal effects that accompany genetic variation in a population, measured by the number of recessive lethal genes carried by individuals in a population; also called genetic burden.

chromosomes, and may differ considerably from one another depending on the lethality of the genotypes. In the sickle-cell anemia example that we will describe later in this chapter, the minimum genetic load must be calculated based on those deaths both caused by the lethal homozygous recessive genotype (about 4% of the population) and those deaths caused by malaria in individuals who possess either the normal homozygous or the heterozygous genotypes. As a rough rule of thumb a high genetic load usually follows a high degree of genetic variability.

HOW VARIATION IS MEASURED

Biological anthropologists study anatomical variation both qualitatively and quantitatively, that is, both in terms of traits that are either present or absent and in terms of traits that vary in degree. Thus, they collect observations on the presence, absence, or frequencies of **genetic markers,** or they collect observations on the variations of certain markers, such as fingerprint patterns. For example, certain populations have the qualitative anatomical trait of ridges of enamel on the back edges of their upper incisor teeth, a feature known as "shovel-shaped" incisors (Figure 11–2). Moderate to marked shovel incisors are almost universal in populations from the Far East, including Eskimos and American Indians (Carbonell, 1963). In other populations very few individuals show even slight development of this trait (Brues, 1977). On the other hand, quantitative traits such as body size (from tall to short), skin and hair pigmentation (from black to white), and hair form (from straight to curly) vary in all populations. Frequency differences of traits between populations are expressed in terms of differences in mean values of a normal curve. For example, the mean height in one population may be 3.6 centimeters (1.4 in.) greater than that of another population, yet the entire range of adult height may be found among individuals in each of the two populations.

Measuring genetic variation allows us to study the effects of natural selection on human populations. Let us take as an example of a quantitative genetic marker the human ABO blood groups. The various blood types of this system are found in individuals in all populations, but the types vary in frequency from one population to another. We can illustrate how genetic variation is measured in human populations.

Human populations vary in frequencies of the different ABO blood types, and they can be distinguished in part on the basis of these frequencies (Table 11–1). American Indian groups, for example, have a very low proportion of B blood types and a relatively high proportion of O blood types compared with most other human populations.

Certainly as markers, the frequencies of particular alleles among the various blood group systems can serve to detect genetic affinity between groups. For example, the suggestion that the Hungarian gypsies originated in India—a suggestion that followed from a linguistic comparison of these two populations—can be supported by the frequency distribution of the ABO blood group system.

genetic markers—traits whose genetic causation are known and which can be used in the study of populations.

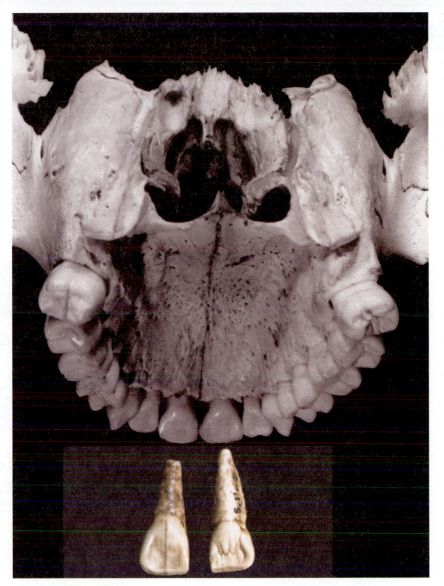

Figure 11–2 • Top, a view of the upper dentition of a modern human (a European) from the inside of the mouth. The inside surface of the middle incisors is smooth, lacking the characteristic indentations seen in the two isolated middle incisors, pictured below, from the *Homo erectus* site of Zhoukoudian in north China. Termed shovel-shaped incisors because this indentation gives the tooth a shovel-like appearance, these teeth are found more frequently in modern Asian peoples and their close kin, such as Native Americans, than in other human populations. Shovel-shaped incisors are also found with a high frequency in Asian archaic *H. erectus* and *H. sapiens* specimens, suggesting a regional continuity in evolution from Asian *H. erectus* through archaic *sapiens* to modern Asians.

Most genetic markers are not visible to a human observer. It is impossible, for example, to tell whether a person has A, B, or O Type blood by looking at any of his or her external features. However, external features also may serve to define human populations. In many cases, though, the underlying genetic cause of these traits is not simple and cannot be tied to any one gene. Although the genetic control for some discrete anatomical traits is known (McKusick, 1989), for many traits, such as stature or skin color, the exact genetic causes are unclear. As a number of loci and their alleles must be responsible for such measurable features, they are referred to as being under polygenic ("many gene") control.

Table 11–1 • Worldwide Distribution of the ABO Blood Group[1]

Geographic Area	Sample Size	Blood Type O	A	B	AB	Allele Frequency A	B	O
Europe								
France	30,810	.42	.45	.09	.04	.29	.07	.67
Italy	11,679	.46	.36	.13	.05	.23	.09	.68
Eastern Europe								
Russia (Leningrad)	54,447	.35	.37	.20	.08	.26	.15	.59
"Armenians" (Russia)	44,632	.29	.50	.13	.08	.35	.11	.54
Asia								
Japan	12,253	.30	.37	.23	.10	.27	.19	.54
Vietnam	114,022	.42	.22	.31	.06	.15	.20	.65
Middle East								
Iran	16,368	.41	.28	.24	.07	.19	.17	.64
Egypt	10,000	.36	.34	.24	.06	.23	.17	.60
Africa								
Nigeria	9,240	.52	.24	.21	.03	.14	.13	.73
Botswana !Kung	114	.70	.25	.03	.02	.15	.02	.83
Pacific Islands								
Hawaii (Natives)	4,670	.41	.53	.04	.02	.33	.03	.64
Easter Islands	1,056	.32	.66	.01	.01	.42	.10	.58
Americas (Natives)								
North America (Cherokee)	166	.95	.04	.02	.00	.02	.01	.97
Greenland (Eskimos)	377	.36	.55	.05	.04	.35	.05	.60

[1]Shows from worldwide population samples the frequencies of the ABO blood groups and the frequencies of the A, B, O alleles. Populations with high frequencies of blood type "O" tend to be peripheral in Europe and Asia, with the highest frequencies reaching nearly 100% among Native Americans. Frequencies of "A" are higher in Europe and in Native Americans of western North America. The "B" blood group is almost totally absent from Native American populations. It reaches its highest frequencies in Asia.

From Mourant et al. (1976).

THE PROCESS OF GEOGRAPHIC ISOLATION

Changing gene frequencies in geographically defined populations is evolution in action. The formation of geographically delimited populations within a species is sometimes termed "raciation." Subspecies or races created by raciation represent those geographical subdivisions or populations that differ in gene frequencies. The factors creating subspecies or races take into account (1) partial geographic and partial genetic isolation that may exist between populations at any point in time; (2) the amount of time in which gene flow has been reduced between

two populations; and (3) mutations that occur and spread in one population but not in another.

Today, laboratory techniques have allowed us to compare different individuals within a population, or to compare populations and subspecies. We can quantify these differences. At the DNA level, where the base pairs can be directly sequenced, the average individual is somewhat less than 1% different in sequence from any other randomly chosen individual. However, this 1% difference represents thousands of different genetic combinations when one considers that there are 3 to 4 $\times 10^9$ base pairs in the human haploid genome. If we compare individuals and populations, it appears that up to 80% of all variation in humans is found within any one population, and that only 20% of the variation is found in differences between populations.

There are no single features of modern populations that clearly set one group off from the next. What defines a race is a suite of morphological and genetic features that statistically can be related to the origin of a particular population group in a geographical location. In today's populations the results of migration make the definition of races a complex question resolvable only by studies of quantitative traits. But this lack of precision in defining modern human races does not mean that population structure and the process of race formation were not important in human evolution. Our knowledge of both the human fossil record and the human genome indicate that an understanding of human population history is important in understanding our modern genetic diversity.

EARLY STUDIES OF HUMAN VARIATION

Darwin showed that inherited variation was a key element in natural selection. Scientists interested in human evolution thus began in the nineteenth century to study human variation and to interpret variation in evolutionary terms. The first attempts were clumsy.

The prevailing theoretical and philosophical debate concerning human origins before and around Darwin's time was between supporters of the unitary (**monogenism**) and of the separate (**polygenism**) origin of the human species. Debate centered on whether the differences seen in modern populations were of such a degree that different human groups should be considered separate species, or whether they were varieties of the same species. Those who emphasized the differences, such as the early American anthropologist Samuel G. Morton of Philadelphia in his *Crania Americana* (1839), were strong proponents of polygenism. Polygenists supported the clear-cut separation of the major human races, usually into separate species. Monogenists emphasized the similarities among populations and pointed that all individuals of the different groups could interbreed. Monogenism had the support of Western religious doctrine because it upheld the single origin of humanity, in accordance with the Book of Genesis. Major proponents of

monogenism—in the history of anthropology, relating to a single or unitary origin of the human species, connoting that all human races were part of one species; an early point of agreement between the Church and Darwinism.

polygenism—in the history of anthropology, relating to a multiple origin of the human species, connoting that human races were different species; used by some to defend slavery and by others to justify colonial mistreatment of indigenous peoples.

monogenism were Johann Friedrich Blumenbach and Erasmus Darwin, the grandfather of Charles Darwin.

What Is "Race"?

The initial ideas about human races were developed around a series of "types," defined by morphological or metric features of body, head, facial, or hair forms. If an individual possessed the one or two characteristics considered essential for inclusion in that type, then that was the type or race he or she was assigned to. There are several problems with this "typological" approach. First, there is little provision for variability. And second, there is no provision for cases that are on the ends of the distributions of populations—for example, an individual who has as parents members of two different populations.

Anthropology has been involved since its inception in the study of human variation. Blumenbach, the founder of biological anthropology, studied the variations in cranial form in living human groups and categorized them into five major "races," which he termed "Caucasian," "Mongolian," "Malayan," "Ethiopian," and "American." Blumenbach, foreshadowing modern population biology, however, stressed that his division of the human species was arbitrary. As more and more research is undertaken on the molecular evolutionary aspects of human populations, conceptions of human races are changing radically. We will review both traditional and newly emerging views of human variation.

There has been a long-standing historical confusion in anthropology concerning the interrelationships of race, language, and culture, a confusion that is manifested in common usage as well. Standard U.S. government usage requests individuals applying for jobs to fill in their "ethnic group," which used to be termed "race." The categories used by the U.S. government are *Hispanic,* largely a language-based term, referring to Spanish speakers (but these individuals can be "white," "black," or also "Native American"); *African-American* and *Asian-American,* geographically based terms that can relate to real population affinities; *Native American,* which can refer to a wide array of geographic populations of broadly Asian affinities ranging from Florida to Alaska to the Pacific Islands; and *white,* a purely descriptive grouping based on skin color, or *Caucasian,* an old term referring to a European "type" from eastern Europe. Widely used terms such as "Jewish" and "Muslim" have a clearly religious connection. But do these terms connote separate "races" because they share certain genetic characteristics distinct from other human populations, separate linguistic groupings because they share a common original language (Hebrew and Arabic, in this case), or separate cultures because they are bound together by common religions, Judaism and Islam, respectively? Or are they all three? What about a population that has a very distinguishing physical characteristic, such as the small stature of the Central African Mbuti (pygmies), but that is not linguistically distinct, instead speaking the languages of their Bantu neighbors? What about two populations, such as the Hopi and Navaho

Indians, that are physically and genetically very similar but have quite different languages and cultural adaptations to the same environment? There are no straightforward answers to these questions, although it is clear that the categories "race," "language," and "culture" should be decoupled from one another, as they can all vary independently. The far-reaching and usually negative effects that "race" often has on such disparate areas as social mores, religious doctrine, educational planning, public health policy, and medical practice, among others, is called **racism** (Shipman, 1994).

When population biological theory began to exert an important influence in human evolutionary studies in the 1940s, an opinion predominated that human populations had been for the most part **panmictic** (Latin, meaning "all mixing") in the past—that is, they had interbred freely over almost their entire range. This theoretical predisposition meant that there must have been relatively little racial differentiation because of the high degree of gene flow between geographic regions in the human past.

General opinion now holds that, although human species seem to have passed the threshold from one ancestral species to its descendant across the species' worldwide range in a more or less synchronous fashion, there is also strong evidence in certain anatomical markers for regional continuity. For example, we do see a high incidence of shovel-shaped incisors in Asian *Homo erectus* and modern Asian (and American Indian) human populations and in the midfacial prognathism of Late Pleistocene European populations and modern Europeans. This means that, although there has been enough gene flow between regions in the past to ensure that all human populations are interfertile and thus in the same species, there has also been enough regional inbreeding to account for higher incidence of certain traits in geographically defined human populations.

Inadequacy of Traditional Racial Classifications

Genetic studies have now added substantially to our understanding of human population variability. The reconstruction of gene lineages in some ways parallels the use of discrete anatomical marker traits in deciphering the history of human variation in the past. New molecular studies have not supported the traditional human racial divisions based on morphology. Cavalli-Sforza and Edwards (1967) used the available genetic data to categorize fifteen distinct human populations. Mitochondrial DNA (Mt-DNA) studies have been at the forefront of this research. Cann (1988) and colleagues have surveyed worldwide mt-DNA diversity and analyzed the data in terms of cladistic patterns. They suggest that the major division in human races lies at a split between Euro-Asian and African populations. The degree of genetic polymorphism in Africa is five times that of the rest of the world's populations. Using these data and the criteria of genetic distance as indicative of race, the traditional racial category of "Africans" would have to be broken up into a number

racism—a policy or opinion that unfairly generalizes real or perceived characteristics of a specific ethnic group, population, or "race" to every member of that group, and that may be used to deny resources or fair and equal treatment to an individual on the basis of membership in that group.

panmictic—"all mixing," referring to populations in which the breeding structure approximates the condition in which an individual male or female has the same probability of mating with another individual of the opposite sex anywhere in the population.

FRONTIERS

Dissecting the Human Genome

by Kenneth K. Kidd and Judith R. Kidd

What is the human genome? The human genome is the approximately 3 billion nucleotide base pairs organized into 23 pairs of chromosomes that each individual possesses. It is also the variation in these 3 billion base pairs as well as the organization of the variation among individuals both within and between human populations. The human genome, like the genome of any other complex species, is not homogeneous. It is composed of a variety of elements that vary from individual to individual. Just as a single representative "consensus" sequence of the genome (the objective of the Human Genome Project) will be a major aid to understanding the function and expression of all human genes, a detailed description of variation in sequence (the objective of the Human Genome Diversity Project) will be a crucial element in under-

standing our evolutionary history as a species.

The genome contains clues to aspects of our evolutionary history such as human and primate relationships and origins, where and when we arose as a species, and how different populations are related. There are also clues to the social structures of populations, for example, whether there has been a pattern of marrying outside the group ("exogamy") or marrying within the group ("endogamy"). [The genome also carries traces of migrations of individuals between populations and of whole populations.] Finally, there are important indications from human genome data as to how we have adapted, and are presently adapting, to our environments, especially as affected by such parameters as disease, diet, and altitude.

Two recent scientific developments are allowing us to examine these clues as never before and are revolutionizing the field of physical anthropology. First, extraordinarily large amounts of data and molecular resources are now being produced by the Human Genome Project. This project is a

major international research effort to sequence the human genome with primary emphasis on functional genes and their genetic controlling elements. Understanding which DNA sequences control morphology and how they control it will allow physical anthropologists to understand better how we evolved from our hominoid ancestors and the genetic changes involved in adapting to new niches. Second, the vast and ever-increasing amount of DNA sequence variation being discovered is relegating the classical markers of variation, such as blood groups and serum protein polymorphisms, to a minute fraction of the known variation available to study. Such data are coming from the Human Genome Diversity Project (HGDP), which is being organized to coordinate the systematic and broadly representative study of genetic variation at the DNA level. It is the huge amount of hitherto unknown genetic variation now being characterized that makes feasible such a project to understand human diversity and variation and ensures the successful coordination of the work necessary for it.

of separate races equal to those traditionally defined. For example, mt-DNA data have shown that an individual from English ancestors is more similar genetically to an individual from Japanese ancestors than are two individuals drawn from any number of contiguous African populations. Future work in molecular anthropology will undoubtedly change our understanding of human races even further.

USING GENETIC MARKERS TO TRACE POPULATION RELATEDNESS

Neutral mutations, discussed first in Chapter 2, are one source of variation that contributes to the formation of genetic polymorphisms in human populations. The spread of neutral mutations within populations

The results of some of our own research on DNA variation indicate the types of understanding of the human species that we expect to come from the HGDP. The data at the DNA level are beginning to suggest scenarios for the geographical and temporal origin of humans. Preliminary work on both nuclear and mitochondrial DNA variation corroborate paleoanthropological evidence for an African origin for *Homo sapiens* (Stoneking, 1993; but see Templeton, 1993, and Bowcock et al., 1994). The continuous nature of the distribution of variation within the human species is another emerging conclusion. Although as yet fragmentary, data on the global distribution of DNA variation demonstrate the continuous distribution of genetic variation between populations. Variation is being seen as quantitative rather than qualitative, that of frequency and not type. For example, virtually all of the polymorphic alleles originally discovered and characterized in Europeans are seen in nearly all populations in all regions of the world. The HGDP is also helping us to understand the effect of the speciation events and different species histories separating humans from their nearest primate relatives. We are beginning to observe that *Homo sapiens*, compared to other living hominoids (*Pan troglodytes*, *Pan paniscus*, *Gorilla gorilla*, and *Pongo pygmaeus*) has far less DNA variation. If these observations prove to be more than anecdotal, they will shape both our view of the nature of the speciation events that separate us from our evolutionary cousins and our understanding of the effects of differing species-wide population structures on genetic variation.

We are better able than ever before to study who we are as a species, where we came from evolutionarily and geographically, and how we came to be what we are today—a single species, genetically quite homogeneous, yet with a rich and fascinating genetic and population diversity.

References

Bowcock, A.M., A. Ruiz-Linares, J. Tomfohrde, E. Minch, J.R. Kidd, and L.L. Cavalli-Sforza. 1994. High resolution of human evolutionary trees with polymorphic microsatellites. *Nature* 368:455–57.

Stoneking, M. 1993. DNA and recent human evolution. *Evolutionary Anthropology* 60–73.

Templeton, A.R. 1993. The "Eve" hypothesis: a genetic critique and reanalysis. *American Anthropology* 95: 51–72.

Kenneth K. Kidd is Professor of Genetics at Yale University School of Medicine and has helped to develop the Human Genome Diversity Project.

Judith R. Kidd is Research Scientist in Genetics at Yale University School of Medicine and an active investigator into human genetic variation.

is the result of genetic drift, as we saw in Chapter 3. In Chapter 3, we showed how two selectively neutral alleles, where there is no apparent advantage of one allele over the other, may exist over a considerable period of time. The frequency of the resulting polymorphic genotypes varies over time only by chance.

Sections of the DNA molecule exist with no apparent function; that is, they do not code for polypeptide chains. These sections consist of short runs of nucleotides repeated in tandem perhaps thousands of times. We have known for a number of years about some of these noncoding tandem repeats, called **satellite DNA.** Other nonfunctional tandem repeats have also been identified and labeled according to their size as either minisatellite or microsatellite DNA loci. Recently it was discovered that their loci, like those of many of their functional counterparts on DNA, are polymorphic: there are different numbers of repeats in different individuals.

satellite DNA—DNA that consists of short sequences repeated many times in the genome; so named because it forms a subsidiary "satellite" band when DNA is spun in a laboratory centrifuge.

These loci, called VNTR's (variable noncoding tandem repeats), are found by the hundreds and are distributed across all chromosomes.

There are a number of reasons why VNTR's are potentially useful for study by anthropologists. As they make up the noncoding regions of the DNA, being relatively unaffected by natural selection, their observed variability must be selectively neutral. As we have seen in our studies of primate phylogeny, neutral polymorphisms (differences) are more useful than selectively maintained polymorphisms for analyzing the relatedness of species. Because VNTR polymorphisms also appear by chance and are fixed by genetic drift, their high rate of production makes them especially useful for studying how populations within species are related and for estimating the amount of genetic distance that separates them. The greater the number of polymorphisms and the higher the rate of heterozygosity, the more useful VNTR's can be in resolving issues of recent human migration history and, perhaps, even the issue of the origin of modern *Homo sapiens* (Harding, 1992).

Neutral mutations have proven useful in evolutionary studies. However, we may also consider the role of neutrality at higher levels in the phenotype. For example, several known variable phenotypes might fall into the category of neutrality because none has been demonstrated to affect individual fitness. The first example involves the excretion of a substance called **methanethiol.** Probably a single dominant allele controls the excretion of methanethiol once it has entered the body's system, usually after an individual has eaten asparagus. One estimate of the frequency of this allele in an English population is 0.23 (23 in 100). Carriers of this allele can be identified because of the strong odor of their urine after they eat asparagus. Individuals, on the other hand, who are homozygous for the recessive allele can eat as much as a pound of asparagus without any detectable odor. Studies have not confirmed any selective advantage for either the excretion or nonexcretion of methanethiol.

A second example that is also under genetic control involves the ability to taste different substances. R. J. Williams, a biochemist, investigated taste sensitivity for a number of substances and found that individuals had different "taste profiles" or responses to the different substances used (Williams, 1951). For example, while 251 individuals said that sugar tasted sweet, 21 unrelated individuals reported a bitter taste. Identical twins usually agreed in their responses, indicating the genetic basis for differences in one's ability to taste.

Neutrally selective genetic markers such as these are useful in studying population movements and gene flow, because their frequencies will not be affected by selection. The movement of genes through populations can be tracked by gene frequencies, revealing (as discussed in Chapter 3) a gradient of populations, each successively less genetically related. These gradients in populations are termed clines. Some researchers prefer to use this term to describe human variation rather than the term "race."

A particularly good example of a cline in human populations is the incidence of **cerumen,** or ear wax, types in Eurasia (Figure 11–3). In

methanethiol–a chemical breakdown product of asparagus with a detectable odor, excreted by individuals heterozygous for the gene.

cerumen–ear wax; a waxy secretion of glands located in the external ear canal.

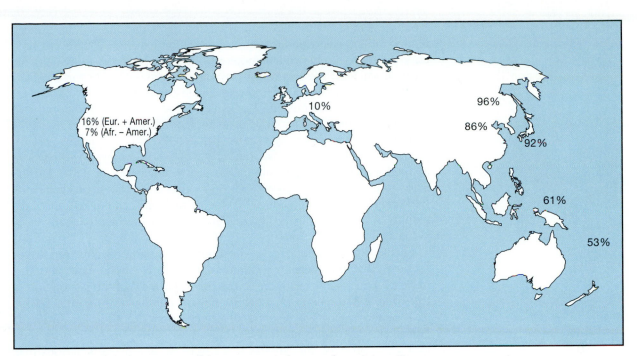

Figure 11–3 • Allele frequencies of dry cerumen in humans from Asia to Europe, an example of a cline.

northern China dry cerumen, that is "nonsticky" ear wax, occurs in 96% of the population. These individuals are homozygous for the recessive allele that causes dry cerumen. In western Europe, on the other hand, over 90% of individuals have "wet" cerumen, a very different type of ear wax, indicating high frequencies of the dominant wet cerumen allele.

Over the geographical area intervening between northern China and western Europe there is a gradient of cerumen types, with dry frequencies increasing west to east and wet frequencies increasing east to west. Because no selective advantage has been determined for the two cerumen types—both types apparently serve to provide a protective barrier to small foreign particles entering the ear canal—their frequency variations have been interpreted on the basis of selective neutrality and are indicative of past gene flow. Historically, the major event that may account for this cline is the Mongol invasion, a mass movement of northern Asian peoples into western Asia and Europe in the fifth century AD.

HOW NATURAL SELECTION CAUSES HUMAN VARIATION

Although biological anthropologists and geneticists have documented much variation in human populations, under most circumstances they have been unable to ascertain either the selective advantages or the evolutionary forces that produce the variation. In those cases where we have determined the reason for variability, large fitness differences among individuals within the study population usually exist. Such a situation exists for sickle-cell hemoglobin. In this example, individuals in West Africa who are heterozygous with the mutant allele for the beta chain of hemoglobin have protection against **malaria.**

Hospital data demonstrate that patients with normal hemoglobin can be infected with the malarial parasite 20% more frequently than those individuals who are heterozygous for sickle-cell trait (see Chapter 3). One particular study showed that out of 1,013 heterozygotes, 132 or only about 13% had heavy parasite infestation, whereas out of 2,858 AA homozygous individuals 955 or about 33% tested for the same degree of parasitic infection. The death rate due to malaria for homozygous individuals is also considerably higher than that for the heterozygous individuals.

Such a high genetic load, or death rate of the homozygous recessive, suggests that this genetic accommodation between humans and the malarial parasite is a relatively recent one. About 4% of the population is lost (due to the lethal homozygous mutant combination) so that about 32% of the population can be protected from the effects of malaria. However, a 4% death rate per generation is a severe genetic load. Natural selection over time should favor possible alternative solutions that reduce genetic load. An "ideal" solution would be a single-locus protection against malarial infection that is not detrimental to individuals carrying the mutant gene.

Adaptation through evolution can occur only when a population has sufficient variability. Mutations, the source of population variability, do not occur because they are needed. Rather, the process of mutation is continuous and random. As the environmental situation changes, some mutations will by chance turn out to be adaptive. Given the relative infrequency, however, of mutations and the finite nature of populations (there are only so many individuals in any given species), we would not expect to find the same adaptation in two different populations. Throughout the world many human populations have been exposed to malaria (Figure 11–4), but genetic adaptations to malaria are varied. In Africa, for example, the adaptation of highest frequency is sickle-cell hemoglobin (Hb^s). In Southeast Asia a different mutant (Hb^e) works to protect individuals from malaria. Hb^e, however, is much less lethal than Hb^s when in the homozygous state.

Hb^s, Hb^e, and a West African allele, Hb^c, are found in fairly large areas of the world at heterozygote frequencies of 10% to 30%, the highest in populations in tropical Africa and in a few locations around the Mediterranean and in India. In addition to these, at least three other variants exist whose local heterozygote frequencies may reach 50%.

In areas where Hb^s and Hb^c both occur, the frequency of Hb^s is lower than that of Hb^c. Predictably the Hb^c allele with its higher degree of fitness (lower genetic load in the homozygous recessive genotype) is spreading.

malaria—from Italian for "bad air," from the original, mistaken belief that the disease was airborne; occasionally fatal disease caused by a protozoan infecting the red blood cells and transmitted from one carrier to another by the bite of a female *Anopheles* mosquito; symptoms include chills, sweating, and convulsions.

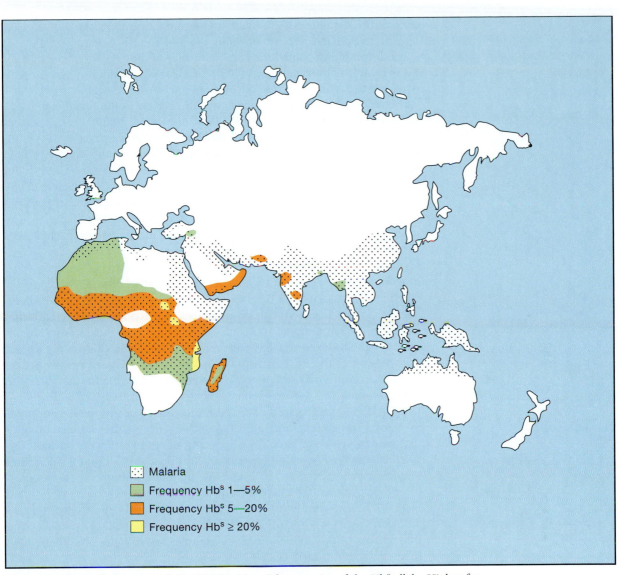

Figure 11–4 • Malarial areas of the Old World and frequencies of the Hb^s allele. Higher frequencies of Hb^s correspond with higher frequencies of sickle-cell anemia.

Time is again the important ingredient. If a situation requiring some genetic intervention persists for a long enough period and certain chance factors (mutations) occur enabling alternative solutions, a shift will take place from a single-locus to a two-locus (or more) mechanism. Substantiating this prediction, we again look at West African and Mediterranean populations in which other loci exist that contain specific alleles whose frequencies correlate with the presence of malaria. At one of these loci, alleles produce the enzyme **G6PD** (glucose-6-phosphate dehydrogenase), important in red blood cell metabolism.

G6PD—glucose-6-phosphate dehydrogenase, an enzyme necessary for red blood cell metabolism; G6PD deficiency is caused by recessive genes and can result in the disease "favism."

Where the frequency of Hb^s is high, the mutant forms of the G6PD gene, leading to deficiency in the enzyme, are also found (Greene, 1993).

Under ordinary conditions carriers of one of the G6PD deficiency alleles exhibit no abnormal effects. Only if a carrier is administered an antimalarial drug will he or she develop anemia. Anemia will also occur if a carrier eats or comes into contact with the pollen of the fava bean, *Vicia faba*. The disease caused by G6PD deficiency and brought on by the fava bean is commonly known as "favism," and is characterized by fever, abdominal pain, anemia, and coma. It was originally found chiefly in Italy and was associated with long-term diets of the raw bean. G6PD deficiency is now known to be widespread in populations exposed in the past to malarial infection. In Israel, for example, among Kurdish Jews the frequency of the G6PD-deficiency alleles may reach higher than 60%. The unexpected relationship between G6PD and malaria demonstrates how evolution in some human populations responded to malaria and developed a defense that affected red blood cell metabolism, which must have in some way protected individuals against the lethal effects of malaria.

The second locus that has been associated with malaria possesses alleles that are concerned with the synthesis of the polypeptide chains that make up the hemoglobin molecule. Individuals who have one of the alleles for β-**Thalassemia** have defective hemoglobin due to the partial suppression of the formation of the normal β-chain. As a consequence, these individuals may be anemic. On mainland Italy the frequency of the heterozygotes for β-Thalassemia reaches 20%, and in some Sardinian populations it approaches 40%. The high frequencies of these genotypes in many populations, and the frequent severity of the anemia, suggest that natural selection should be reducing these frequencies through differential fitness. That this has not occurred is again good evidence of natural selection at work. We presume that the counteracting selection is for protection against malaria, and as with sickle-cell hemoglobin and G6PD deficiency, a lowered efficiency of red blood cell activity and metabolism apparently retards the propagation of the malarial parasite. The frequencies of the anemia-producing alleles are like the Hb^s allele, high in areas where malaria is also prevalent.

A study of the relationships between malaria, β-Thalassemia, and G6PD-deficiency alleles was undertaken in Sardinia. Here the frequency of the alleles was correlated with altitude, the interpretation being that the higher the altitude, the lower the incidence of malaria (Figure 11–5). The prediction borne out by this study was that, as the effects of malaria on the human population diminished, the incidence of malaria-related alleles would also decrease in frequency.

The malarial example illustrates the interaction between disease, genetics, and natural selection. A heterogeneous group of genetic variants of various red cell components (including hemoglobin S, α- and β-Thalassemia, and G6PD deficiency) appear to impart in common an increased fitness in malarial environments, the end result of which is the production of a common phenotype, one in which the red cell environment is less favorable for the malarial parasite.

Thalassemia—from Greek meaning "sea blood," in reference to the blood's "dilute" nature; genetic disorders affecting hemoglobin metabolism that can range from negligible clinical effects to fatal anemia.

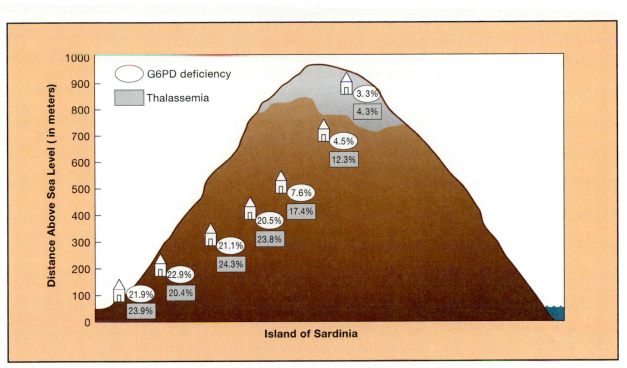

Figure 11–5 • Incidence (average frequency) of G6PD deficiency and the Thalassemia trait among villagers on the island of Sardinia. These traits are lower at higher altitudes, away from coastal malarial areas.

Blood Group Polymorphisms

The idea of transfusing the blood of one individual into that of another dates back several centuries. As early as the seventeenth century, blood transfusions were attempted, but the patients often died. The question of why some patients survived transfusion was not correctly answered until the turn of this century by K. Landsteiner. He discovered what ultimately became one of the most widely known genetic systems, the **ABO blood group.** Individuals may have an A, B, AB, or O blood type. The genotypes for these types are AA or AO, BB or BO, AB, and OO, respectively.

The ABO system was the first of many blood groups to be discovered, and the reason that it was first is relatively simple. Individuals who do not have the A antigen possess a preexisting, "natural" antibody to A. Likewise, individuals who lack the B antigen possess anti-B. In this respect the ABO system is different from other blood group systems, such as the **Rh blood group,** in that in these latter systems antibodies are not initially found within an individual if certain system antigens are absent. Antibodies that do exist to specific antigens are manufactured only if foreign antigens are introduced, as, for example, by transfusion. Because of this difference, the reaction to foreign antigens of the ABO system is immediate, whereas in the other systems, reactions may be delayed. In short, the ABO system was discovered first because it is the first to respond to foreign substances.

ABO blood group—blood group system discovered by Landsteiner in 1900 defined by agglutination (clotting) reactions of red blood cells to natural anti-A and anti-B antibodies. Blood type A reacts to only anti-A, type B reacts only to anti-B, type AB reacts to both, and type O reacts to neither.

Rh blood group—a complex system of blood antigens originally discovered by Landsteiner and Wiener in 1940 using blood from the rhesus monkey, which lent the first two letters of its name to the system. Rh antigens are controlled by 8 major genes or gene complexes yielding some 18 different phenotypes.

When incompatible blood is mixed together, a reaction results between the antigens present on the surface of the red blood cell and the antibody to it, which is present in the blood of a recipient. The antibody makes the foreign red blood cells clump together in clots. These clots are capable of blocking small blood vessels, often with fatal results.

Frequencies of the different blood groups have been shown to vary geographically, as Table 11–1 on page 280 demonstrates. How might natural selection have played a role in the origins of this variation in the first place?

When we look carefully at the data, we see that blood group polymorphisms cannot result from neutral mutation and genetic drift. One clue explaining blood group polymorphisms comes from their great antiquity. Antigens for the ABO system, for example, have been found to exist in all mammals and even in birds. The fact that polymorphisms still exist after such vast amounts of time demands the explanation that these polymorphisms must be balanced polymorphisms. Yet for a balanced situation to exist, some selective advantages must be found for the heterozygote. In a few examples that we have for heterozygotes the opposite has been found to be true. Heterozygotes are at a disadvantage in examples that involve **hemolytic incompatibility** between the mother and her fetus for both the ABO system and, especially, the Rh system (Figure 11–6).

Until quite recently, heterozygous fetuses were at direct risk for spontaneous abortion, a risk that increased as the mother conceived succeeding offspring. The blood group data, therefore, present a considerable paradox. The existence of multiple alleles, on the one hand, can be explained only by a balanced polymorphic situation, yet the supposedly favored heterozygote may be fatally at peril.

Blood group antigens stimulate the production of antibodies, which, in turn, function to eliminate foreign substances, including disease-causing agents, from an individual's circulatory system. Most of the studies attempted so far, however, have looked at individual antigen systems, such as the ABO system, and studied the various gene frequencies as if they existed in isolation from the other antigen systems. As with malaria, one, two, and perhaps three independent systems, each having something to do with the blood environment, may interact to produce a combined heterozygote advantage. In the blood group systems a dozen different antigen groups have been identified. If each one of these evolved as a response to a particular situation, such as malaria, we should easily be able to identify a causal relationship. That we have not yet been able to do so strengthens our assumption that the multiplicity of the blood groups themselves are the results of natural selection over long periods of time. With this thought in mind let us turn to the second-best-known blood group: the Rh system.

Rh incompatibility occurs in a pregnancy in which the fetus is an Rh+ (Dd) heterozygote while the mother is Rh– (dd). Because of the nature of the placental membrane, D antigens on the red blood cells of the offspring may cross over into the blood supply of the mother. As the

hemolytic incompatibility—destruction of red blood cells caused by the action of antibodies, resulting in release of hemoglobin into the plasma.

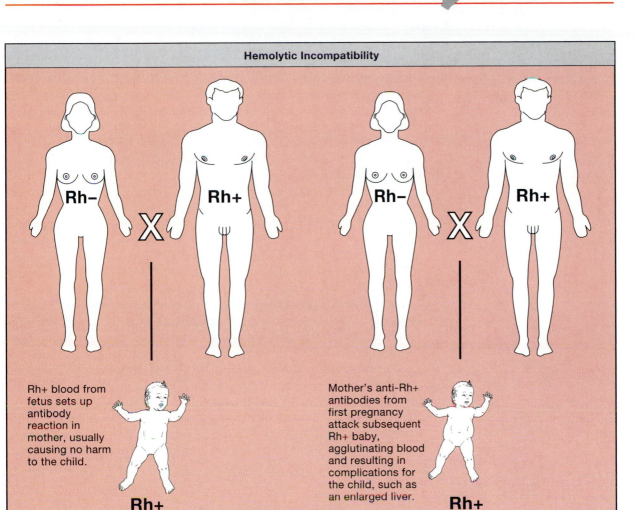

Figure 11–6 • Mechanism of hemolytic incompatibility between mother and fetus.

mother has no D alleles, her immune system responds by manufacturing an antibody to them, anti-D, which functions, as all antibodies do, to agglutinate the foreign D antigens and remove them from the mother's system. However, as red blood cells can cross the placental barrier from fetus to mother, so can the maternal anti-D antibodies travel from mother to offspring. If enough maternal anti-D is transferred to the fetus, it can incur hemolytic disease.

A mother's first pregnancy is generally a safe one, at least in regard to hemolytic disease. Under normal conditions no blood passes directly between mother and fetus. But about the time of birth, fetal red blood cells can transfer between the fetus and mother, at which time the mother's immune system begins to produce anti-D antibodies. In subsequent pregnancies residual anti-D antibodies can have a cumulative effect and do serious harm to the fetus.

If the fetus dies of hemolytic disease, its two alleles, D and d, are lost to the population gene pool. If a balanced polymorphism favoring the heterozygote genotype did not exist and each of the alleles D and d were of equal fitness, chance processes alone would lead to the loss over time of one or the other. In the Rh example hemolytic incompatibility clearly selects against the heterozygote, yet both D and d alleles remain in the gene pool. That this is true is a puzzle for human geneticists. The case of double incompatibility between the Rh and ABO blood groups may shed some light on the solution.

Like the Rh system, the ABO system also provides situations that may result in hemolytic incompatibility in the fetus. In fact, all ABO phenotypes are potentially incompatible if the fetus possesses an antigen that the mother does not. Cohen (1970a, b), supporting earlier work, showed how maternal–fetal pairs who were doubly incompatible for both ABO and Rh ran less risk of fetal death than if the fetus was incompatible only for one system or the other. We do not know why this is the case.

The protective effect of double incompatibility for the Rh system is better understood. Apparently, antibodies to A or B, which may normally circulate in the mother's system, attack those fetal red blood cells if they manage to get into the maternal circulation. The fact that the fetal red blood cells are destroyed thus prevents the mother's body from recognizing the presence of the D allele in the first place, preventing the production of the anti-D antibody.

Recognizing the possibility of many more instances where multiple incompatibility will have a selective advantage allows us to look at the blood group frequency data from a new perspective. Future research will probably shed light on the remainder of the blood group polymorphisms.

Skin Pigmentation

The anatomy, physiology, and genetics of the skin and its coloration are complicated. The skin is composed of two layers, an outer epidermis and an inner dermis. The coloration of the lower levels of the epidermis is what determines skin color. Coloration, on a light to dark scale, depends on the pigment **melanin.** Melanocytes, cells found in the epidermis, produce this brown pigment; actual skin color depends on how active the melanocytes are in producing melanin, since the number and density of these cells are the same in light- and dark-skinned individuals. In lighter skin one environmental factor affecting coloration is the sun's ultraviolet radiation. The red color of a "sunburn," the body's first response to excessive ultraviolet light, is the result of a concentration of hemoglobin near the skin's surface. A "suntan," the body's usual second response to excessive UV (ultraviolet) light, can also darken lightly pigmented skin by stimulating the production of additional melanin.

The genetics of skin color is not completely understood. Some researchers believe that, rather than a single locus of a major gene, many loci and their multiple alleles work in combination to determine a per-

melanin—from Greek meaning "black"; a dark brown or black pigment that occurs in the skin and hair.

son's pigmentation. One of the most common misconceptions about race concerns skin pigmentation. The lay public, in particular, often confuses race with skin color, as in "white race," "people of color," and "black race." Skin color is, indeed, a very noticeable anatomical characteristic of inherited human variation. However, it is not in itself a reliable indicator of population affinities. For example, Africans, the Dravidians of southern India, and native Austral-Asians all have darkly pigmented skin, but otherwise they share no particularly close genetic affinities. They are probably more closely related to lightly pigmented populations than to one another. This conclusion implies that skin color has been under strong selective forces and has changed relatively rapidly in recent human evolutionary history. To understand the variation in human skin color we must investigate its adaptive significance.

Human skin serves in a general adaptive sense to regulate the penetration of UV light. In the lower latitudes near the equator that experience intense UV radiation, pigmented epidermal skin serves to block the harmful rays of the sun from reaching the dermis. This prevents sunburn and, eventually, skin cancer from developing. For these reasons dark skin color has a great adaptive advantage for peoples of equatorial regions. That peoples living farther away from the equator are subjected to lesser amounts of ultraviolet radiation does not explain why lighter skin color is characteristic of those regions. The question of why lightly pigmented skin evolved is not so clearly answered.

We do know that sunlight, in addition to producing harmful effects on the human body in excessive amounts, also has beneficial effects. Vitamin D is produced in the skin and subcutaneous tissue when light penetrates and is absorbed there. Although Vitamin D can also be eaten in the form of fish or fortified milk, experimental results indicate that most of the body's content of the vitamin derives from sunlight (Cardinali and Wurtman, 1975). If Vitamin D is insufficient during growth, a condition known as **rickets** develops. In this disease the lower limbs become bowed outward and the pelvic bones are deformed because the bones are under-mineralized. Rickets has occurred frequently in many populations, such as African-Americans, whose darkly pigmented skin does not allow sufficient sunlight to penetrate to the dermis or with poor dietary intake of Vitamin D. The fossil record also shows that rickets occurred in the Neandertals in Ice Age northern Europe. With these facts in mind, many researchers believe that a more lightly pigmented skin in areas of reduced solar radiation would have been advantageous.

Thus, a model explaining the distribution of skin pigmentation was developed on the basis of Vitamin D requirements for individuals living in different environmental conditions. The Vitamin D hypothesis, however, fails to explain conclusively why various shades of skin color persist at different latitudes. Whereas an excess of Vitamin D can cause vitamin poisoning, affect proper kidney functioning, and cause calcification of soft tissues and abnormal calcification on bone, excessive exposure to UV light does not lead to such high levels of Vitamin D that toxicity occurs. Robins (1991) has leveled other criticisms at the

rickets—from Old English, meaning "twisted," a disease caused by deficiency of Vitamin D and characterized by the symptoms of poor calcification of bones, skeletal deformities, disturbance of growth, and generalized muscular weakness.

Vitamin D hypothesis, claiming rickets to be a disease of urbanization, not one particularly worrisome to our Paleolithic ancestors.

One other explanation for skin color distribution is based on wartime observations of different groups of soldiers and the effects cold climates had on them. Light-skinned soldiers were four times less likely to suffer frostbite than dark-skinned soldiers. Although the reason for this is not clearly understood, lighter-skinned people may have an advantage in cold climates, and this may have been a main factor that selected for lighter skin in early human populations migrating northward from Africa.

Clearly, skin color has adaptive value for people living under different environmental conditions. Nevertheless, the picture is clouded by many factors that may have contributed to the overall pattern of skin color distribution of modern peoples. We can be confident, however, that skin color is a product of natural selection and not a characteristic that can be or should be used as the primary criterion to delimit one specific population of people from another.

GENETIC INFLUENCE ON BEHAVIORAL VARIATION

Although human behavior has as its primary component the patterned learned behavior adopted by living and growing up in a society (*culture*) (Figure 11–7), many human behaviors also have a direct genetic basis. Among the mammals, primates show the highest amounts of behavioral variability, and humans show the highest level among primates. How much of this variability is due to the responsiveness of culture and learning, and how much is due to genetic variation, has been examined by our looking at behavioral differences between groups where cultural and genetic influences can be minimized. For example, studies on differences between males and females in the same culture, coupled with a functional interpretation of hormonal differences in behavior, attempt to relate behavior to biological sex differences. Studies of identical twins, who share the same genes, but may have different cultural experiences as they mature, have also provided important insights into the interplay of genetics and culture in behavior.

Part of the folklore of any human culture are stories describing behavioral differences. Of these, those stories that describe differences between men and women are probably the most common. For example, before the advent of empiricism Aristotle thought that men had more teeth than women. It would have been simple for Aristotle to open up the mouths of a number of men and women and simply count teeth, but he never did. The idea that men are more "intelligent" than women has been shown in scientific studies to be insupportable, but for centuries this idea has remained in place. It was not until 1920, for example, that U.S. society held women to be competent to vote. In many countries of the world, women's suffrage has yet to come to pass.

Figure 11–7 • The process of enculturation—learning a culture.

Twin Studies

Identical (monozygotic) twins who have been reared apart provide one of the simplest and most powerful focuses for disentangling the influence of environmental and genetic factors on human characteristics and their variable expression (Figure 11–8). The published report of *The Minnesota Study of Twins Reared Apart* (Bouchard et al., 1990) offers a basis for understanding the contributions of genetics versus environmental influences.

The total variance between any two individuals for a given trait is composed of variance caused by genetic differences and variance caused by environmental factors. In the twin study, for traits such as IQ, variance caused by genetic factors has been found to equal approximately 70% of the total. This suggests that, although parents may be able to affect their children's rate of cognitive skill acquisition, they probably have little influence on the ultimate level attained. These findings do not imply that traits like IQ cannot be enhanced. The Bouchard study did not define or limit what might conceivably be achieved in an optimal environment, but it did indicate that in the broad middle class of an industrial society, two-thirds of the observed variances of IQ could be traced to genetic variation.

Race, IQ, and Social Class

The heritability of intelligence has been difficult to predict, because the actual genetic basis of intelligence is not well understood. The Minnesota Twin Study may provide us with one estimation of heritability, but we must consider a number of other factors before we can apply the data from specific individuals to whole populations.

In a variety of ways, quantitative individual differences in intelligence can be recognized, and these differences may roughly indicate the genetic component that relates to them. However, when we step away from measurements based on individual differences and attempt to apply them to broader categories, such as populations, we must ask additional questions. One question concerns the range of intelligence for all populations. Is there any evidence to suggest that whole groups of people fall below (or rise above) some hypothetical worldwide average?

The consequences of the answers to these questions are not simply academic. For example, for many years the Commonwealth of Virginia had a law in effect that allowed the state to sterilize any "mentally deficient" individual without his or her consent. This law permitted the state to perform over 7,500 sterilizations during the period 1924 to 1972. In theory, such a law had the potential to include whole groups of people considered to be "mentally" inferior.

What is "intelligence" and how has it been measured? From a biological point of view we might consider intelligence as a manifestation of the innate intellectual capacity of the brain (Birdsell, 1981). However,

Figure 11–8 • Identical twins studied in the Minnesota Study.

innate intelligence cannot yet be defined in precise genetic terms. Psychologists have usually looked at intelligence by testing such skills as memory, problem solving, ability to synthesize information, and motivation (more difficult to measure). Some psychologists have listed up to 120 different components for intelligence (Bodmer and Cavalli-Sforza, 1976).

Intelligence is usually measured by administering a standardized test to an individual and then scoring that test. One common intelligence test is the well-known Stanford-Binet IQ test. **IQ** or "intelligence quotient" measures a person's "mental age" based on the test score and divides it by his or her chronological age. The test sets the average response at 100, with the range for average intelligence falling between 90 and 110. Because the test supposedly measures a number of abilities, often individuals score differently on the various test sections. Furthermore, over an individual's life span an IQ can change as much as 30 points.

In the United States the most questionable use of IQ testing has been in response to a fairly consistent and large body of data that suggests the average IQ of African-Americans to be about 15 points below that of white Americans. In a number of cases (Jensen, 1969, 1980) educators and others have attributed these differences to genetics. This contention, however, is rejected by most anthropologists and evolutionary biologists. A number of tests have confirmed their stance. If white Americans on the average were more intelligent than African-Americans and the difference were due to genetics, African-Americans with a high degree of European admixture should do better on IQ tests than African-Americans who do not have a high degree of European admixture. They do not.

Japanese children from a socioeconomically disadvantaged group, the Buraku-min, scored on the average 16 points below other Japanese children, roughly comparable to the difference between white Americans and African-Americans. Yet there is no genetic way to distinguish the Buraku-min as a group; they can be distinguished from other Japanese only by their place of birth or current residence. Such examples indicate that "intelligence" as measured by standardized tests has a strong environmental component (Birdsell, 1981:386–387).

Other environmental factors affecting IQ scores—diet, disease, educational quality, and social class—all must figure into the formula. Also the design of IQ tests is socioeconomically biased because of the cultural differences between those making up such tests and those taking them. No one yet has constructed a culture-free IQ test.

Whatever the ancient origins and functions of genetic variability are, repercussions of variation in contemporary society are pervasive and important. A human species whose members did not vary genetically with respect to significant cognitive and motivational attributes and who were uniformly average by current standards would have created a very different society from the one we know. Modern society not only augments the influence of genotype on behavioral variability, but permits this variability to contribute reciprocally to the rapid pace of cultural change.

IQ—Intelligence Quotient; a score on a standardized psychological test designed in western Europe and North America to measure "an individual's aggregate capacity to act purposefully, think rationally, and deal effectively with his environment."

SUMMARY

1. Humans are one of the most biologically variable of animal species, a fact that reflects the wide range of environments and habitats in which people live. Biological anthropologists measure this variability both quantitatively, as in stature and weight, and qualitatively, as in the presence or absence of the shovel-shaped incisor.

2. Although the level of heterozygosity (between 10 and 15%) at loci among individuals within a population is only slightly lower than the differences seen between populations, population variation shows a geographic component that is a result of evolution. Local, geographically defined populations of humans are sometimes termed "races." "Race," however, is a term that has been frequently misused and is not synonymous with "ethnic group."

3. Although we know that geographically isolated populations develop their own unique characteristics by mutation, genetic drift, and natural selection, it is difficult to categorize human "races" because of the continual ebb and flow of genetic exchange that occurs between individuals. It is also not scientifically useful to do so. Modern genetic studies show that some traditionally measured characteristics, such as skin color, are not good guides to actual population groupings.

4. The evolutionary forces of mutation, genetic drift, migration, and natural selection contribute to other aspects of human variability. Certain characteristics arise in individuals and spread by chance that have no discernible selective advantage. Other variable conditions, such as sickle-cell anemia, provide heterozygotes in malarial areas an advantage in their ability to resist the disease.

5. There may be considerable genetic influence on behavioral variation, as well as on morphophysiological variation, an area where twin studies have been useful, especially in the area of the inheritance of intelligence. No convincing evidence, however, exists for genetic differences in intelligence between human populations.

CRITICAL-THINKING QUESTIONS

1. Name three factors that influence human biological variation.
2. Describe the process of geographic isolation and the role it plays in human biological variation.
3. Explain the heterozygote advantage selected for in malarial regions and how this relates to human genetic variability.
4. Is skin color a good indicator of a person's racial group? Elaborate.
5. Are IQ tests a valid indication of intelligence? Explain.

SUGGESTED READINGS

Brues, A. 1977. *People and Races*. New York: Macmillan. Discussions of genetics and human variation and the concept of race. This 8-chapter volume focuses on specific aspects of human variation such as blood groups and pigmentation. It concludes with a statement on new and future races of humankind.

Harrison, G. A., J. M. Tanner, D. R. Pilbeam, and P. T. Baker. 1988. *Human Biology: An Introduction to Human Evolution, Variation, Growth, and Adaptability,* 3rd ed. Oxford, England: Oxford University Press. Detailed text that reviews the subjects of human evolution, human genetics, biological variation in modern human populations, human growth, and human ecology. The concluding section includes material on nutritional ecology, climatic adaptation, disease, and population stability.

Johnston, F. 1973. *Microevolution of Human Populations*. Englewood Cliffs, N.J.: Prentice Hall. Population genetics and the Hardy-Weinberg equilibrium are discussed in relation to natural selection and microevolution in human populations. Major contribution of this text is its discussion of the search for natural selection.

Molnar, S. J. 1998. *Races, Types and Ethnic Groups: The Problem of Human Variation,* 4th ed. Englewood Cliffs, N.J.: Prentice Hall. Discussions include the biological basis for human variation, the perception of human differences, and the distribution of those differences in world populations. The text reviews what we know about the adaptive value of human variation. Race, behavior, and intelligence, along with some speculations on the future of the human species, are also discussed.

Woodward, U. 1992. *Human Heredity and Society*. St. Paul, Minn.: West Publishing Co. General review of genetics, evolution, populations, and species. Includes discussions of human behavior and intelligence, social Darwinism, sociobiology, and genetic engineering.

CHAPTER 12

The Human Life Cycle: Human Biology, Growth, and Adaptability

We have seen how populations adapt to changing environmental conditions over time. This is evolution, a long-term response involving changes in the genetic makeup of a population. As a result of evolution, the human organism is a compendium of physiological and morphological adaptations. Some of these basic adaptations are very old, extending back to early vertebrate and even prevertebrate ancestors (see Chapters 2 and 4). Others are much more recent evolutionary acquisitions.

We have already determined that individuals in a population vary genetically from one another (see Chapter 3). Variability in gene pools offers the possibility that some individuals will be successful under different or changing environmental situations. The **genetic plasticity** of a species is the degree to which individuals can survive under increasingly diverse environmental situations. The different ways that individuals respond to changing environmental circumstances are measures of a species' genetic plasticity. Throughout an individual's life cycle, a dynamic interaction exists between environment and physiology, and this interaction is the subject of this chapter.

A species' ability to adapt to different environmental conditions and the relation of this ability to the evolution and biology of the population is **adaptability.** This term refers also to an individual's reaction to changes in environmental conditions, and it includes any biochemical, physiological, or behavioral response that improves the ability to function. Within the genetic limits of any species, each individual can, in

genetic plasticity–ability of a developing organism to alter its form and function in conformity with demands of the immediate environment.

adaptability–range of physiological and anatomical changes and adjustments allowed by a species' adaptation.

varying degrees, make short-term changes in his or her physiological response to specific environmental situations. In higher altitudes, for example, the body's response to hypoxia (the lowering of the level of oxygen in the blood) is to increase both breathing and heart rate. This response increases both blood flow and the partial pressure of oxygen in the lungs.

HUMAN GROWTH STUDIES

In this chapter on adaptability, the subject of growth and development is also examined. The study of growth is important from at least two different perspectives. First, as J. M. Tanner (1989), the British growth specialist, put it: Growth is a mirror of the condition of society. Growth rates and development respond to the environmental conditions that surround an individual during its life. Less than optimal environmental conditions can retard the realization of the genetic potential of an individual, for example in the case of stature, which will not be recouped even as that individual matures. Second, the study of growth provides important clues towards an understanding of evolution (Bogin, 1995).

The process by which human beings develop biologically from conception to death is *growth*. The study of human growth is a broad field and one to which biological anthropologists and human biologists have made and continue to make significant contributions. Tanner suggests in his *A History of the Study of Human Growth* (1981) that there were three main "impulses," or themes, in the development of the field.

First, there have been social motivations for growth studies. Investigations of the physical and physiological development of children began, for example, in Britain in response to the child labor reform movement during the nineteenth century. At this time, eruption of the second molar began to be taken as a sign that a child had reached puberty and was old enough to work. The second molar thereby became known as the "factory molar."

Second, some studies of growth are motivated by medical concerns. Included in this category are studies undertaken to monitor the physical and developmental progress of children. The earliest modern studies in biological anthropology in the United States were human growth studies supervised by Franz Boas. Boas, sometimes referred to as "the father of American anthropology," undertook in the late 1890s large-scale anthropometric studies of American school-children in order to establish for the U.S. Department of Education standards for weight and height at each chronological age. Also included in this category of growth studies are those relating to nutritional requirements for normal growth, the effects of environment on growth, and medical aspects of growth and its abnormalities.

Third, evolutionary studies of growth are prompted by a desire to understand the interaction of growth and the evolutionary biology of the human species. Of the three kinds of study, these have the longest history. For example, Louis Bolk's (1926) **homunculus theory** of human evolution was the most clearly enunciated version of the idea that early human fossils would be discovered looking very much like fetal and preadult stages in human development.

Comparing the rates of growth between closely related species can provide important insight into the different biology of each (Figure 12–1). Brain growth rate in humans is different from that in the apes.

homunculus theory—held that human ancestors when discovered would look similar to early stages of modern human development.

Figure 12–1 • Transformation grids comparing (*a*) fetal and adult chimpanzee skulls to (*b*) fetal and adult human skulls. The relative amount of distortion of the grid lines overlying the adult skull proportions indicates the amount of growth of different parts of the skull. (From Bogin, 1988)

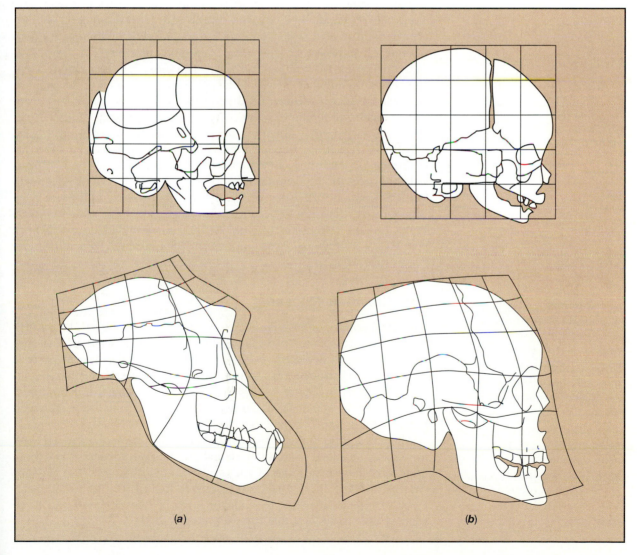

(*a*) (*b*)

The accelerated fetal brain growth rate in humans continues postnatally to about one year of age. In the apes, postnatal brain growth slows to the adult rate immediately after birth. This is in part due to the extension of childhood years in humans as well as a reflection of the birth process. In humans, birth is a difficult process, as large-headed newborns exceed the normal dimensions of the mother's birth canal. Such a situation at birth demands the smallest possible head size (and, thus, brain size). The accelerated rate of postnatal brain growth is a way by which humans, less developed at birth, "catch up" with the comparably aged apes.

How Growth Is Defined

Growth is usually distinguished from **development,** or that part of growth that occurs prior to birth and consists of the differentiation of various tissues and body parts of the embryo and fetus. "Growth" has sometimes been defined as "increase in size," "development" as "increase in tissue diversity." Here, both growth and development are considered as components of the same continuous process.

Growth takes place in several ways. The most common pattern is an increase in the number of cells. Soft body structures, such as the brain or muscles, develop by **interstitial growth,** where cells proliferate from many centers within the structure. Muscle tissue represents a unique pattern of growth in that fibers are formed by the fusion of several cells, which means that each fiber has more than one nucleus. Hard or rigid structures, on the other hand, such as bones or teeth, develop by **appositional growth,** the laying down of new layers on top of those already formed. Counting these layers can tell us how old an individual is or was. Growth does not proceed at the same rate in all tissues (Figure 12–2). Indeed, differential growth, defined as the relative growth rates between two structures, is an important distinguishing characteristic between species.

How Growth Is Measured

Biological anthropologists measure growth and other physical attributes of living humans using instruments designed for the purpose. The subdiscipline that is dedicated to the measurement of the human body is known as **anthropometry.** As in the study of skeletal remains, a number of landmarks (Figure 12–3) have been defined for the living body. These serve to standardize measurements and comparisons between human groups and between individuals.

There is a good but not absolute correlation of chronological age with measures of skeletal maturation, dental eruption, and increase in overall body size. In assessing age by the use of biological criteria, as many criteria as possible should be used to ensure the most accurate estimate. Even so, precision within a range of error of between two and three years is usually the best that can be accomplished.

development–embryological differentiation of organs and tissues; sometimes considered the earliest stage of growth.

interstitial growth–growth by new cell formation throughout the mass of a structure, tissue, or organ.

appositional growth–growth by adding of layers at a specific point or plane.

anthropometry–the portion of physical anthropology concerned with measurement of the human body.

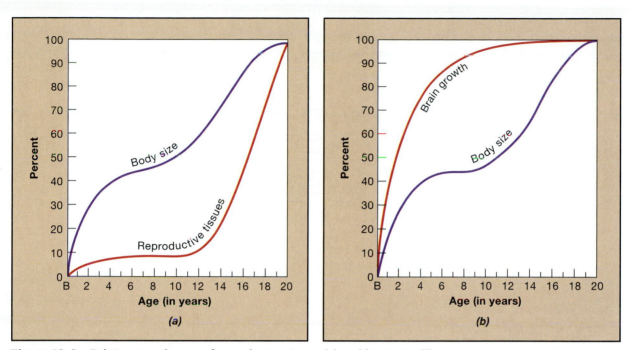

Figure 12–2 • Relative growth rates of reproductive tissues (*a*) and brain size (*b*), compared to overall body size.

The Seven Stages of Human Growth

There are seven stages of growth (Bogin, 1995): **embryonic,** which takes place before birth, during which there is rapid growth but little differentiation in function of various tissues; **infancy, childhood, juvenile,** and **adolescence,** during which a balance between growth and differentiation of tissue functions exists; **maturity,** when functional activity is the primary activity and a steady replacement of cells takes place; and **old age,** when the rate of cell death is greater than the rate of replacement. Primates have a proportional relationship between the length of the seven stages that remains relatively constant throughout the order (Figure 12–4). As maximum life span increases, the embryonic, prematurity, maturity, and old age life periods proportionally lengthen. Humans have the longest life span of the primates and the longest period of prematurity growth.

Bogin has characterized each of the early stages with both biological and behavioral features. Infancy is defined as that period when the individual is nourished almost exclusively by its mother's milk. This stage ends upon weaning, which in preindustrialized societies occurs at about three years of age. Childhood is a period of continued dependency, characterized by reliance on others for feeding and protection. It ends when the brain has reached its adult weight, somewhere about seven years of age. The juvenile period occurs between the end of childhood and puberty, the onset of which for girls is about age ten and for boys

embryonic–that period of growth prior to birth, especially weeks 3 through 8; growth during the last six months of gestation is sometimes referred to as fetal growth.

infancy–earliest stage of postpartum growth, extending from birth to the time of weaning.

childhood–the period of growth from weaning to the attainment of adult brain size.

juvenile–the period of growth between attainment of adult brain size and the onset of puberty.

adolescence–the period of growth between puberty and the attainment of full adult stature and sexual maturity.

maturity–life cycle stage typified by steady state replacement of cells and cessation of growth.

old age–life cycle stage typified by a greater rate of cell death than replacement.

Figure 12–3 • Somatological landmarks used in measurements and assessments of growth. (From Georges Olivier, *Practical Anthropology,* copyright © 1969. Courtesy of Charles C. Thomas, Publisher, Springfield, Illinois.)

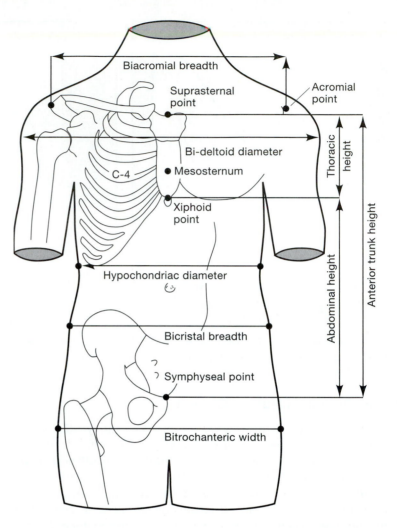

about two years later. Postpubescent growth and the development of secondary sexual characteristics marks the adolescent stage, which ends when adult stature and full reproductive maturity are reached. On the average, adolescence ends, and maturity or adulthood begins, by about 19 years of age for women and 21 to 25 years of age for men.

The human pattern of growth after birth is unique among the mammals. Several stages, such as childhood and adolescence, have no counterpart in the growth patterns of other animals. For the largest-brained member of the primates the relatively slow physical growth of childhood holds advantages in that it extends the period of brain development and provides time for the development of technical as well as social skills. In addition, Bogin (1995:53) believes that childhood should also be viewed as a feeding adaptation in which the child may be provisioned with food by kin, removing this exclusive burden from the mother.

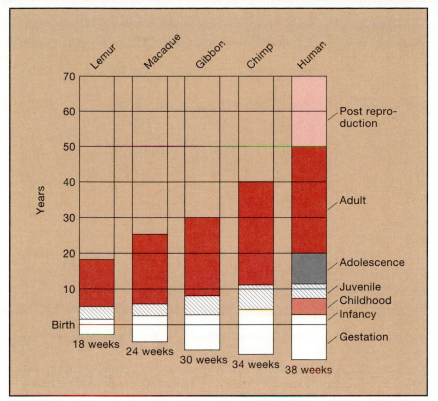

Figure 12–4 • Progressive prolongation of the life stages among the primates.

Evolutionarily speaking, there is a reproductive advantage to humans in shortening the length of infancy by inserting childhood between the end of infancy and the juvenile period. The childhood stage frees the mother from nursing and the impediments that continuous nursing places on ovulation. Thus, human females have a potentially shorter interval between births of offspring, an adaptation offering a reproductive advantage over the closely related apes (Table 12–1). The reduction of the birth spacing interval enables humans to produce more offspring as compared with apes.

The stage of human adolescence is also unique among the primates in that it is marked by a rapid acceleration in growth of the skeleton that accompanies the onset of sexual maturation. Growth seems to seek a *target,* rather than to proceed according to a strict schedule. If a spurt in growth that would normally have occurred at a certain age is delayed because of poor nutrition or illness, when conditions improve there is a rapid period of growth to "catch up." This aspect of growth is termed **canalization,** because there are certain channels or paths that it will follow. For normal and healthy individuals this growth spurt at its peak for stature velocity averages 9 to 10.3 cm (3.5 to 4 in.)/year in boys and 7.1 to 9.0 cm (2.8 to 3.5 in.)/year in girls (Tanner and Whitehouse, 1976). This growth spurt is primarily responsible for the average 12.6 cm (5 in.)

canalization—the directed trajectory of growth in certain directions even if normal growth spurts are delayed.

Table 12–1 • Comparative Fertility in Three Different Human Groups and in the Chimpanzee				
	Chimpanzee	!Kung (Botswana)	Agta (Philippines)	Ache (Paraguay)
Menarche (Age in years)	8.8	16.6	17.1	14.3
Age at First Birth (Years)	14	19.9	20.1	18.5
Birth Spacing (Years)	5.6	4.1	3.05	3.2
Fertility Rate (Average Number of Children)	2.0	4.7	—	—
Average Reproductive Life-Span (Years)	25–30	36	—	—

Data from Smith (1992a).

in height difference between males and females. The timing of adolescent growth is different for males and females (Figure 12–5). Females complete the growth spurt before becoming fertile. Males, on the other hand, begin the growth spurt after they have begun to produce sperm.

For many girls around the world, adolescence begins at menarche, about the age of 12.5 years, on average, usually followed by a period of one to three years of sterility. During this period menstrual cycling occurs but without ovulation. Females, also, do not attain adult pelvic inlet size until 17 to 18 years, as the pelvis has its own pattern of growth, slower than that of the reproductive tract. Taking everything into account, a female does not reach adult reproductive maturity until about the age of 20 to 24 years. Younger mothers face higher risks of spontaneous abortion and are twice as likely to give birth to babies of lower than average birth weight.

The pattern of development for boys differs from that of girls in that boys become fertile at an early age and then attain adult size and the physical appearance of adult males. The median age for sperm production is about 13.4 years, yet cross-cultural evidence shows that few males are successful as fathers until they reach an age somewhere in their twenties. In the United States, for example, statistics report that only 4% of all births are fathered by men under 20 years old. The survival advantage of adolescence for boys is that, with increasing blood testosterone levels, they become more interested in adult activities and begin to behave more like adult males, while at the same time continuing to look like boys.

Bogin summarizes his argument for the adaptive value of adolescence with the following. Though they are still infertile, adolescent girls are perceived by adults as adults, and this maximizes their ability to learn fe-

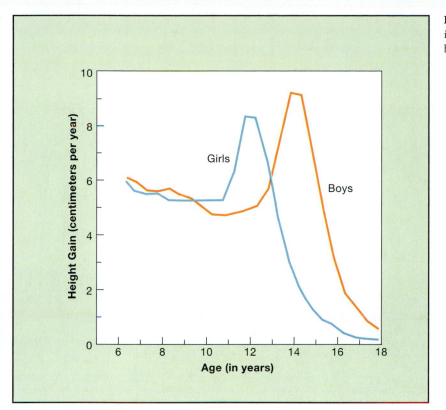

Figure 12–5 • Adolescent spurt in height growth for girls and boys.

male adult social roles. Boys, on the other hand, are sexually mature while they learn male adult social roles, but they are not perceived as adults nor are they taken seriously in their attempts to model adult behavior. The advantage to the adolescent growth spurt is that this unique style of social and cultural learning can occur.

Genetic and Hormonal Control of Growth

The genetic message for growth is mediated through the production of secretions from the *endocrine glands* (Figure 12–6). Several secretions of endocrine glands, known as *hormones,* are important for growth in human beings. The most important of these is **somatotropin** or growth hormone, which is secreted by the **pituitary gland** at the base of the brain. Growth hormone is secreted episodically, and secretion may be affected by a number of factors, including stress and exercise. The actual secretion of the growth hormone is regulated by the **hypothalamus.**

   Thyroid hormone, secreted by the thyroid gland in the neck, is also important in growth from birth through adolescence. The lack of either of these hormones in sufficient quantities will result in retardation of growth and small size. The artificial administering of growth hormones and their chemical substitutes (steroids) enhances muscle development

somatotropin–pituitary or growth hormone, important in initiating the adolescent growth spurt.

pituitary gland–an endocrine gland at the base of the cerebral cortex.

hypothalamus–part of the ancient forebrain; located "below the thalamus" at the base of the brain's third ventricle, and important in autonomic nervous system functions such as endocrine gland activity.

thyroid hormone–also known as thyroxine, an iodine-containing hormone secreted by the thyroid gland and important in regulating the rate of tissue metabolism.

Figure 12–6 • Endocrine glands of the human body.

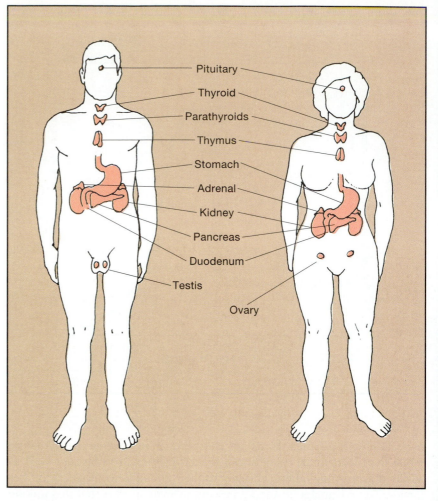

in athletes, but it also leads to hypertrophy, or excessive development, and damage to certain internal organs, especially the liver. At adolescence, gonadal hormones (from the ovaries in the female and from the testes in the male), particularly *testosterone* in the male, and the hormone secreted by the adrenal gland (above the kidney), *androgen,* are added to the already present pituitary and thyroid hormones.

Growth and Development: A Guide to Evolutionary History

The study of growth is one important way biologists shed light on how evolution works. There is a general correspondence in the stages of a species' embryological growth and the major stages of its phylogenetic history. That this is so is not surprising. Evolution utilized the structural blueprint at hand to adapt to new conditions. As evolution has proceeded, the end results of development and growth of species through time have changed dramatically, but the early stages of differentiation have been much more conservative. For this reason the embryos of sharks, chickens, dogs, and humans are all similar, but as growth proceeds the species-specific pattern becomes clearly expressed. The brain in human embryos, for example, shows relatively more growth than the brain in embryos of other species at the same level of development. Nevertheless, the sequence in which structures develop reflects to some degree the sequence in which they evolved. This principle can be of use when paleontologists attempt to determine the "primitive" or "derived" nature of anatomical traits. The embryological development of the horse, for example, clearly shows that its single-toed foot develops from a five-toed appendage, a conclusion well-documented in the fossil record.

One of the ways in which evolution produces species differences is by altering growth patterns, that is, by retarding, accelerating, or truncating the growth of certain parts of the body relative to others. Generally, species that are far removed phylogenetically from one another diverge in their patterns of growth early in their developmental histories. More closely related species diverge in growth patterns much later. The later stages of growth have been the foci of evolutionary changes that separate humans from our closest primate relatives. Human and chimpanzee embryos are virtually indistinguishable until just before birth. A chimpanzee embryo, for example, could grow into near-human form if its brain and lower limbs grew relatively faster or for a longer time, and its lower face, canine teeth, and arms grew more slowly or for a shorter time. The evolutionary changes in rates of growth are termed **heterochrony** (McKinney and McNamara, 1991).

There are two categories of heterochrony. The first alters growth patterns by retarding the growth of certain parts of the body while normal sexual development proceeds. This results in an adult of the new species looking like the juvenile form of the ancestral species. This juvenilization is known as **pedomorphosis.**

Pedomorphosis is important in human evolution because it explains many specific human anatomical traits. Adult humans in many characteristics resemble juvenile nonhuman primates (see Figure 12–1). Like infants of other species, adult humans have relatively large heads, the head is flexed toward the ventrum of the body, the body is largely hairless, and there is a relatively high retention of body fat. There are likely a number of selective reasons for these pedomorphic characteristics in humans. No doubt large brain size (accounting for a large head), bipedalism (accounting for balanced or "flexed" head position), regulation of temperature (relating to hairlessness allowing effective sweating), and long-term energy storage (accounting for fat retention) all play a role in the selection for pedomorphic characteristics.

The second category of heterochrony is **peromorphosis,** or adultification of body form. Evolution can produce species differences by continuing growth for a longer period of time, accelerating development in some of the life stages, or adding additional stages to the end of the life cycle of descendant species. An example of peromorphosis in human evolution is the growth of the relatively long lower limbs (Shea, 1993).

heterochrony—Greek meaning "different time"; refers to the changes in rate of growth characteristic of species' evolutionary divergence from an ancestral species.

pedomorphosis—the retention of a juvenile stage in some part of a descendant species' morphology or behavior, in comparison with its ancestral species.

peromorphosis—the extension of growth or "adultification" of some part of the morphology or behavior of a descendant species, in comparison with its ancestral species.

secular trends–trends in growth or morphological characteristics that are attributable to transient environmental factors, such as nutrition and disease, and not to genetic adaptation.

Secular Trends in Growth and Maturation

The reduction in the number of infectious diseases and overall improved nutrition has allowed certain populations to achieve more of their genetic potential for growth. In many countries we have, over time, observed increases in height and weight and a decrease in the age of menarche. Because these trends are not always confined to the upper economic segment of a population, we deduce that a better balance in diet, with the regular consumption of essential minerals and vitamins, must certainly be more important than some single factor increase, such as calories. We study **secular trends,** those that we observe from one generation to the next, to understand the effects, over time, of nutrition, socioeconomic factors, and general health conditions on populations.

In Western Europe and North America studies have demonstrated several important trends. J. M. Tanner (1981) has shown that there was a decrease in the age of menarche: from average ages of between 15 to nearly 17 in the 1800s to the current 12.5 to 14.5 years in the 1940s (Figure 12–7). However, women in advantaged socioeconomic conditions experience menarche about 12 to 18 months earlier than poor women. This is primarily due to the generally better level of nutrition in the advantaged group. Studies have shown that when lean body mass (LBM) has reached a critical point, menarche will occur. The ratio of body fat to lean body mass prior to puberty is about 1 to 5. At menarche this ratio increases to about 1 to 3.

Figure 12–7 • Graph of secular trend in decrease in age of menarche in Western European and North American girls. (From Malina, 1975)

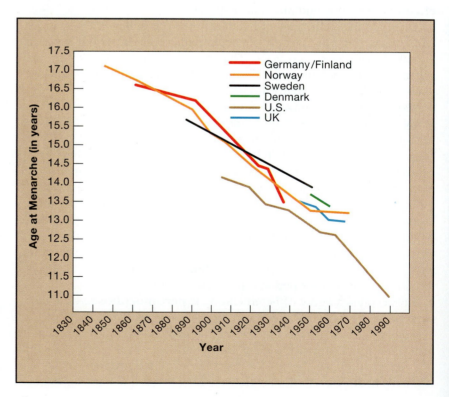

In one of the classic studies of human growth, the anthropologist Franz Boas measured the stature and head diameters of European immigrants to the United States, and then compared them with the same measurements of their children who were born and reared in the United States. He found that stature in the children was somewhat higher than in their European parents and that head diameters were larger as well. At the same time, secular trends were observed in European-American males who lived in North America. At all ages, males living in the 1960s were taller than their counterparts living in 1880 (Figure 12–8).

Growth and Development in Different Human Groups

The genetic messages for growth may differ from one human population to another. For example, anatomist A. Abbie (1977) found that Australian aborigines showed growth curves similar to Europeans' up to the age of five to six. After that point the length of the lower limbs in aborigine children increased rapidly. Adult aborigines have on average longer legs than do Europeans. Similar patterns also show up when comparisons between individuals of European and African descent are made (Figure 12–9).

Bogin, Wall, and MacVean (1992) studied two ethnic groups in Guatemala: Mayas and members of a higher socioeconomic group called *ladinos*. Mayan children are on average shorter than *ladino* children of the same age. Is this difference due to genetic differences or to nutritional and environmental differences? The mean difference in height between Mayan and *ladino* boys is established during childhood and maintained without significant change during adolescence. Girls of the two groups, on the other hand, established differences in mean height during childhood that increased during adolescence, and Mayan girls, even though their adolescent period was shorter than *ladinas,* had a

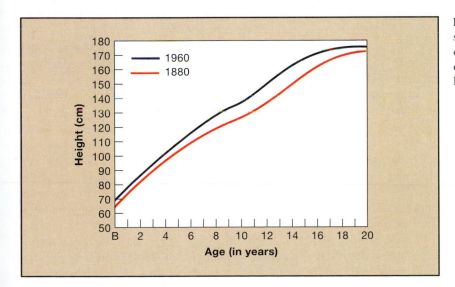

Figure 12–8 • Comparison of stature between American-born children of European descent and earlier populations of the same heritage. (From Malina, 1975)

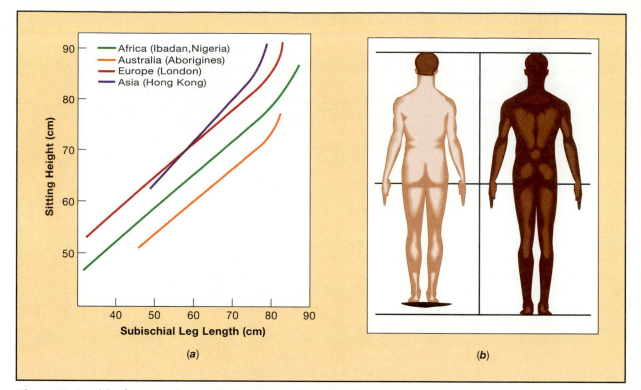

Figure 12–9 • (*a*) Africans and Australian aborigines have longer legs compared to Europeans and Asians, relative to sitting height. (*b*) Olympic 400 m runners. Comparison of physiques of two individuals, European (left) and African (right), both having the same sitting height. (From Tanner, 1964)

slower rate of growth at all ages. In contrast to the Mayan boys, Mayan girls do not show a delay in maturation. From many studies it seems that girls in general possess genetics that override or "buffer" some environmental effects on adolescent growth. As a consequence, Mayan girls appear to proceed through adolescence more in accordance with genetically determined timing for development than Mayan boys.

Although genetics may play a greater role in the timing of growth in girls than in boys, it is not necessarily a useful explanation for the differences between the two ethnic groups of children. When we compare the Mayan and *ladino* study with others in which poor nutrition and health are environmental factors, similar patterns of difference emerge. Data from rural India and Gambia reveal boys who, along with the Mayans, show slower growth velocities and longer periods of growth during childhood and adolescence and end up significantly shorter in stature than cohorts who are better nourished and healthier.

Secular studies of Mayan children living in Florida and Los Angeles have shown that these immigrants are significantly taller and heavier than Mayan children living in Guatemala. Although they are still shorter, on the average, than children of African-Americans or Mexican-Americans living in the United States, they appear to be in the process of a trend leading to increased stature. The average increase of 5.5 centimeters (2.2 in.) in height for Mayan children reared in the United States is substantial. This illustrates clearly the fact that socioeconomic improvement is an important factor influencing growth, and that the greater the deprivation the more it affects growth potential.

A case in which genetics overrides environment is among the Efe pygmies of eastern Congo (formerly Zaire) (Figure 12–10), studied by Bailey (1991). The Efe are among the smallest of modern humans, males averaging 1.42 meters (4 ft. 8 in.) and females 1.35 meters (4 ft. 5 in.). Efe babies at birth are smaller than babies born to a neighboring group, the Lese, even though nutritional and environmental factors are similar. Efe show slower growth throughout childhood and a slower peak velocity of growth at adolescence. Their small body size has evolved through natural selection, possibly for greater heat dissipation in their hot, humid environment, or possibly in response to negotiating dense forest undergrowth.

Figure 12–10 • The Efe of eastern Congo.

Tanner makes an important distinction between the nutritional effects on rate of growth during development and those affecting the adult condition. He observes that nutrition appears to affect rate first: growth slowdowns occur in undernourished children (along with the young of animals in general). This regulation of growth is an important adaptation among animals to counter the uncertainties of the food supply; that is, as a conservation method, slowdowns are periods awaiting better times for growth optimization.

Responses to Modernization and the Urban Environment

Living in modern urban environments has put other kinds of stress on human populations. Changes in diet, in the routine of physical activity, in stress levels, and in lifestyle may all, in various ways, affect human biology. Any of these factors may have an immediate effect on increasing blood pressure, for example, that in itself can contribute to many health problems, such as heart disease and stroke (Figure 12–11). There also may be longer-term consequences that affect growth.

In previous sections we have discussed the fact that, in our evolutionary history, urban life has been a relatively recent cultural situation. Up until 1950, much of the world's population still lived as peasant farmers in small social groups, much as humans have done since the agricultural revolution 12,000 years or so ago. Urban life has created both environmental and social situations that have considerably modified our earlier lifestyles. While improvements in health and nutrition have allowed individuals in many populations to reach more of their genetic potential for growth, urban environments have exacted a price.

To give one example, although the majority of the world's societies permit some use of tobacco and alcohol, consumption has been overwhelmingly reserved for males; however, urban environments allow the

Figure 12–11 • One example of the effects of modernization on male diastolic blood pressure is that blood pressure tends to increase with age. These are common findings in studies such as this one, performed in the Gilbert Islands, South Pacific. (From Eaton et al., 1989)

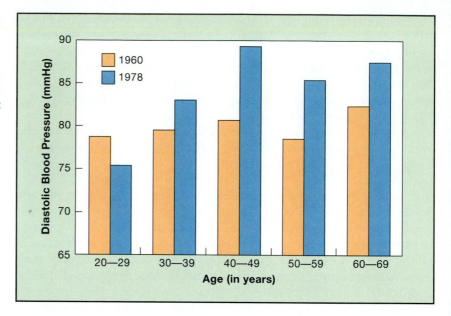

relaxation of these cultural rules and sometimes encourage women of childbearing years to drink and smoke. Both tobacco and alcohol use are clearly responsible for poor fetal health and slower postpartum growth: the average birth weight of children born to women who smoke is less than that of children born to women who do not smoke. Although there is medical controversy as to just how much alcohol pregnant women can safely consume, an excess can cause "fetal alcohol syndrome," which may result in newborns who have overall smaller body size, smaller heads with possible facial deformities, organ disorders, and a chance of reduced intelligence.

Psychological stress also has been proven to affect growth. Infants and children who have been exposed to continual emotional stress from family breakups, among other factors, show reduced growth patterns. Psychological stress may contribute to a reduced appetite and difficulty in sleeping. We know, for example, that growth hormones are commonly secreted into the bloodstream during the first few hours of sleep. If the normal level of growth hormone is reduced as a consequence of disturbed sleep, overall growth may also be reduced.

Certainly urban societies, as opposed to traditional ones, are affected by greater levels of many different kinds of pollution. For example, some decreases in average height may be attributable to the presence of toxic waste and noise. In a study of Japanese children who lived close to Osaka International Airport, Schell and Ando (1991) concluded that their observations of shorter than average height in their sample could be attributed to noise pollution and psychological stress generated by continual noise, which creates disturbed sleep patterns and reduced secretions of growth hormones.

HUMAN ADAPTABILITY TO ENVIRONMENT

Individual humans respond physiologically to changes in many different environmental conditions. However, it seems that whereas humans adapt to a wide range of climates, climate apparently has little effect on growth rate. If the age at menarche is used as one criterion of growth rate, studies show that for well-nourished girls this event is not perceptibly affected by major climatic differences. For example, girls in Nigeria average 13.3 years of age at menarche, while Eskimo girls average 13.8 years of age. Compare this to the average 13.2 years of age for girls raised in Burma, who grow up in hot climates where temperatures frequently reach 45°C (113°F). All three of these groups also closely approximate the age of menarche of European girls (Tanner, 1989:146).

Newman (1970) characterized humans as "linear in build, large, meaty, hairless, and sweaty." These attributes came about by adaptation to a certain set of environmental conditions (hot, dry, terrestrial) and a certain ecological niche (large terrestrial home range, omnivorous, and culture-bearing), yet they allow the human species to be extremely adaptable throughout a range of modern environments. By understanding the limits of human adaptability and how adaptation to the environment takes place we can understand much more of the essence of human biology.

Human adaptability to changing environmental conditions consists of genetically shaped responses within the range that is characteristic of the species' *adaptation,* as determined by natural selection (see Chapters 2 and 3). Within their range of adaptive responses individuals react to changes in their environment in three different ways. (1) **Acclimatization** is accommodation over a period of months or years to environmental conditions. Acclimatizing to living in high mountains is an example. (2) **Acclimation** is short-term physiological response to changed environmental conditions. Acclimating over several days to a new time zone, as in "jet lag," or light-skinned individuals acclimating to increased exposure to sunlight by **tanning,** are examples. (3) **Habituation** is an even shorter-term accommodation to a temporary environmental stimulus. Tuning out the monotonous sound of an air-conditioner during a lecture is an example. Individuals within populations, as well as entire populations, may differ in their thresholds and responses to stimuli.

Heat and Cold

Physiological responses to heat and cold constitute human **thermoregulation,** an important part of the human adaptation. Humans have a tropical origin, a fact demonstrated not only by the fossil record but by human biology. No other indication of this origin is stronger than the range of temperature at which human beings achieve thermal equilibrium—that is, neither gaining nor losing heat. This temperature for a naked adult at rest is approximately 25°C (77°F), depending on humidity. Once sweating starts, either because of exercise or increasing

acclimatization—long-term physiological adaptation, which may have some morphological effect, but which occurs during the lifetime of one individual and which is not passed on genetically.

acclimation—short-term physiological adaptation, occurring over a period of several hours to several days.

tanning—a response of lightly pigmented skin after exposure to sunlight that increases the amount of melanin in the cells of the skin; an example of acclimation.

habituation—neurophysiological mechanism for "tuning out" unwanted stimuli, an accommodation that takes only a few minutes.

thermoregulation—controlling the body's temperature by a number of physiological and behavioral means.

temperature, the temperature of the skin is maintained at between 35°C and 36°C (95°F and 102°F). When internal body temperature or local skin temperature increases, **eccrine sweat glands** in the skin become active, producing a watery liquid that evaporates, cooling the skin. When internal body temperature decreases, the body produces more heat by muscular contraction (shivering), by increasing the body's metabolic rate, and by **vasoconstriction,** the contracting of the small arterioles near the skin's surface to reduce the temperature of the skin. An even older physiological response to cold is "goose bumps." This is a reflex standing-up of hairs that served to increase the insulating effect of fur, which disappeared from the hominid body probably several million years ago.

If the temperature continues to drop, a "warming response" can be seen in European and Asian populations, in which the hands or feet become vasodilated to increase circulation and raise the temperature of the extremity. Africans do not show this response, which seems to be a genetically controlled part of thermoregulatory physiology evolved by northern hemisphere, cold-adapted populations.

Light and Solar Radiation

The **pineal body** at the base of the brain (where the French philosopher Descartes thought the soul was located) controls daily rhythms relating to light and dark (Cardinali and Wurtman, 1975). The primitive human adaptation to light was undoubtedly tropical, with day length virtually the same all year long. But as hominids expanded into increasingly northern and southern latitudes, they had to adapt to changing day lengths. As yet, the details of this adaptation are poorly understood. But we have ample evidence that when days shorten or lengthen with the seasons, humans can suffer emotional changes. Light therapy, in which an individual is subjected to bright, intense light, has been found to be an effective treatment for some conditions, such as symptoms of depression in night-shift workers resulting from light deprivation. Furthermore, modern people spend much of their lives, particularly in the winter months, indoors. Their relationship to light has changed in three major ways: the spectrum of artificial light has changed, the irradiance level is drastically different, and the number of hours per day that an individual is exposed has increased dramatically.

High Altitude

Living at altitudes greater than about 3,000 meters (9,840 feet) above sea level causes a number of physiological changes. Biological anthropologists have studied these changes in order to learn how rapidly nonacclimatized individuals can adapt to the low oxygen levels (**hypoxia**) found at high altitudes. For visitors to these altitudes, as we described at the beginning of this chapter, the immediate response to hypoxia is increased breathing and heart rate. Although this response increases par-

eccrine sweat glands—glands that excrete a watery liquid over much of the surface area of the head, face, neck, and upper body during heat stress.

vasoconstriction—the contraction of small blood vessels next to the skin's surface; a response to cold.

pineal body—small cone-shaped part of the brain located below the *corpus callosum;* synthesizes the hormone melatonin, which is important in mediating estrus cycling in mammals, and reacts to ambient light in the environment.

hypoxia—a condition of reduced oxygen supply to tissues despite adequate blood supply.

tial oxygen pressure in the lungs and, at the same time, blood flow, it also contributes to difficulty in sleeping and to bouts of hyper- and hypoventilation.

A longer-term physiological response to low oxygen pressure is the reduction, somewhere between 20 to 30%, in the amount of oxygen that the body can absorb. As a consequence, work capacity for high altitude visitors is diminished. One study did suggest, however, that individuals who grow up in high altitudes somehow acclimatize themselves and, in terms of oxygen consumption (and, thus, work) capacity, measure closely to those individuals born at sea level (Frisancho et al., 1995). Although hypoxia is the primary stress factor in high altitude environments, there are others, such as high solar radiation, cold, aridity, rough terrain, and a limited nutritional base.

NUTRITIONAL AND DIETARY ASPECTS OF ADAPTATION

Humans are omnivores. They and their primate ancestors have eaten a very wide range of plant and animal foods, with little or no preparation prior to consumption, for many millions of years (Harding and Teleki, 1981; Table 12–2). This adaptation confers a large degree of dietary adaptability, but it has its limits.

With the advent of fire and cultural food preparation techniques, the potential range of edible foods expanded. Or did it? Newman (1975) suggested that the early hominid reliance on animal meat relaxed selection on the body's synthesis of several important amino acids. Although

Table 12–2 • Daily Diet of Pre-Agricultural Humans[1]

	Grams[2]	Percent Total Energy
Protein	250	33
Animal	190	
Vegetable	60	
Fat	70	21
Animal	30	
Vegetable	40	
Carbohydrate	340	46
Total Fiber	150	
	1130	100

[1]Based on an average modern human hunter-gatherer diet of 3000 kilocalories, composed of 35% meat and 65% plant foods.

[2]Represents weight less water content. Weight of actual ingested food is 2250 g (5 lbs.). Equivalent food weight for same energy in modern American diet is 3 lbs.

From Eaton et al. (1989).

hominids lost the ability to synthesize these substances, they were not at a selective disadvantage because their diets supplied these essential nutrients. However, during the Neolithic Revolution, that period of time about 10,000 years ago in the Middle East when farming and village life became predominant and the food supply more stable, the overall human diet may have been less nutritious, with a dependence on single plant food staples. A similar problem exists in many of the world's cultures today, such as those in which dependence on rice or manioc has led to malnutrition and even nutritional diseases.

Jared Diamond, physiologist at the University of California, Los Angeles, describes (1992) recent studies of a diabetic epidemic on the Pacific island of Nauru and points out other problems when changes in diet occur. Only a few generations ago, the 5,000 or so Micronesians living on this island engaged in a lifestyle that depended on fishing and subsistence farming. However, the discovery of phosphate deposits, and the substantial income that mining this substance produced, dramatically changed the Nauruans' energetic way of life. Now virtually all food is imported, the caloric intake is more than double the norms set by the nearby Australians, and obesity is practically universal. Non-insulin-dependent diabetes mellitus (NIDDM), which, prior to 1950, was unknown in this population, now affects almost two-thirds of adults by the age of 55 to 64, contributing to most nonaccidental deaths and to one of the world's shortest life spans.

Unfortunately, this example is not uncommon among developing peoples in other parts of the world. It is the extent of the problem on Nauru that is remarkable. Studies, however, show that the epidemic may have passed its peak, though not because of a decline in the environmental risk factors. Rather it appears that natural selection has reduced the number of individuals who are genetically susceptible to NIDDM. Because it often occurs in women during their peak reproductive years, NIDDM results in increased stillbirths and decreased numbers of live births. As a consequence, over a few generations the number of islanders who possessed the lethal NIDDM genotype has been reduced.

This question remains to be answered: If NIDDM represents a major world health problem (50 million diabetics are estimated in China and India alone by the year 2000) then why is the genotype so common? One hypothesis was proposed by J. V. Neel (1962), which he labeled the "**thrifty genotype.**" Neel suggested that whenever the daily food supply becomes sparse and varies unpredictably in amount, the individuals with an advantage would be those who, during times when food is plentiful, could convert most of their ingested calories into fat through quick insulin release. Because these calories will be stored instead of immediately burned, they can be drawn on during times when food is scarce. Under such circumstances the NIDDM genotype would be advantageous, but it would lose its advantage in individuals recently introduced

thrifty genotype–the adaptation of storing "excess calories" as fat, and then burning them during periods of famine or scarcity of food.

to modern high-calorie diets and sedentary lifestyles. As Boyd Eaton, Marjorie Shostak, and Melvin Konner (1989) conclude:

> Our bodies today simply haven't "learned" that there is no longer an advantage to carrying extra weight. We are still essentially Late Paleolithic hunters and gatherers, and our appetite-control centers continue to operate as if the food surplus may come to a crashing halt at any time. We persist in storing up against that eventuality and, because the shortages fail to materialize, we become obese. Fat people . . . are stocking up for a famine that never comes.

MODERN LIFE AND HUMAN EVOLUTION

As we have seen, over 90% of our species' evolutionary history has been spent in tropical environments, in small groups of related individuals, eating for the most part low-sugar, high-fiber foods and leading physically demanding lives. Modern, technologically advanced humans, many of whom lead sedentary lives and eat highly processed foods that are high in sugar, salt, and polyunsaturated fats, suffer from "diseases of civilization" that are virtually unknown among technologically primitive hunter-gatherer peoples (Table 12–3). Among these are **hypertension** and the related problem of heart attack, cancer, gastric ulcers, and stress-related disorders. Studies also show among urban dwellers an increase

Table 12–3 • Diseases of Civilization: The Leading Causes of Death in the United States

Cause of Death	Percent of Total Deaths
Heart Disease (chiefly coronary atherosclerosis)	37.0%
Cancer (lung, colon, rectum, breast, and prostate cause 54% of cancer deaths)	22.1%
Stroke	7.3%
[Accidents	4.5%]
Chronic Obstructive Lung Disease	3.4%
Pneumonia	3.2%
Diabetes mellitus	1.8%
Atherosclerosis (not including heart or brain, but including aortic aneurysm)	1.8%
[Suicide	1.4%]
Cirrhosis	1.3%
Total	83.8%

From Eaton et al. (1989).

hypertension–persistently high blood pressure; above 140 mm Hg systolic (contraction) and 90 mm Hg diastolic (dilation) pressures of the heart.

serum cholesterol–cholesterol is a lipid (fat), deriving from the diet, that when in high concentrations in the blood serum causes lesions and plaque buildup in arteries.

Table 12–4 • Serum Cholesterol Values In Different Human Hunter-Gatherer Groups	
Population	Average Serum Cholesterol Value
Hadza (Tanzania)	110
Eskimos (Canada)	141
San (Botswana)	120
Aborigines (Australia)	139
Pygmies (Congo)	106
Caucasians (United States)	210
From Eaton et al. (1989).	

in blood pressure and **serum cholesterol** levels (Table 12–4) and a tendency for higher blood pressure to increase with age. In contrast, traditional populations show lower blood pressure and no tendency for blood pressure to increase with age (Little and Baker, 1988). In an attempt to counter some of the deleterious effects of civilized life, Eaton and colleagues (1989) have suggested a "Paleolithic prescription," which calls for the return, within modern technological limits, to many of the practices of diet and exertion employed by our ancestors.

On the other hand, our Paleolithic ancestors never faced the problems of overpopulation (Figure 12–12). Quite the contrary. Rather than curbing the birth rate, societies, until recently, attempted to maximize child production and minimize infant mortality. Today, the world population problem poses a new challenge to human adaptability and may

Figure 12–12 • World population growth and growth estimates. "X's" represent projected growth, given no change in the current world birth rate.

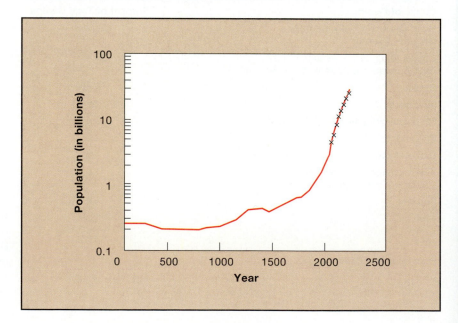

force significant changes still only vaguely contemplated by modern peoples. The one-child policy that China has set in motion, even though morally repugnant to some, may presage things to come in many of the world's societies.

There are other less dramatic possibilities for change. Our diet, as we have seen, is a mixture of plant and animal foods. Whether we hunted or scavenged, animal proteins have been a necessary component of our diet, because they are relatively complete in their contents of essential amino acids. Even today in many parts of the world animal protein is almost the only way to secure a complete and balanced pattern of amino acids in a diet consisting predominantly of plant foods. However, conditions of overpopulation require a hard look at land use because they make us view the domesticated animal as a competitor to humans. Cropland produces 10 to 20 times the amount of human food that we can obtain from animals grazing on the same land (Almquist, 1969).

As all of our food originates in plants, the animal is only a converter. What has kept animals in use as converters? Originally, they earned their place by their value in locating and converting food items that humans could not, or would not, consume, such as seeds, roots, and wild grasses. Today, however, under the conditions of the modern feed lot, where animals consume supplemental food that humans could use, animal food is an ever-increasing luxury. Furthermore, with the advances in genetic engineering, plant varieties have been developed that are no longer deficient in particular amino acids.

Our knowledge of nutrition can help to improve our efficiency in how we use plant food. Protein blending, adding soybean, which contains a surplus of lysine, to corn, and supplementing this mixture with a synthetic methionine (lacking in soybean) would produce an adequate diet. Technologically, as the world population situation becomes more critical, we can gradually shift from a diet based on animal food to one predominantly derived from plants. Although such an adaptation will pose no physiological problem, such changes will inevitably be strongly culturally challenged by our traditional eating patterns and may become acceptable only after no alternative exists.

The crowded, noisy, and generally "artificial" conditions of modern urban life are very recent environments for humans to live in. The consequences to human biology and psychology are profound though still not fully understood. Yet cities being cultural entities, they are environments that can be changed if necessary to better fit human adaptations evolved over millions of years.

SUMMARY

1. Growth patterns in all species are, to a certain extent, reflections of their evolutionary history. The prolonged period of human adolescence, coupled with the delayed maturation of the brain, is adaptive to the needs of our species to learn.

2. The study of growth patterns provides a measure of how well a population is adapted to its environment. Poor nutrition, pollution, stress, and a number of sociological factors, such as family size, can retard growth. Different populations around the world, however, respond differently to adverse conditions.

3. Studies of growth show us how much genetics is involved in regulating rates and stages, and how much the environment can modify the genetic program. Studies of boys versus girls, for example, show that nutritional factors affect girls' maturation much less than they do boys'.

4. Neoteny describes the situation in which growth of certain parts of the body is retarded while normal sexual development proceeds. Neoteny, or pedomorphism, helps explain why humans have retained so many juvenile characteristics as adults, such as a relatively high retention of body fat.

5. Human individuals have adapted to a wide range of environments, even though for millions of years our ancestors were primarily a tropical species. In the course of this adaptation humans have responded to changes in temperature, light, and altitude, among many factors that are now part of the broad human ecosystem.

6. Humans have a varied diet, but there are limits to our adaptability, which become apparent when we consume too much of any particular food. Many plant foods lack essential amino acids, and, if eaten without supplements, can cause deficiencies and, ultimately, disease.

7. Perhaps the most telling limitations of our diet come from studies of "modern" diseases of the heart and arteries, those related to high blood pressure and diabetes. Modern lifestyles that incorporate high sugar, salt, and saturated fats, coupled with a lack of exercise, have proved to be a deadly combination.

CRITICAL-THINKING QUESTIONS

1. Define growth in terms of biological development.
2. Describe the seven stages of human growth.
3. Explain allometry and how it can be used to better understand growth relationships.
4. How do different environments affect human variation?
5. How did the advent of fire affect nutritional diversity?
6. In what ways has human development responded to modernization and urban living?

SUGGESTED READINGS

Bogin, B. 1999. *Patterns of Human Growth,* 2nd ed. New York: Cambridge University Press. Text on human growth written from an evolutionary point of view. Attempts to place human growth into an ecological and phylogenetic context.

Eveleth, P., and J. M. Tanner. 1991. *Worldwide Variations in Human Growth,* 2nd ed. New York: Cambridge University Press. Text in the comparative studies of growth including 82 tables presenting the means and standard deviations of various anthropological measures and indices. Exhaustive list of references to other growth studies.

Tanner, J. M. 1989. *Foetus into Man: Physical Growth from Conception to Maturity,* 2nd ed. Cambridge, Mass.: Harvard University Press. Text describes the process of growth in children, the maturation rate of different tissues, the chromosomal and endocrine control of sexual differentiation *in utero,* and the further differentiation that takes place at puberty. Explores further the interaction of genes with the environment.

CHAPTER 13

The Modern Human Condition in Evolutionary Perspective: Applied Biological Anthropology

The subject of human evolution has excited both the public and scientific imaginations for many years. But the application of biological anthropological knowledge has lagged behind the intellectual popularity of the subject. Although many professional and lay people alike know about, and are fascinated with, australopithecines and Neandertals, they may doubt whether these dusty relics of our evolutionary past have any relevance to our current life and problems. There are signs that this attitude is now changing. We now know that our hominid ancestors can teach us a tremendous amount of useful information about how to conduct our daily lives.

As the perspective of evolutionary biology has pervaded both the natural and social sciences, so also has it affected such applied areas as medicine, psychotherapy, education, and conservation. We begin this chapter with a discussion of the basis for applying biological anthropology to the modern human condition.

PREMISES AND GOALS OF APPLIED BIOLOGICAL ANTHROPOLOGY

Although a distinct discipline of **applied biological anthropology** is still developing, biological anthropologists have been active in practical applications of their research for many years. One of the most prominent nineteenth-century German biological anthropologists, Rudolf Virchow (Figure 13–1), founded the public health service in Berlin, for example. And the great French anthropologist Paul Broca made many contributions to medical treatment of brain disorders. In the twentieth century the list of applications of biological anthropological research is diverse and wide ranging, from designing the dimensions of fighter plane cockpits, to assistance in apprehending criminals, to urban planning. This chapter will discuss the major areas of applied biological anthropology, keeping in mind that the field is a dynamic one and new applications are being developed every year.

applied biological anthropology—use of the method and theory of biological anthropology to solve problems or address questions of practical significance.

epidemiology—the study of the geographic distribution, spread, and control of disease.

Definition

Certain attributes of applied biological anthropology set it off from other disciplines. In general, applied biological anthropology is "holistic, evolutionary, cross-cultural, comparative, and population-based" (Lasker, 1991:2). For example, an anthropological research project on the incidence of disease in a certain population will generally differ from a project in the public health field of **epidemiology** by investigating more biological parameters than the presence or absence of disease and whether patients survived or died.

Anthropologists bring an approach that includes a broad comparative perspective on human biological response to the environment, and thus may look at, in addition to the manifestations of the disease in question, birth weights of babies, growth rates of children, and many other biological parameters that may escape medical attention. Anthropologists are also human evolutionary biologists; they consider the overall human adaptive response within the contexts of evolution, different cultures, and different environments. Biological anthropology becomes applied biological anthropology when it focuses on solving practical problems of human well-being.

Anthropology is a population-based biological science, and, unlike medicine, it does not focus on the individual (Figure 13–2). Its conclusions are statistical and its statements are probabilistic. This aspect of anthropological research is very important for physicians or other health professionals to remember when using anthropological data. An example will suffice. A six-month-old child is brought in for his medical checkup, and the examining nurse notes that he seems to have an enlarged head. A second appointment is made for the child with a growth specialist, who measures the child's head and compares his measurements with an anthropological study of head growth. The specialist finds that according to the study the child is in the 95th percentile of children

Figure 13–1 • Rudolf Virchow, one of the first applied physical anthropologists, who founded the public health service in Berlin in the late 1800s.

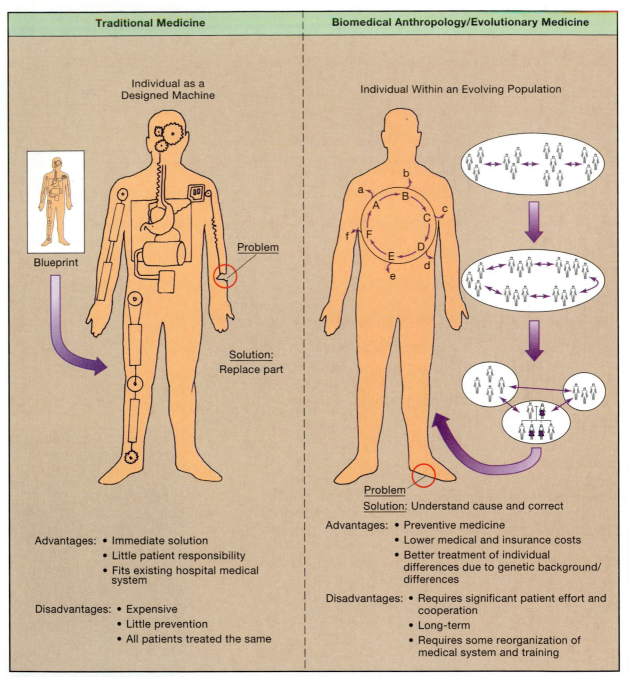

Figure 13–2 • Difference in approach of traditional medicine and biological anthropology in regard to the individual. Traditional medicine is more typological and focuses on the individual, whereas anthropology places the individual within the context of a population.

his age; that is, only 5 out of 100 children would have heads as large as his at his age. The specialist recommends further tests, including a brain scan. The parents do not want this procedure performed on their child unless absolutely necessary. At this point a biological anthropologist enters the picture and is able to show, by reference to the results of a second study, that the child has head dimensions in the same proportion in the general population as his parents. Anthropologists do not make individual diagnoses, nor should they, but they do show that the child's head dimensions are within the "normal" population limits of the original growth studies. The parents decide, after consultation with their child's physician, against a brain scan.

Human Adaptation and the Modern Environment

Human beings are remarkably adaptable, as we have seen in the last chapter. But there are limits to this adaptability. Obviously people cannot live underwater or in outer space without the aid of technology. But are there less obvious examples of a lack of fit between human beings and their environment? The answer is a definite yes, and for those of us living in the technologically sophisticated Western world, many of the examples of this lack of fit are close to home.

The conflict between the conditions of the modern world and basic human adaptations is known as the **Discordance Hypothesis.** The evolutionary perspective that applied biological anthropology provides can help people bring their living environment into closer congruence with their biological adaptation as human beings.

Underlying the goal of "concordance" in applied biological anthropology is the realization that natural selection has produced through millions of years of evolution a good fit between human adaptive capabilities and the environment, as these have **co-evolved.** An evolutionary perspective indicates that human beings are the product of a long process of change that has perfected a certain way of solving problems and getting work done. A static machine metaphor for human adaptation has been replaced by the more sophisticated idea of a **feed-back system** that has been designed and perfected over immense spans of time and under many different circumstances. Like the proverbial auto mechanic who ignores the directions and ends up with a few pieces left over from the engine he has just reassembled, applied human scientists who ignore the overall evolutionary context of human biology and behavior may well find that their solutions to human problems are less than optimal. If human beings think that they can devise a better system than evolution, they must first at least know how that system operates.

The agenda of applied biological anthropology, then, is **adaptationist.** There is an assumption that, if a trait or characteristic is present in human beings, then there is or was some adaptive reason for it to be there. Not all evolutionary scientists agree. Stephen Jay Gould, for example, holds that specific traits may be the result of evolutionary processes more random than adaptation. The nipples on male humans

Discordance Hypothesis—the thesis that human biology and behavior, as shaped by evolution, are at odds with modern human environments.

co-evolution—the concept that organisms sharing the same environmental resources will evolve along with one another, as well as with environmental changes.

feed-back system—in information theory, the concept that change in one step of a loop will affect a subsequent step that will in turn affect the starting point.

adaptationist—the theoretical position that most if not all morphological and behavioral traits of a species have been crafted by natural selection to adapt that species to its adaptive niche; criticized by S.J. Gould as the "Panglossian paradigm," from Voltaire's *Candide,* in reference to Dr. Pangloss's explanation that "all things are for the best."

Figure 13–3 • Human pectoral nipples. The male nipple is cited as a possible example of a biological trait with no adaptive value, but the female nipple is an important reproductive adaptation for suckling infants. Viewed in a populational context, the male nipple is a reflection of an important species adaptation to infant care, shared with other mammals.

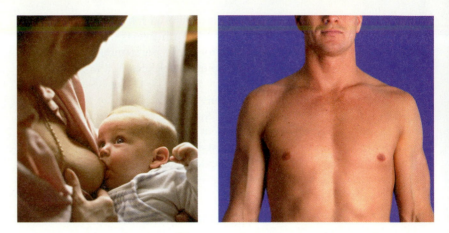

(Figure 13–3), he points out, never had an adaptive reason to be there and do not have an adaptive reason today because men cannot and do not suckle infants. Despite the fact that men in some South Sea Pacific cultures are known to use their nipples as pacifiers for infants, Gould is largely correct in this assessment if one focuses only on individuals. A focus on the species, however, reveals that breasts are a very important part of the biology of reproduction. Men have nipples because women have nipples with which to suckle infants, a trait that ensures infant survival; it finds expression in males because of similarities in the early embryological development of males and females.

The goals, then, of applied biological anthropology are to construct an explanatory framework for the many physical and behavioral traits of the human species within evolutionary and environmental contexts and to seek ways to maximize their function. These are broad goals, and they will certainly be applied much more widely in the future of this still new discipline. This chapter will discuss the major areas of applied biological anthropology to date.

BIOMEDICAL ANTHROPOLOGY AND EVOLUTIONARY MEDICINE

Biomedical anthropology is the field that specifically relates knowledge of human biology and evolution to medical research and treatment of disease. Medicine has long recognized this close connection, and biological anthropologists who teach gross anatomy are frequently among the first instructors that entering medical students encounter. But until recently this connection between biological anthropology and medicine was viewed as largely static. Using the machine metaphor again, anthropologists and anatomists were needed to supply the parts, but the physicians, the master engineers, knew how to put them together. Medicine became more concerned with the machinelike functioning of genes and cells, and less with the overall functioning of the organism.

New initiatives in biomedical anthropology, however, have begun to have an effect in medicine. Perhaps the most noticeable of these is **evolutionary medicine,** also sometimes termed Darwinian medicine (Williams and Nesse, 1991). Evolutionary medicine is the study and treatment of the causes, distributions, and cultural correlates of disease within a framework of evolution by natural selection. It is one of the most important new areas of applied biological anthropology and holds particular relevance to people's everyday lives.

The following case studies represent the range of issues dealt with by biomedical anthropologists and physicians who work in evolutionary medicine.

Sudden Infant Death Syndrome

Anthropologist James McKenna of Pomona College was by training an expert in nonhuman primate mother–infant behavior when he became interested in the problem of human **Sudden Infant Death Syndrome** (SIDS). SIDS, also known as "crib death," is the leading cause of death of very young infants in the United States. Standard medical research has failed to find either a cause or a cure for the syndrome. McKenna believed that the practice, very unusual from an evolutionary and nonhuman primate standpoint, of parents isolating young infants in a crib away from the parents had something to do with the problem. He undertook extensive studies of other cultures in which there are standard parent–infant "co-sleeping" arrangements and of other primates where infants and mothers sleep together (Figure 13–4), and he found that SIDS did not occur. In association with medical researchers he then began to investigate the neurological development of infants who died of SIDS. This research strongly implied that these infants were neurologically not yet fully capable of breathing on their own during sleep, and needed the pacemaker effect of nearby maternal breathing and heartbeat (McKenna et al., 1990). Further work showed that co-sleeping young infants responding to parents' movements slept less deeply and were less likely to stop breathing during deep, uninterrupted sleep. McKenna's research is continuing but his evolutionary approach has succeeded in directing research away from a search for elusive viruses or hidden trauma as a cause of the innumerable infant deaths resulting from SIDS.

Neonatal Jaundice

Newborn babies may develop a yellowish cast to the skin (Figure 13–5), similar to that of jaundiced adults, between the second and fifth days after birth. Adult jaundice is a condition in which the pigment known as **bilirubin,** caused by a normal breakdown of red blood cells, builds up in the body, due to impaired liver function or to a lack of necessary enzymes to break hemoglobin down. Neonatal jaundice is also due to an elevated amount of bilirubin and has been explained as a byproduct of a

Figure 13–4 • Co-sleeping human infant and mother; co-sleeping nonhuman primate infant and mother.

evolutionary medicine–the application of evolutionary principles and deductions from biological anthropology and human biology to the practice of medicine; also termed "Darwinian medicine."

Sudden Infant Death Syndrome–"crib death" or "cot death"; sudden and unexpected death of apparently healthy infants, usually between 3 weeks and 5 months of age.

bilirubin–a bile pigment from the liver that results from the breakdown of hemoglobin in red blood cells; bilirubin normally circulates in the blood in a complex with albumin but can increase in certain pathological conditions such as hepatitis.

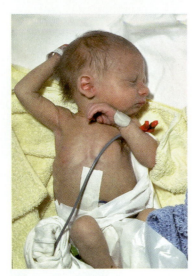

Figure 13–5 • Infant with neonatal jaundice.

free radicals—highly reactive "active" molecules of oxygen (mainly O_2^-) formed from the breakdown of oxygen molecules in the body.

morbidity—showing evidence of disease or infection.

still immature and not fully functioning liver. Traditionally, it was treated primarily by phototherapy, the application of bright light, which oxidizes the excess bilirubin and makes the yellowish pigmentation disappear. One evolutionary explanation for this treatment was that early hominids lived outdoors and newborn babies would normally have been exposed to significantly greater amounts of light than modern indoor-living babies receive.

Two biomedical anthropologists, John Brett and Susan Niemeyer (1990), questioned this treatment and also the medical reasons for it. They contend that the presence of bilirubin enables a newborn's body to rid itself of **free radicals** that can damage developing tissues, particularly the brain. While the baby was in its mother's uterus her bloodstream and immune system removed these and other harmful substances. Excess bilirubin, contend Brett and Niemeyer, is an excellent method that evolution has developed of protecting a baby's first few days in its own oxygen-rich environment before its own immune system is fully functioning. They further argue that under normal conditions bilirubin is excluded from the brain and that, if it is present there, another disease is responsible, not neonatal jaundice. They suggest that pediatricians do not need to treat this "disease" and that they should not tamper with a process that has been designed by millions of years of evolution and that still works well.

Coping with the "Diseases of Civilization"

At the same time that Western medical researchers were making advances in understanding the genetic mechanisms of diseases and their more effective treatment, biological anthropologists studying the health and physiology of non-Western peoples made the startling discovery (see Chapter 12) that the very diseases that Western medical practitioners considered an intrinsic, genetically coded part of human biology did not account for any major part of the mortality or **morbidity** of hunting-and-gathering peoples. Such maladies as cancer, stroke, heart attack, and diabetes, termed "diseases of civilization" (see Table 12–3) by Eaton et al. (1989), simply did not occur. Instead, trauma, parasites, and infectious diseases were the major killers of non-Western peoples. Another important discovery was that many individuals in hunter-gatherer groups, and by extension early hominids, who survived the high mortality period of early childhood lived remarkably healthy lives and had excellent chances of living to advanced ages.

The genetic code of hunter-gatherers is largely the same as that of "civilized" populations because all human beings alive today are part of the same biological species. The conclusion from this research was, then, that there must be something about the environment or lifestyles of Westerners that caused diseases that otherwise would not occur.

Obesity and the Human Ecology of Fat Deposition   Recent medical surveys indicate that some 20 to 30% of Americans are overweight, defined as being 20% or more above the "normal" mean weight for their height. Although strong societal and medical forces encourage individuals to moderate food intake, increase exercise, and lower body weight, obesity continues to be a major health problem. It contributes directly or indirectly to heart disease, high blood pressure (hypertension), diabetes, and musculo-skeletal problems ranging from back pain to flat feet.

There are four types of fat in the human body, defined on the basis of their location in the body and how they are metabolized. (1) *Brown fat* is found mainly in babies and young children and functions to provide heat to protect them from hypothermia. It exists on the back between the shoulder blades. (2) *Subcutaneous fat* occurs over almost all the body, but is found especially in the abdominal region and in the female breasts. It is directly related to "excess nutrition" built up during times of plenty. It serves as a long-term reservoir of energy and is metabolized during periods of famine or starvation. (3) *Hip/Thigh fat* is found predominantly in adult females and shows a different metabolic pattern than generally distributed subcutaneous fat. This fat serves solely as an energy reservoir for pregnancy and lactation; even in cases of near-starvation, females who are not pregnant or nursing do not metabolize this energy reservoir. (4) *Intra-abdominal fat* occurs inside the abdominal cavity, especially in a structure that drapes over the stomach known as the greater omentum. Males have a predominance of this type of fat, which is metabolized the most rapidly of all the types of fat. It is a short-term energy reservoir that may have evolved to assist males in the short-term fasting that accompanies hunting. In modern humans it is this fat deposit that is associated with increased risk of heart disease.

Except for brown fat, human fat deposits are an adaptation for storing energy in a seasonal round of feast or famine, the "thrifty genotype" (see Chapter 12). Hunter-gatherer studies indicate that in the wet season of the year when food is plentiful, individuals build up their fat reserves, only to use them during the dry season when food is scarce. The percentage of fat compared to bone and muscle in the body fluctuates from about 10% to 15% in men and between about 20% to 30% in women (Eaton et al., 1989:63). In modern humans of the Western world, however, there is no season of scarcity and thus the fat reserves that build up in the body remain there unless exercise or moderation of food intake (dieting) take place.

Obesity contributes to high blood pressure by creating an internal physiological environment in which *cholesterol* builds up and plaque is deposited on the inside walls of arteries, constricting their diameters (Figure 13–6). The heart must pump harder to push the blood through these constricted arteries. When the arteries of the heart itself become constricted or occluded, the heart muscle can no longer get adequate oxygen for its work and a heart attack results.

Diverticulitis   Over millions of years, hominids have evolved their eating patterns, which are also related to the "feast or famine" seasonal round. Ancient diets had a high proportion of roughage—fibrous fruits

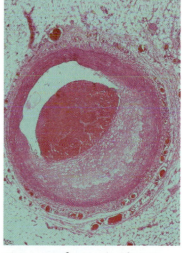

Figure 13–6 • Inside of artery showing buildup of plaque, which causes high blood pressure and, in turn, contributes to heart disease.

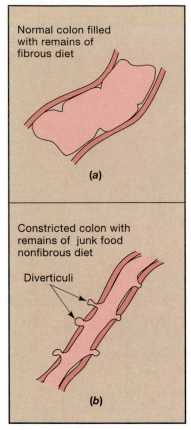

Normal colon filled with remains of fibrous diet

(a)

Constricted colon with remains of junk food nonfibrous diet

Diverticuli

(b)

Figure 13–7 • Cross-sections of human colon with (*a*) normal fibrous diet, and (*b*) junk-food diet and diverticuli.

diverticulitis–inflammation of an outpocketing of the wall of the large intestine.

and plant material low in energy but filling—and relatively small amounts of high-calorie animal fat and sugar. Nevertheless, natural selection ensured that the latter foods were craved, for the balance in diet and the excess energy that they conferred. Similar cravings occur with certain important minerals, particularly salt. Potato chips and pizza, both loaded with fat and salt, are excellent examples of what early hominids, not knowing any better, might have imagined as the ideal food. But not only does excess dietary fat in people contribute to heart disease, as noted above, and excess sodium (versus potassium) also raise blood pressure, but these sorts of "junk foods" also lack the fiber that early hominid foods had.

The lack of dietary fiber leads to chronically underfilled large intestines—that part of our digestive tracts that stores large volumes of the undigestible components of dietary intake (Painter and Burkitt, 1975). In consequence, the large intestines contract into smaller and smaller diameters, and the increased pressure inside creates small outpocketings of the intestinal walls known as "diverticuli" (Figure 13–7). When these become infected and burst, a serious disease known as diverticulitis results. **Diverticulitis** can be avoided by eating a diet high in fiber and plant roughage.

Breast Cancer   Eaton et al. (1994) have recently related the late onset of first pregnancies in Western women and the high proportion of reproductive time they spend nonpregnant and without nursing infants as the primary contributing factors to breast cancer. In a comparative study of Asian and American women, Eaton noted that early onset of menarche, late menopause, fewer children born, and lower frequency of suckling infants all positively correlate with higher incidences of breast cancer. Mechanisms for this correlation are still under study.

Human Populations, Infectious Diseases, and Parasites

Arguably the most significant agent of natural selection for any population is disease, which has produced most of the polymorphic variation that is found in gene pools. Devastating plagues have spread recurrently through human populations, causing the death of tens of thousands of people. The European Black Death of the mid-fourteenth century killed from 30% to 90% of those infected. Researchers have estimated that about one-third of Europe's population died in this epidemic.

Most recently, the worldwide epidemic caused by HIV has already killed 6,400,000, with an estimated 29,400,000 persons currently infected. An effective medical strategy to develop a cure that would prevent HIV replication in infected persons has proven elusive. The ability of HIV to mutate has made a vaccine approach difficult, as any vaccine can attack only a single type of virus, and vaccines are mostly ineffective against viruses that can change their outer protein coats quickly. Curiously enough, an evolutionary approach to finding a cure or preventative for HIV infection has not been among the popular strategies employed—until recently. A number of significant pieces of information have helped change the direction that new research has taken.

Fact #1: Over a period of many years, through the painstaking collection of blood samples, it has been discovered that a number of high-risk individuals never became infected with HIV.

Fact #2: Substances secreted by CD8 lymphocytes suppress the replication of HIV. These substances turn out to be members of a poorly known class of hormonelike molecules called *chemokines,* which are thought to help cause inflammation, among other things. As part of their overall function, they bind to a chemokine receptor, called CCR5, found on a CD4 cell, the primary initial target of HIV. When chemokines bind to their receptors they block HIV from doing the same thing, thus preventing HIV from entering the CD4 cell and replicating within it (Figure 13–8).

Fact #3: In some individuals, the gene that codes for the CCR5 receptor protein is defective, and in some cases the protein produced is so badly misshapen that the CD4 cell destroys it before it can become a surface feature on the CD4 cell wall.

Fact #4: Without the CCR5 receptor, HIV cannot penetrate the CD4 cell.

These facts led researchers to the discovery that, indeed, there is a defective chemokine receptor gene, and that about 1 in 100 Caucasian-Americans is homozygous for the defective gene. These people are immune to HIV infection. In addition, about one in five individuals are

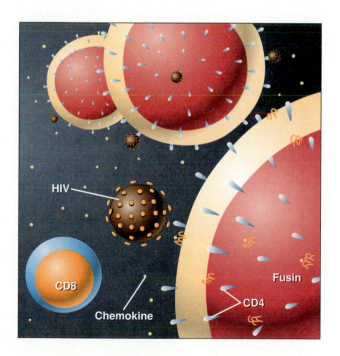

Figure 13–8 • Immunity to HIV in some individuals is achieved by the blocking of CD4 receptor sites with hormonelike proteins called chemokines that are produced by CD8 cells.

heterozygous, and, apparently, heterozygous individuals stay healthy two to three years longer than infected individuals who are homozygous nondefective.

From what we already know about other epidemics and the presence of genes that offer protection against disease, one could predict that in the case of HIV, natural selection might have offered an opportunity for resistance. However, from the high numbers of individuals who carry the defective chemokine receptor gene, it is apparent that the mutation that causes this condition could not have arisen recently and spread opporrtunistically as a result of HIV. Many researchers argue that the initial spread of the defective gene may have been the result of an ancient epidemic as much as 100,000 years ago in Caucasian populations. The survivors of that epidemic carried the defective gene, resulting in its commonplace appearance in modern populations. But for this gene to remain common for so long, natural selection must still be operating in its favor. It is this bit of detective work that must be done to unravel the rest of this mystery.

What about other populations? People of African and Asian descent may also have their own unique genetic protection against HIV. There are uninfected African and Asian high-risk people, and they don't carry the defective chemokine receptor gene. The prediction from the perspective of evolutionary medicine is that there are many other human resistance genes. The recent discoveries of HIV-resistant individuals and the chemokine defective receptor gene must surely be only a small part of what is out there.

Evolutionary medicine has also contributed to a better understanding of the response of the human body to disease. Williams and Nesse (1991), for example, note that the increased body temperature (**fever**) that frequently accompanies infectious disease is actually adaptively beneficial, because it creates an internal environment in which enzymes can work faster and bacteria can be killed more effectively. The standard medical practice of reducing fever thus may actually work against the patient's best interests. Children with chickenpox whose low-grade fevers were lowered actually recovered from the disease more slowly than children whose fevers were untreated (Ewald, 1994).

Populations of some hunter-gatherers have exceedingly high levels of parasite loads in their bodies, as was probably the case over most of our evolutionary history. The Mbuti pygmies of Congo (formerly Zaire), for example, have elevated white blood cell counts and widespread occurrence of malarial, **bilharzia,** and other parasites. Indications are that the relative parasite loads of our ancestors were high, and we probably have a number of genetically defined defense mechanisms as holdovers of our adapting to these loads. Sometimes these mechanisms themselves, as in the case of sickle-cell hemoglobin which evolved as a defense against the malarial parasite (see Chapter 11), result in disease.

Another recent discovery demonstrates this same type of co-evolutionary relationship between a genetic defense and disease. This is the case of **cholera,** a bacterial disease that can cause death by dehy-

fever—elevation of body temperature above normal; in disease, caused by infection by microorganisms.

bilharzia—infection by the parasitic blood fluke *Schistosoma,* which lays its eggs in the liver; leads to liver and occasionally kidney damage; also known as schistosomiasis.

cholera—infectious disease caused by the bacterium *Vibrio cholerae,* and spread usually by contaminated drinking water; symptoms include severe diarrhea, dehydration, shock, and kidney failure.

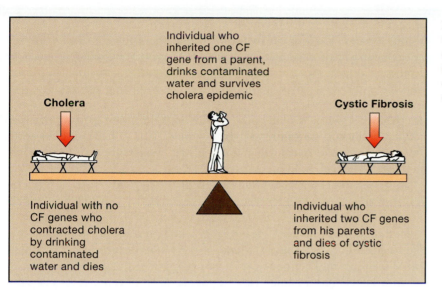

Figure 13–9 • Schematic view of the balanced polymorphism of cholera (left), cystic fibrosis (right), and heterozygote CF gene carrier, protected against cholera (middle).

dration though diarrhea, and **cystic fibrosis,** an inherited disease caused by a recessive gene in homozygous condition that results in a number of pathological pancreas, lung, and other physiological functions (Figure 13–9). Cystic fibrosis is the "most common, fatal, homozygous recessive disorder of the Caucasian population" (Gabriel et al., 1994:107). In populations of European ancestry, 5% of individuals carry one gene, leading to 1 in 2,500 live births being homozygous and affected with the disease. Why the gene is so common has been a mystery. New research with genetically engineered strains of mice has shown that cystic fibrosis individuals are immune to the toxins produced by the cholera bacterium. These individuals of course die of cystic fibrosis, but heterozygote individuals are protected from the cholera toxin at a 50% level. Because cholera must have taken a heavy toll in the evolutionary past of European populations, a balanced polymorphism exists, and we can explain through this evolutionary mechanism the high percentage of cystic fibrosis genes in the population.

Structural Problems

A number of medical problems that beset human beings are traceable to our bipedal stance and locomotion, a relatively recent adaptation in evolutionary terms. And as body size has increased in human evolution and obesity in modern Westerners becomes more common, some of these problems have become more severe.

Our feet have many problems that are related to our ancestors' being climbing hominoids. Basically, the ape foot is a grasping organ designed by evolution for holding on to large vertical branches and supporting the body with the foot inverted (sole facing inward). The human foot, on the other hand, is a rigid supporting organ that, although built on the

cystic fibrosis—hereditary disease of children and young adults affecting the pancreas and exocrine glands and associated with chronic lung disease.

longitudinal arch—the up-wardly arched structure composed of bones and connecting ligaments on the medial side of the human foot.

meniscus—from Latin meaning "lens"; the cartilage rimming the articular surface of the tibia at the knee joint and which forms a basin for the articular end of the femur.

basic ape plan, supports the body's weight with the sole of the foot flat on the ground. The human **longitudinal arch** in the foot is an important component of our ability to stride and "toe-off" in walking and is a feature lacking in the ape foot. The human great toe, brought into line with the other toes, plays an important role in stabilizing the longitudinal arch, but if, like that of apes, it diverges away and is mobile, flat feet result (Figure 13–10). When body weight in a standing human presses down, a rolled in or "pronated" foot results. This condition can cause foot pain from the excessive muscle effort needed to compensate for the lack of skeletal and joint support.

The knee joint is a rather fragile part of the human body, as runners and football players will readily admit. This fragility is also a residue of our nonbipedal heritage. Joints have a functional trade-off between strength and mobility. The knee joint is a quite mobile and very shallow joint formed between the distal end of the femur, which sits on the flat top of the tibia, and is rimmed with an up-lipped cartilage ring known as the **meniscus,** and the knee cap, or patella, in front (Figure 13–11). The evolutionary heritage of our knee joints is the ability to flex and extend through a wide range of movement while supporting the weight of the body, usually with a pronated foot, which grasps the vertical support,

Figure 13–10 • X-rays showing hypermobility of the first metatarsal and hallux in the human foot (left), leading to *pes planum* or flat feet, compared with the normal condition in the gorilla foot (right).

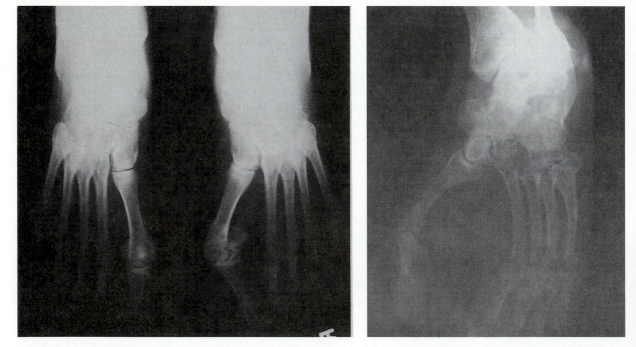

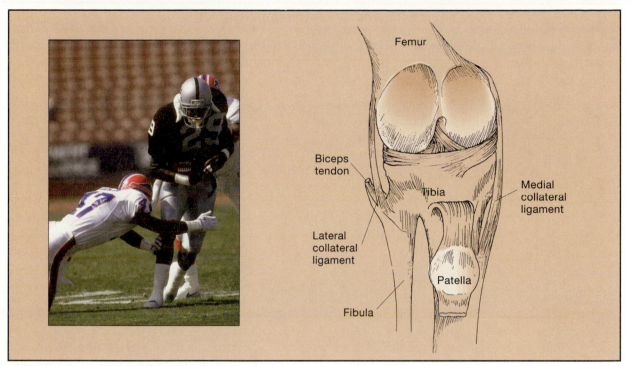

Figure 13–11 • Bone and ligament structure of the human knee, showing the stronger structures on the lateral side, with inset of side tackle in football, tearing medial collateral ligament.

for example a tree trunk. Thus, the lateral (outside) ligaments that support the knee joint are the strongest, exactly the opposite to the force administered in football tackles to the lateral side of the knee. The knee is similarly not adapted to the vertical forces resulting from long-distance running on hard pavement, exercise that can result in ligament and meniscus tears and pain. Fortunately, running with cushioning shoes can help alleviate this problem.

FORENSIC ANTHROPOLOGY

Forensic anthropology is the applied side of that branch of biological anthropology known as skeletal biology, also termed **osteology.** It is the study of human skeletal remains for the purpose of solving crimes and for personal identification (Ubelaker, 1995). Forensic anthropologists collaborate extensively with law enforcement officers, the military, international human rights organizations, and medical examiners' offices. Not surprisingly, forensic anthropology is the largest applied subdiscipline of biological anthropology.

osteology—study of bones.

Facial and Dental Reconstruction

Perhaps the oldest and most well-known, but also most problematic aspect of forensic anthropology is facial reconstruction, widely popularized by the 1981 murder mystery and subsequent movie *Gorky Park*. The character of the Russian forensic anthropologist in this story, who recreates the face of one of the victims from the skull, is based on the late Mikhail Gerasimov of the University of Moscow, perhaps the most well-known practitioner of facial reconstruction in the last several decades. In the West, facial reconstruction has been less widely practiced in forensic anthropology because of its arbitrariness. Years ago it was shown that one skull can lead to markedly different facial reconstructions, depending on the sculptor. Although the skull can provide a general outline to the face and average tissue thicknesses can provide some indications of soft part anatomy (Figure 13–12), many of the facial features that are critical to personal identification leave no marks on the skull. Nevertheless, facial reconstruction remains one weapon in the arsenal of the forensic anthropologist that may be used when all else fails. Ubelaker (1995) suggests that facial reproduction be "used only to inform the public through the media that the remains of a person of that general appearance has been recovered." This publicity may lead to further leads in solving a case. Occasionally a photograph of a missing individual may be matched with a skull by a process of overlaying the images in a computer, controlling for orientation and exact measurements (Ubelaker and O'Donnell, 1992).

Teeth are particularly useful in identifying individuals, because of their idiosyncratic nature and because they can be matched to dental records. A telltale gap between the front teeth proved the most important single determining factor in forensic anthropologist Clyde Snow's positively identifying the Nazi SS officer Josef Mengele, the Auschwitz "Angel of Death," from a skull exhumed in Brazil (Joyce and Stover, 1991).

Figure 13–12 • One skull, two stages of the forensic reconstruction made from it, and a photograph of the victim in life.

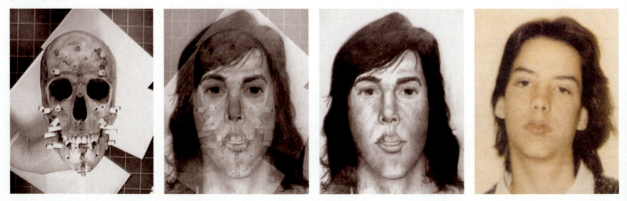

Skeletal Reconstructions

Forensic anthropologists use many clues left on bones to determine the identification and history of a skeleton. Using standard osteological techniques, specialists can determine sex, age, and population affinities ("race") if the remains are complete enough. Any remnants of clothes associated with the bones can give valuable clues as to weight and height.

Cause of Death

Forensic anthropologists categorize most trauma that they can detect in bony remains to (1) gunshot wounds, (2) blunt force trauma, or (3) sharp force trauma. These types of damage are readily identified in broad outline, but the details can be bedeviling. For example, if a skeleton shows both gunshot and blunt force trauma, which injury caused death? Or, if a victim was killed by blunt trauma to the head, and the accused murderer claims that the victim was kicked in the head by a horse rather than being hit with a hammer, can the forensic anthropologist distinguish between these two types of blunt trauma force? And can anthropologists be confident enough of their conclusions to testify in court in cases where their expert testimony may be critical in determining the guilt or innocence of the defendant? These and similar questions make forensic anthropology a challenging subdiscipline of applied biological anthropology (Iscan and Kennedy, 1989).

Human Rights Investigations

As challenging as identifying individual criminal cases may be for forensic anthropologists, identifying the victims of state-sponsored human rights abuses can be even more so. Joyce and Stover (1991) describe the long-term work of Clyde Snow and the Argentine Forensic Anthropology Team (EAAF) in unearthing and identifying the remains of thousands of "the Disappeared," mainly young political dissenters who were detained, tortured, and executed without trial by the military junta that ruled Argentina in the late 1970s. Risking death threats and overcoming bureaucratic obstacles, Snow and his team succeeded in focusing attention on and investigating a number of the execution-style murders of over 9,000 missing individuals. Working with the courts, Snow's forensic team excavated cemeteries (Figure 13–13) and matched up medical and dental records of persons reported missing with exhumed skeletons. To gain an estimate of the magnitude of the problem, they gathered cemetery records thoughout Argentina that showed that after the 1976 military coup, the numbers of anonymous burials rose drastically in those cemeteries located near prisons and detention centers. Absolute numbers of anonymous burials rose dramatically between 1976 and 1977, the height of the military's repression. There was a demographic shift as well. Before the coup most of the anonymous burials had been of destitute men older than 35 years of age. The percentage of individuals between the

Figure 13–13 • Excavation of anonymous graves in the Avellaneda Cemetery, Buenos Aires, by the Argentinian Team for Forensic Anthropology, 1988.

FRONTIERS

Evolutionary Medicine

by S. Boyd Eaton, M.D.

In prestigious universities around the world, theoretical physicists are attempting to find a modern day Holy Grail. They want to unravel basic relationships between the four fundamental natural forces—gravity, electromagnetism, and the strong and weak forces of atomic nuclei—with the ultimate aim of integrating these into a "unified field theory." A Nobel Prize awaits this achievement, which will rank with the discoveries of Newton and Einstein.

On a less exalted plane, evolutionary medical theory attempts to unify or integrate important disciplines related to health care: genetics, epidemiology, pathophysiology, and disease prevention. Genetics deals with the building blocks basic to all biomedical science. Epidemiology studies disease distribution: for example, why breast cancers are more common in Boston than in Tokyo. Pathophysiology seeks to explain disease mechanisms: just how does an elevated serum cholesterol level lead to atherosclerosis? And, of course, disease prevention is dedicated to finding lifeways that can delay or forestall indefinitely the development of serious illnesses. Evolutionary theory is central to all these endeavors and provides a conceptual framework that facilitates the interrelationship of each to the others.

Health status reflects the interaction of genetic makeup (for individuals) or the gene pool (for populations) with lifestyle factors:

Genes (+) Lifestyle = Health Status

When viewed as an equation, our gene pool represents the constant, over time, because humans living in the twentieth century are less than 0.005% different, genetically, from their preagricultural ancestors of 10,000 years ago. In contrast, lifestyle factors can change drastically in only a generation or two; therefore, they represent the equation's variable element.

Members of recently studied gatherer-hunter societies, present-day surrogates for our Late Paleolithic ancestors, have cholesterol levels averaging less than 150 mg/dL and their diets provide superample amounts of antioxidant vitamins. In contrast, the "new" (in evolutionary terms) life circumstances of affluent Americans show elevated average serum cholesterol concentrations to over 200 mg/dL and reduced antioxidant intake. Pathophysiologically, this phenomenon results in greater production of oxidized cholesterol (specifically, oxidized low density lipoprotein cholesterol, or LDL); it is this material which accumulates within developing atherosclerotic plaques and leads ultimately to hardening of the arteries, heart attacks and strokes.

ages of 21 and 35 buried in unmarked graves rose from 15% before 1976 to 56% after the coup (Joyce and Stover, 1991:260–261). These figures and statistics provided irrefutable evidence of the thousands of the Argentinian "Disappeared" who would, in the main, never be identified further.

Molecular forensic anthropology also played a part in the resolution of the human problems associated with the Argentinian "Disappeared." In 1984, Mary-Clair King, a geneticist at the University of California, Berkeley, developed a genetic screening test for determining the relatedness of grandparents to missing children. King and her Argentinian collaborator Ana Maria Di Lonardo used the HLA (human lymphocyte antigen) proteins for testing grandpaternity (Di Lonardo et al., 1984). This was necessary because, when the government death squads abducted and executed political opponents, they also abducted their victims' children, whom they adopted out to Argentinians who were in favor with the government. In one case, King and Di Lonardo took small blood samples from an eight-year-old girl suspected of being the

Epidemiological studies increasingly link breast cancer incidence to reproductive events. Early menarche, delayed first birth, failure to breastfeed, lower parity (number of births), and late menopause are all significant risk factors. In each instance, the reproductive experience of women in Western nations heightens susceptibility: compared with foragers, we Americans experience menarche earlier, are older at first birth, breastfeed far less, have fewer babies, and our menopause occurs later. The experience of Japanese women is closer to that of foragers than is that of Americans, hence the epidemiological findings (higher incidence of breast cancer in Boston than in Tokyo) might have been anticipated.

In the light of evolutionary medical theory, health promotion recommendations reprise the life circumstances of our ancestors, either directly, as for diet and exercise, or indirectly, as for reproductive factors. Early first birth and increased parity would be socioeconomically disadvantageous for most women, but fortunately the hormonal correlates of these factors can be recreated independently by endocrinological manipulation (in much the same way that oral contraceptives permit birth control), thereby substantially increasing the women's resistance to carcinogenesis.

Traditional medical practice historically has been oriented toward diagnosis and treatment of disease. Now, as economic considerations exert ever more influence on the health care system, we must place more emphasis on the importance of health promotion activities. However, the American public has become somewhat disenchanted with the conflicting results of epidemiological studies and with advice about diet and exercise that seems to fluctuate as capriciously as the stock market. The unifying influence of evolutionary medical theory can combat this jaundiced view by providing a consistent, rational framework for health promotion recommendations, a logic for ordering research priorities, and a compelling incentive for individual preventive activities.

The scientific impact of evolutionary medicine pales beside that expected from the unified field theory of physics, but its effect on health care costs, and, more importantly, on the well-being of individuals in affluent nations will nevertheless be profound.

S. Boyd Eaton, M.D., is Adjunct Professor of Anthropology at Emory University, and is a pioneer in the development of evolutionary medicine.

child of a Disappeared couple, along with samples from the couple's parents (the girl's grandparents). Although a retired police chief and his wife claimed the child to be their biological daughter, the HLA tests conclusively proved the girl to be the granddaughter of the Disappeareds' parents. Consequently, the courts awarded custody to her maternal grandmother.

BIOLOGICAL ANTHROPOLOGY, HUMAN ECOLOGY, AND QUALITY OF LIFE

As biological anthropology succeeds in laying out the limits of human adaptation, opportunities to design better and more evolutionarily consistent living arrangements will increase. This area of applied biological anthropology is sometimes referred to as "human ecology."

Environmental pollution has become a major factor in lowering the standards of living for millions of people in the modern world. Increased noise pollution near busy airports leads to decreased birth weights in babies (Schell, 1991) and only recently, with modern medicine and nutrition, have secular trends in body size approached those of our Paleolithic hunter-gatherer ancestors (see Chapter 11). Nevertheless, the dosage effects of the many substances foreign to our biological adaptations that are now common in our drinking water, in the foods we eat, and in the air we breathe create an environment that is hostile to human health and survival. Ridding our environment of these disease-causing substances while ensuring an adequate supply of food and energy to a growing world population is a major challenge for the entire human species.

Anthropologist Lionel Tiger has argued in his 1992 book *The Pursuit of Pleasure* that all humans have some basic entitlements to certain aspects of the environment that are basically "normal" and therefore "pleasureable." If we accept this premise and its implication that society and governments should take it upon themselves to foster such environments, then much needs to be done. If, for example, Tiger is correct that expansive views of trees and bodies of water are "psycho-pleasures" born of human evolutionary adaptation over millions of years, then how do dwellers in urban glass towers surrounded on all sides by similar towers meet this need? If having an open fire with its warm glow, heat, and smoky smell are also evolutionary entitlements, how does the equally pressing need for clean air in our urban centers get met?

Another aspect of human ecology that perhaps is of even more importance than humans' relationship with the environment is intraspecific relationships. As more and more people are born and inhabit the earth, more and more crowding and interaction will become inevitable. The scale of the world's population of more than six billion people is simply incomprehensible to a hominid evolved out of a context in which groups of between 25 and 150 people were his or her entire life-long social environment (Allman, 1994). The myriad of social and economic problems that besets the modern city-state—from racism to poverty to homelessness to unemployment to crime to bureaucratic inefficiency—are possibly symptoms of this discordance between human evolution and modern human living conditions. Modern urban environments need to mimic the small groups, the intimate settings, and the natural and unpolluted surroundings of our ancestors. Such a utopian solution is clearly very far off, but one thing remains certain. It will be easier to change our surroundings to fit our adaptation than to change our adaptation to fit surroundings that are outside the limits passed on to us from our ancestors.

 **SUMMARY**

1. Applied biological anthropology takes the lessons of anthropological research and relates them to solutions of real-world problems and concerns. It is "holistic, evolutionary, cross-cultural, comparative, and population-based."

2. Much of applied biological anthropology is based on finding a resolution between the discordance of the human evolutionary past, to which we are still adapted, and modern living conditions.

3. Biomedical anthropology and evolutionary medicine are concerned with the clinical aspects of this relationship. Anthropologists have studied such health problems as Sudden Infant Death Syndrome, various cancers and other "diseases of civilization," including obesity, diverticulitis, and structural problems.

4. Forensic anthropology helps to solve individual criminal cases as well as human rights cases.

5. How humanity copes with the increasing problems of global human ecology will have to take into consideration human evolutionary history and adaptation while maintaining a technological infrastructure necessary for modern standards of living.

 ## CRITICAL-THINKING QUESTIONS

1. What is applied biological anthropology?
2. Discuss the "Discordance Hypothesis" of human adaptability.
3. Discuss three medical conditions and how knowledge of the evolutionary origins of these conditions has contributed to their treatment and prevention.
4. How can biological anthropology contribute to the investigation and solution of criminal cases?
5. Define "eugenics" and discuss how modern biological anthropology has contributed to society's altered view of this movement.
6. What contributions can applied biological anthropology make to improving the educational process?
7. What are some of the practical, applied reasons why we need to have a good knowledge of our early hominid forebears? Give examples.

 ## SUGGESTED READINGS

Allman, W. F. 1994. *The Stone Age Present*. New York: Simon & Schuster. An introduction to evolutionary psychology.

Eaton, S. B., M. Shostak, and M. Konner. 1988. *The Paleolithic Prescription: A Program of Diet and Exercise and a Design for Living*. New York: Harper and Row. One of the first books to establish the basis for evolutionary medicine—the application of anthropological principles to human disease, especially "diseases of civilization," in the modern world.

Ewald, P. 1994. *Evolution of Infectious Diseases*. London: Oxford University Press. A view of the co-evolutionary relationships between human populations and contagious diseases.

Joyce, C., and E. Stover. 1991. *Witnesses from the Grave: The Stories Bones Tell*. New York: Ballantine. A popular book about the career of Dr. Clyde Snow, a forensic anthropologist.

Trevathan, W. 1987. *Human Birth: An Evolutionary Perspective.* New York: Aldine de Gruyter. Looking at birth not as a medical emergency but as a normal life-cycle process of the human organism.

Williams, G. C., and R. M. Nesse. 1991. The dawn of Darwinian medicine. *Quarterly Review of Biology* 66:1–22. A succinct review of the evolutionary medicine movement.

Ubelaker, D., and H. Scammell. 1992. *Bones: A Forensic Detective's Casebook.* New York: Harper Collins. Discusses the methods used by forensic anthropologists using examples from missing persons and homicide investigations.

The Language of Biological Anthropology: Human Anatomy

Finding one's way around the structures in the human body requires an understanding of some navigational terms. First, we must "pin down" the body. Anatomists have done this by defining **anatomical position,** a standard placement of the human body standing erect with head looking forward, arms at the side with palms facing forward, and feet flat on the ground facing forward. The front part of the body is termed **anterior** or **ventral** ("belly"). The back part of the body is termed **posterior** or **dorsal** ("back"). And upper and lower parts of the body are called **superior** and **inferior,** respectively. Anatomical structures are always defined in reference to anatomical position. For example, we would say that an acrobat's chin is inferior to his forehead even though he might be swinging upside down from a trapeze. When discussing limbs, **proximal** refers to a part near the center of the body, and **distal** refers to a part farther away from the body.

Anatomical position for nonhuman animals differs somewhat from that of humans. Because four-footed animals normally do not stand erect, their anatomical position is defined as facing forward with all four feet on the ground. Anterior, posterior, inferior, and superior, then, are defined in the context of this orientation. In comparative anatomy, unlike human anatomy, ventral is synonymous with inferior, and dorsal is synonymous with superior. This system of terminology is also used in describing the brain.

Planes in the body are also important to understand and visualize. A **median (or midsagittal) plane** cuts the body in half lengthwise, into right and left halves. **Sagittal** planes cut the body parallel to the left or right of the median plane. A **transverse plane** cuts the body in half crosswise, at a right angle to the long axis of the body. And a **coronal plane** cuts the body into ventral and dorsal halves.

Orientation and description of teeth also has its own terminology. We can think of a set of teeth as a triangle, with the apex at the front of the mouth. A direction along the tooth row towards this apex is termed **mesial,** and away from the apex is termed **distal.** The sides of teeth are termed **lingual** if they are on the side facing the tongue, and **labial** (for front teeth facing the lips) or **buccal** (for teeth facing the cheeks).

Basic Movements

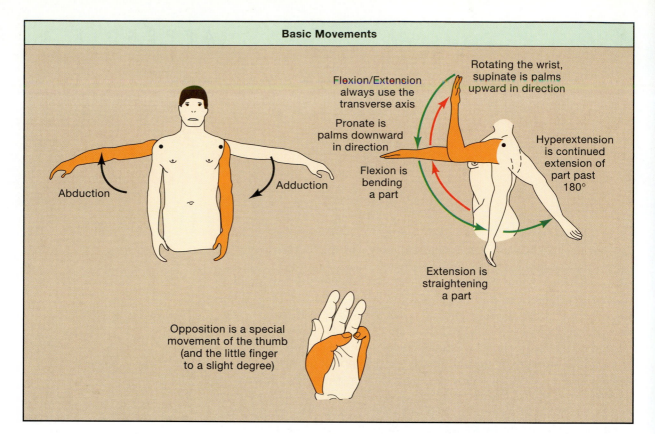

Abduction

Adduction

Flexion/Extension always use the transverse axis

Pronate is palms downward in direction

Flexion is bending a part

Rotating the wrist, supinate is palms upward in direction

Hyperextension is continued extension of part past 180°

Extension is straightening a part

Opposition is a special movement of the thumb (and the little finger to a slight degree)

Mammalian Tooth

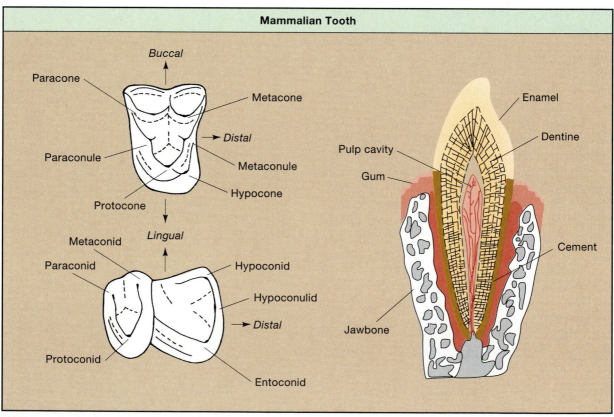

Buccal

Paracone

Metacone

Distal

Paraconule

Metaconule

Hypocone

Protocone

Lingual

Metaconid

Paraconid

Hypoconid

Hypoconulid

Distal

Protoconid

Entoconid

Enamel

Pulp cavity

Dentine

Gum

Cement

Jawbone

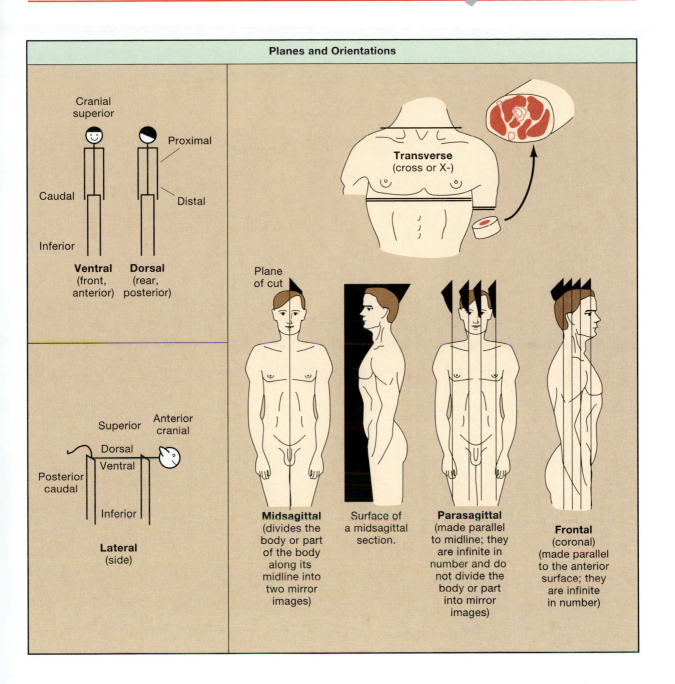

Planes and Orientations

Cranial superior

Proximal

Caudal

Distal

Inferior

Ventral
(front, anterior)

Dorsal
(rear, posterior)

Superior   Anterior cranial

Dorsal

Ventral

Posterior caudal

Inferior

Lateral
(side)

Transverse
(cross or X-)

Plane of cut

Midsagittal
(divides the body or part of the body along its midline into two mirror images)

Surface of a midsagittal section.

Parasagittal
(made parallel to midline; they are infinite in number and do not divide the body or part into mirror images)

Frontal
(coronal)
(made parallel to the anterior surface; they are infinite in number)

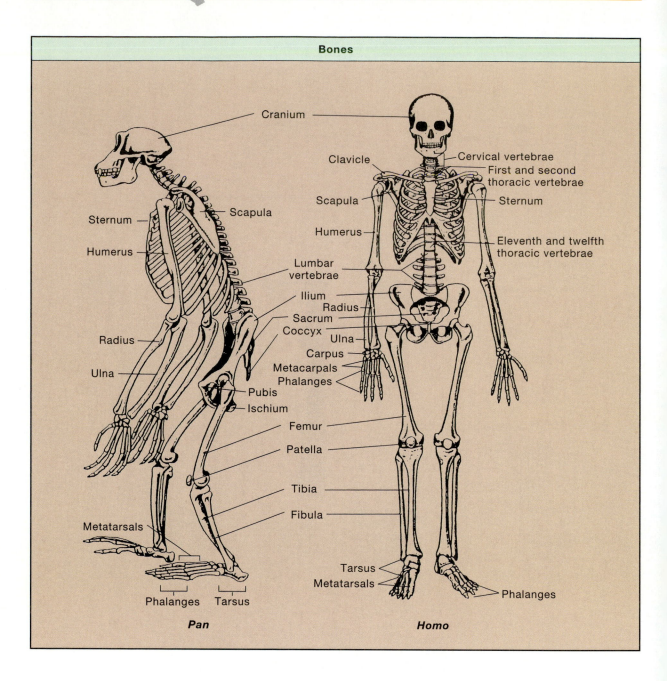

Bones

Pan

Homo

The Brain

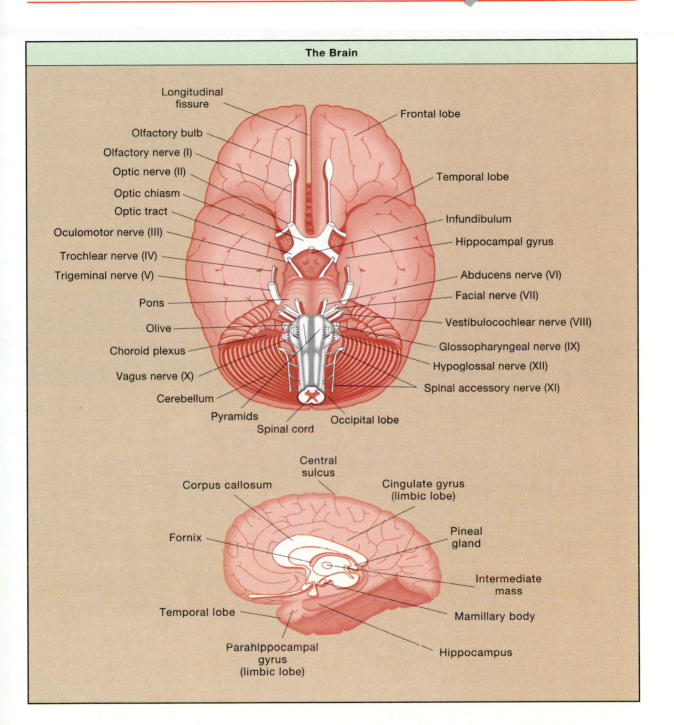

Longitudinal fissure

Olfactory bulb

Olfactory nerve (I)

Optic nerve (II)

Optic chiasm

Optic tract

Oculomotor nerve (III)

Trochlear nerve (IV)

Trigeminal nerve (V)

Pons

Olive

Choroid plexus

Vagus nerve (X)

Cerebellum

Pyramids

Spinal cord

Frontal lobe

Temporal lobe

Infundibulum

Hippocampal gyrus

Abducens nerve (VI)

Facial nerve (VII)

Vestibulocochlear nerve (VIII)

Glossopharyngeal nerve (IX)

Hypoglossal nerve (XII)

Spinal accessory nerve (XI)

Occipital lobe

Central sulcus

Corpus callosum

Fornix

Temporal lobe

Parahippocampal gyrus (limbic lobe)

Cingulate gyrus (limbic lobe)

Pineal gland

Intermediate mass

Mamillary body

Hippocampus

The Language of Biological Anthropology: Geology

The geological time scale provides an important way to describe how old and in what time context ancient organisms lived. The largest categories of time in the geological time scale are termed **eras.** Eras are divided into **periods.** For the most recent two periods of geological time, there are also smaller divisions known as **epochs.** As methods of determining the absolute ages of fossil sites have improved, so have our ideas of the age limits of the various time boundaries been refined. These boundaries are shown in the table.

Geological Terminology

Time (millions of years ago)	Era	Period	Epoch	Etymology
0.01	Cenozoic	Quaternary	Holocene (Recent)	"entirely recent"
			Pleistocene	"most recent"
1.6–1.8			Pliocene	"more recent"
5.5		Tertiary	Miocene	"less recent"
22			Oligocene	"scanty recent"
40			Eocene	"dawn recent"
50			Paleocene	"ancient recent"
70	Mesozoic	Cretaceous		"chalk-bearing"
140		Jurassic		from Jura Mts., Switzerland
190		Triassic		"three-parts"
220	Paleozoic	Permian		from region in Eastern Russia
280		Carboniferous		"carbon-bearing"
340		Devonian		from Devon, England
390		Silurian		from Welsh tribe of Siluria
430		Ordovician		from Welsh tribe of Ordovices
500		Cambrian		from Cambria, Wales
570	Precambrian	Ediacaran		from Ediacara, Australia

The Language of Biological Anthropology: Biology and Taxonomy

The scientific discipline that studies naming is termed **taxonomy.** Although the naming of new species and the renaming of old species continually keeps classificatory schemes changing, scientists need to agree on the definition of the animal species and higher categories to which reference is being made. A formal taxonomic name at any level is known as a **taxon.**

All biological species are formally classified by a **binomial** system, under which they are assigned two, usually Latin, names. The first of these names, used alone, is the **genus.** Both names used together designate the **species** to which the animal is assigned.

Zoological classification is *hierarchical,* that is, organized in levels, one under another. In practice, the International Code of Zoological Nomenclature establishes the rules of taxonomy for animal species. There are many rules, but, basically, the Code says that names that were proposed first for a species always have *priority* over names proposed later. There must be a clearly designated type specimen with a description of the characteristics that distinguish its species from other closely related species. The classification can be somewhat arbitrary. For example, it does not matter if we call ourselves *Homo sapiens sapiens* or *Gorilla gorilla beringei* so long as everyone understands what group of animals is being referred to. Most classifications attempt to strike a balance between current taxonomic usage and recent findings in both paleontological and molecular realms. The full taxonomic classification of the human species, along with other living primates, is presented on the following page; common names of each classification are given in parentheses.

Kingdom Animalia (Animals)

  Phylum Chordata (Chordates)

    Subphylum Vertebrata (Vertebrates)

     Class Mammalia (Mammals)

      Subclass Eutheria (Placental Mammals)

       Order Primates (Primates)

        Suborder Prosimii (Prosimians)

         Infraorder Lemuroidea (Lemuroids)

           Family Cheirogalidae (Dwarf and Mouse Lemurs)

           Family Daubentoniidae (Aye-aye)

           Family Galagidae (Bushbaby)

           Family Indridae (Indri and Sifaka)

           Family Lemuridae (Lemur)

           Family Lepilemuridae (Sportive Lemur)

           Family Lorisidae (Potto and Loris)

         Infraorder Tarsioidea (Tarsioids)

           Family Tarsiidae (Tarsier)

        Suborder Anthropoidea (Anthropoids)

         Infraorder Platyrrhini (New World Monkeys)

           Family Cebidae (Cebid)

           Family Callimiconidae (Goeldi's Monkey)

           Family Callitrichidae (Marmoset and Tamarin)

        Infraorder Catarrhini ("Old World Primate")

         Superfamily Cercopithecoidea (Old World Monkey)

           Family Cercopithecidae (Cercopithecids)

           Family Colobidae (Langurs, Colobus)

         Superfamily Hominoidea (Apes and Humans)

           Family Hylobatidae (Gibbons and Siamangs)

           Family Pongidae (Orangutan)

           Family Gorillidae (Gorilla)

           Family Panidae (Chimpanzee and Bonobo, or Pygmy Chimpanzee)

           Family Hominidae (Hominid)

            Subfamily Homininae (Hominine)

            Genus *Homo* (Human, "Man")

             Species *Homo sapiens* (Human, "Man")

              Subspecies *Homo sapiens sapiens* (Human, sometimes "anatomically modern human")

Glossary

ABO blood group—blood group system discovered by Landsteiner in 1900 defined by agglutination (clotting) reactions of red blood cells to natural anti-A and anti-B antibodies. Blood type A reacts only to anti-A, type B reacts only to anti-B, type AB reacts to both, and type O reacts to neither.

acclimation—short-term physiological adaptation, occurring over a period of several hours to several days

acclimatization—long-term physiological adaptation, which may have some morphological effect, but which occurs during the lifetime of one individual and which is not passed on genetically

Acheulean—stone tool culture characterized by "hand axes" flaked on two sides, thus termed "bifaces"

adapids—lemurlike prosimians, among the earliest strepsirhines

adaptability—the range of physiological and behavioral responses that an individual can make to adjust to environmental changes

adaptation—biological change effected by evolution to accommodate populations to different environmental conditions

adaptationist—the theoretical position that most if not all morphological and behavioral traits of a species have been crafted by natural selection to adapt that species to its adaptive niche; criticized by S.J. Gould as the "Panglossian paradigm," from Voltaire's *Candide,* in reference to Dr. Pangloss's explanation that "all things are for the best"

adolescence—the period of growth between puberty and the attainment of full adult stature and sexual maturity

"African Eve" Hypothesis—the hypothesis based on studies of modern human mitochondrial DNA, that all modern humans descended from one closely related population, or even one woman, living in Africa approximately 100,000 to 200,000 years ago

agnathans—primitive, "jawless" fish

agonistic—in ethology, referring to behavior that appears in aggressive encounters

allele—alternate form of a gene

amniote egg—an egg characteristic of the reptiles that could be laid and developed out of water

Amphibia—class of vertebrates that includes frogs, salamanders, and extinct species living much of their lives on land but whose reproduction remains tied to water

analogous—similar because of adaptation for similar functions

anthropoids—"higher" primates, including the monkeys, apes, and humans

anthropology—the study of humankind

anthropometry—the portion of physical anthropology concerned with measurement of the human body

apomorphy—in cladistic terminology, a newly arisen or derived trait used in systematics

applied biological anthropology—use of the method and theory of biological anthropology to solve problems or address questions of practical significance

appositional growth—growth by adding of layers at a specific point or plane

archaeology—the anthropological study of past cultures, their social adaptations, and their lifeways by use of preserved artifacts and features

Ardipithecus ramidus—the most primitive species of hominid presently known, dating to 4 to 4.2 million years ago from Aramis, Middle Awash, Ethiopia.

assort—the independent separation of pairs of genes on one chromosome from pairs of genes on other chromosomes; also known as Mendel's Second Law, or Law of Independent Assortment

australopithecine—subfamily of the Hominidae containing the most primitive species within the family; characterized by relatively small crania, large cheek teeth, and according to some researchers enhanced climbing capabilities

Australopithecus afarensis—gracile species of *Australopithecus* found at sites in East Africa and dated from 4.0 to 2.5 million years ago; most famous representatives of this taxon are "Lucy" from Hadar, Ethiopia, and the Laetoli footprints in Tanzania.

Australopithecus africanus—the first species of *Australopithecus* to be named, based on the type of the Taung child; characterized by "harmonious dentition" and relatively "gracile" skull morphology, the species dates to between about 3 and 2.5 million years ago; represented at other sites in South Africa, and probably also in East Africa.

Australopithecus anamensis—new species of *Australopithecus* discovered at two sites around Lake

Turkana, described in 1995 by Meave Leakey and Alan Walker, and dated to 4.0 million years ago.

Australopithecus (=Paranthropus) aethiopicus– earlier form of robust australopithecines in East Africa dated from 2.6 to 2.3 million years ago; most famous representative is the Black Skull discovered in 1986 at a site on the western shores of Lake Turkana.

Australopithecus (=Paranthropus) boisei–robust australopithecines found at site in East Africa and dated from 2.4 to 1.3 million years ago; most famous representatives were found at Olduvai Gorge *(Zinjanthropus)* and East Lake Turkana.

Australopithecus (=Paranthropus) robustus–robust australopithecines found in cave deposits from South Africa and dated from 2.0 to 1.0 million years ago; most famous representatives were found at the site of Swartkrans, South Africa.

autosomes–referring to chromosomes other than the sex (X and Y) chromosomes

basal ganglia–structures in the forebrain of vertebrates that form part of the "R-Complex"

basicranial flexion–the hinging of the base of the skull and the hard palate together to form a more acute angle; seen in both australopithecine lineages.

behavior–patterns of animal activity over time

bilharzia–infection by the parasitic blood fluke *Schistosoma,* which lays its eggs in the liver; leads to liver and occasionally kidney damage; also known as schistosomiasis

bilirubin–a bile pigment from the liver that results from the breakdown of hemoglobin in red blood cells; bilirubin normally circulates in the blood in a complex with albumin but can increase in certain pathological conditions such as hepatitis

biological anthropology–the study of human evolution, biology, variation, and adaptation

blending inheritance–the mixing in equal halves of the contributions of parents in their offspring

bonobo–*Pan paniscus,* a species of chimpanzee distinct from the common chimpanzee, *Pan troglodytes,* and living in a different, nonoverlapping range—the Central Congo (formerly Zaire) forest basin; also termed the "pygmy chimpanzee" but its differences from the common chimp are more in terms of morphology and shape than size

brachiation–hominoid ability, the result of specialized anatomy of the forelimb and upper torso, to move under (branches) by swinging

branchial arches–the tissue between the gill slits in the embryos of vertebrates.

breccia–from Italian, meaning "broken"; a geological term used to refer to the sediment found in cave deposits composed from rock fragments of widely varying sizes cemented together

Broca's Area–portion of the cerebral cortex (posterior part of the inferior frontal gyrus, usually on the left side) that is essential for the motor control of speech

callitrichids–marmosets and tamarins

canalization–the directed trajectory of growth in certain directions even if normal growth spurts are delayed

cartilage–a supporting tissue more elastic and flexible than bone (for example, the "gristle" in meat)

cartilage bone–bone formed by development from cartilage and growth at epiphyses, characteristic of vertebrate limb bones

catarrhines–Old World monkeys, apes, and humans

catastrophism–theory that earth history is explicable in terms of violent and sudden cataclysms that destroyed most living species, after which a new set of creations established new species

cebid–New World monkeys excluding marmosets and tamarins

cercopithecines–Old World monkeys with generally omnivorous or graminivorous diets, frequently ground-living, and sometimes lacking tails

Cercopithecoidea–Old World monkeys

cerumen–ear wax; a waxy secretion of glands located in the external ear canal

Cesarean section–incision through the abdomen and uterus for delivery of a fetus; the name derives from Julius Caesar, whose mother arranged for this method of delivery to assure the proper astrological sign for her son

childhood–the period of growth from weaning to the attainment of adult brain size

cholera–infectious disease caused by the bacterium *Vibrio cholerae,* and spread usually by contaminated drinking water; symptoms include severe diarrhea, dehydration, shock, and kidney failure

chordates–animals with a notochord and a dorsal nerve cord

chromosomes–structures composed of folded DNA found in the nuclei of the cells of eukaryotic organisms

cingulum–a "belt" (from Latin), referring to a raised ridge of enamel encircling a tooth crown

cladistics–the common term for the study of the phylogenetic relationships among a group of related animals by reference to only derived traits shared in common

cladogram–branching diagram showing relative relationships among taxonomic groups of animals; not to be confused with a phylogenetic tree, which postulated ancestor-descendant relationships

cline–a gradient of genotypes or phenotypes over a geographic range

co-evolution–the concept that organisms sharing the same environmental resources will evolve along with one another, as well as with environmental changes

codons–three-unit bases of DNA that code for one of 20 amino acids or that code for a stop on termination of translation of that particular segment of DNA

collector bias–the selection that an individual makes in assembling a collection of specimens, which can vary from one individual to another

colobines–leaf-eating monkeys, mostly arboreal

communication–transmittal of information by sensory means

consort relationships–pairing off of a female and male for the purposes of mating

convergence–the evolution of similar traits in two distantly related animals, such as similar streamlined body form for swimming in dolphins and sharks

corpus callosum–the fiber tract connecting the two halves of the brain across the midline

cortical homunculus–the localized map of the entire body as represented in the cerebral cortex

Cro-Magnon–a cave site in southern France where late Pleistocene anatomically modern humans were first found

crossing over–the exchange of genes between paired chromosomes during cell duplication

cultural anthropology–the anthropological study of human societies, their belief systems, their cultural adaptations, and their social behavior

culture–learned aspects of behavior passed on from one generation to the next in human societies

cut marks–incisions left on bone as a byproduct of skinning or cutting muscle off the bone with stone tools; uniquely characteristic of hominids but sometimes difficult to distinguish from carnivore bite marks or scratch marks made by sand grains

cystic fibrosis–hereditary disease of children and young adults affecting the pancreas and exocrine glands and associated with chronic lung disease

deduction–inferring conclusions about particular instances from general or universal premises

deme–a population within which there is a high degree of gene exchange

demographic–relating to the age composition, proportions of the sexes, size, and other statistical parameters of a population

development–embryological differentiation of organs and tissues; sometimes considered the earliest stage of growth

diachronic–historical; extending through time

dietary hypothesis–hypothesis advanced by John T. Robinson that differences in the dentitions of the gracile and robust australopithecines were to be accounted for by differences in dietary adaptations, the former eating a more omnivorous diet and the latter eating a more herbivorous one.

diploid–having two sets of chromosomes, as normally found in the somatic cells of higher organisms

directional selection–selection that acts to move the mean of a population in one particular direction

Discordance Hypothesis–the thesis that human biology and behavior, as shaped by evolution, are at odds with modern human environments

diverticulitis–inflammation of an outpocketing of the wall of the large intestine

DNA–double-chain molecule that contains the genetic code common to all organisms

DNA hybridization–method of assessing genetic relationships by splitting and "re-annealing" strands of DNA from different species

dominance rank–the relative hierarchical position of an individual in a social group

dryopithecid–family of middle Miocene hominids found mostly in Europe

Early Divergence Hypothesis–hypothesis that postulates an ancient evolutionary split (more than 15 million years ago) of African apes and humans from a common ancestor

eccrine sweat glands–glands that excrete a watery liquid over much of the surface area of the head, face, neck, and upper body during heat stress

ecological niche–the "ecological space" to which a species is adapted, including its habitat, diet, and behavior

ecology–the science that studies the biological relationships between species and their environment

ectotympanic bone–a separate bone covering the ear canal

embryonic–that period of growth prior to birth, especially weeks 3 through 8; growth during the last six months of gestation is sometimes referred to as fetal growth

encephalization–the process of extreme brain enlargement in the *Homo* lineage

endocast–a three-dimensional replica of the inside of the brain case, revealing what the exterior of the brain would have looked like

endocranial volume–synonymous with cranial capacity—the amount of space inside the skull, occupied in life by the brain and brain coverings

enzymes–polypeptides that catalyze or accelerate chemical reactions

epidemiology–the study of the geographic distribution, spread, and control of disease

epistasis–gene masking the effect of another gene

estrus–the period of maximum sexual receptivity and ovulation that may be marked by physiological and behavioral changes in females. Corresponding changes may also be observed in males

ethnocentrism–the pervasive belief present in all cultures that tends to lead individuals within a culture to view their own culture as superior to all others.

ethogram–the behavioral repertoire characteristic of a species

ethology–naturalistic study of animal behavior and its evolution

eukaryotes–organisms that have a nucleus containing DNA in their cells

evolution by natural selection–Darwin's theory that inherited variability results in the differential survival of individuals and in their ability to contribute to offspring in succeeding generations

evolutionary medicine–the application of evolutionary principles and deductions from biological anthropology and human biology to the practice of medicine; also termed "Darwinian medicine"

exon–the expressed segment of a gene, separated from other exons by introns

exoskeleton–a hard and inflexible outer covering of the body of invertebrate animals, such as insects and crustaceans

family–a taxonomic grouping of similar genera

feed-back system–in information theory, the concept that change in one step of a loop will affect a subsequent step that will in turn affect the starting point

fever–elevation of body temperature above normal; in disease, caused by infection by microorganisms

fibrinopeptide–blood protein related to blood clotting

field studies–in primatology, studies of species in their natural habitat, uninfluenced or influenced to a minor degree by interactions with humans

fist walking–a terrestrial quadrupedal form of locomotion characteristic of orangutans involving the placement of the flexed first phalanges instead of the palms on the ground for support; similar in function but probably not homologous to knuckle walking

fitness–the extent to which the genes of an individual survive in its descendants

fixed action pattern–inborn, genetically programmed behavior that is always released by the same stimuli and always shows the same sequence of actions

foraging strategies–behavior patterns that result in the discovery and procurement of food

fossils–remains of animals and plants preserved in the ground

founder effect–a type of genetic drift caused by sampling a small amount of genetic variation from the original population in a group of individuals colonizing a new area

free radicals–highly reactive "active" molecules of oxygen (mainly O_2^-) formed from the breakdown of oxygen molecules in the body

fusion-fission social organization–social organization based on formation and dissolution of groups

G6PD–glucose-6-phosphate dehydrogenase, an enzyme necessary for red blood cell metabolism; G6PD deficiency is caused by recessive genes and can result in the disease "favism"

game theory–the analysis of win-loss combinations in any competitive relationship in order to determine strategy or to predict outcomes of the competition

gene pool–the shared genetic makeup of a population

genes–units of the material of inheritance, now known to be sequences of DNA

genetic drift–gene frequency changes due to chance effects, not affected by selection; most common in small population sizes

genetic load–the deleterious or lethal effects that accompany genetic variation in a population, measured by the number of recessive lethal genes carried by individuals in a population; also called genetic burden

genetic markers–traits whose genetic causation are known and which can be used in the study of populations

genetic mutation–a heritable change in the genetic material, located in the sex cells, that brings about a change in phenotype

genetic plasticity–ability of a developing organism to alter its form and function in conformity with demands of the immediate environment

genetic polymorphism–the existence of two or more genetic variants within a population; can be a balanced polymorphism when selection favors the heterozygotes, as in sickle-cell anemia

genetics–the study of heredity and variation

genotype–the genetic composition of an organism, as compared to phenotype, the manifestation of its genes

genus–a taxonomic grouping of similar species

globin–protein of hemoglobin that comprises red blood cells

grade–a level of organization or morphological complexity in an evolving lineage of organisms

grooming behavior–slow systematic picking through the hair of another individual to remove foreign matter; important in primate social interactions

habituation–neurophysiological mechanism for "tuning out" unwanted stimuli, an accommodation that takes only a few minutes

Hadar—hominid site in northern Ethiopia dating to between 3.0 and 3.4 million years ago

haploid—having a single set of chromosomes, as found in the sex cells or gametes of higher organisms

Hardy-Weinberg equilibrium—a hypothetical condition in which there is no selection or other forces of evolution acting on a population and in which gene and genotype frequencies stay the same from one generation to the next. For two alleles at one locus, alleles p + alleles q = 100%

harem species—in primatology, social groupings characterized by one dominant male and a number of females and their young

hemolytic incompatibility—destruction of red blood cells caused by the action of antibodies, resulting in release of hemoglobin into the plasma

heterochrony—Greek meaning "different time"; refers to the changes in rate of growth characteristic of species' evolutionary divergence from an ancestral species

heterodonty—the condition of possessing teeth differentiated for different functions; contrasted with the homodont dentition of many reptiles, such as living crocodiles

heterozygous—bearing two different alleles at a genetic locus

holotype—the single specimen on which a taxonomic name is based

home range—the area that a group or population inhabits and ranges over, the boundaries of which, unlike a territory, are not defended

homeothermy—the maintenance of constant body temperature; "warm-blooded"

Hominidae—the zoological family to which living humans and their bipedal relatives, all now extinct, belong

hominine—subfamily of the Hominidae containing the members sharing derived characteristics with modern humans; characterized by relatively large brains, small dentitions, and fully modern postcranial adaptations

hominoids—modern apes, modern humans, and their immediate ancestors

Homo erectus—primitive species of the genus *Homo*, generally considered to have evolved from *Homo habilis* and to be the ancestor of *Homo sapiens*

Homo ergaster—taxon assigned by some researchers to remains of *Homo* in East Africa but regarded by most as being an early representative of *Homo erectus*

Homo habilis—earliest generally recognized species of the genus *Homo*

Homo sapiens—species that includes modern humans as well as archaic *Homo sapiens*

homologous—similar because of common descent or common inheritance

homozygous—bearing two identical alleles at a genetic locus

homunculus theory—held that human ancestors when discovered would look similar to early stages of modern human development

hormone—a chemical substance produced by an organ or structure of the body that acts on or affects another distinct organ or structure

human biology—the branch of biology that studies human physiology and adaptation; closely related to biological anthropological study of the same topics

Hybridization Model—evolutionary hypothesis that suggests interbreeding between emigrant African populations and resident human populations in other parts of the world

hypertension—persistently high blood pressure; above 140 mm Hg systolic (contraction) and 90 mm Hg diastolic (dilation) pressures of the heart

hypothalamus—part of the ancient forebrain; located "below the thalamus" at the base of the brain's third ventricle, and important in autonomic nervous system functions such as endocrine gland activity

hypothesis—an explanation of a set of observations that can be disproved or falsified by additional observations or facts

hypoxia—a condition of reduced oxygen supply to tissues despite adequate blood supply

imitative—relating to information gained through observing other individuals and not through one's own experience

imprinting—the fixation in an individual of a specific stimulus or set of stimuli during a particular period of sensitivity to learning that stimulus

inbreeding—the increased incidence of mating within a deme or population that results in an increase in homozygosity within the population

inclusive fitness—the relative reproductive potential of an individual within a group of related individuals in a population

inductive scientific method—inferring a generalized conclusion from particular instances

infancy—earliest stage of postpartum growth, extending from birth to the time of weaning

infanticide—killing of infants

innate releasing mechanism—a sensory cue that triggers a certain behavior or set of behaviors in an animal.

Insectivora—order of insect-eating mammals that includes shrews and tree shrews; similar to early Mesozoic mammals

inter-birth interval—the period of time between births

interstitial growth—growth by new cell formation throughout the mass of a structure, tissue, or organ

intron—noncoding sequence of DNA that is not transcribed by the m-RNA

IQ—Intelligence Quotient; a score on a standardized psychological test designed in western Europe and North America to measure "an individual's aggregate capacity to act purposefully, think rationally, and deal effectively with his environment"

juvenile—the period of growth between attainment of adult brain size and the onset of puberty

karyotype—identified and numbered arrangement of chromosomes

knuckle walking—a terrestrial quadrupedal form of locomotion characteristic of chimpanzees and gorillas involving the placement of the flexed second phalanges instead of the palms on the ground for support

laboratory studies—in primatology, controlled studies of captive primates

labyrinthodonts—extinct, predaceous amphibians of the Carboniferous Period some of whom were ancestral to the first reptiles

lactation—in mammals the period of production of milk following birth of offspring, during which offspring are suckled by the mother

Laetoli—a site in northern Tanzania, south of Olduvai Gorge, where hominids were first found in the 1930s and again in the 1970s; dated to between 3.6 and 3.8 million years ago

Lake Turkana—hominid sites on both the east and west sides of Lake Turkana (formerly Lake Rudolf), closely associated with Omo and dating to between 4.0 and 1.4 million years ago

laryngeal sacs—outpocketings at the sides of the voice box (larynx) used as resonating chambers in certain primates; remnants of the laryngeal sacs can be seen in human individuals who, like trumpet players and glassblowers, create high air pressure in their throats

Late Divergence Hypothesis—hypothesis that postulates a recent evolutionary split (5 to less than 15 million years ago) of the African apes and humans from a common ancestor

learn—remember information or experience and retain for use in future behavior

life history strategies—behavioral decisions that each animal in a species must make to acquire food, avoid predators, and find mates. These decisions may increase inclusive fitness and, thus, vary the reproductive success of different individuals

limbic system—a mammalian adaptation of the primarily olfactory part of the forebrain, important in sexual and maternal behavior

linguistics—the anthropological study of languages, their diversity and connections, and the interaction of language and culture in society

linkage—the tendency of genes to be inherited together because of their location and proximity to one another on one chromosome

locomotion—the means of moving about

locus—a "place" on a chromosome or segment of DNA where a gene is located

longitudinal arch—the upwardly arched structure composed of bones and connecting ligaments on the medial side of the human foot

macroevolution—large-scale changes in gene frequencies or other biological traits in a species or higher level taxonomic grouping, generally over a relatively long period of time

malaria—from Italian for "bad air," from the original, mistaken belief that the disease was airborne; occasionally fatal disease caused by a protozoan infecting the red blood cells and transmitted from one carrier to another by the bite of a female *Anopheles* mosquito; symptoms include chills, sweating, and convulsions

mammal-like reptiles (therapsids)—reptiles with a skull opening behind the eye (subclass Synapsida) and with differentiated teeth.

mandible—the lower jaw of mammals, composed of a fusion of the reptile dentary and articular bones

marsupials—pouched mammals

maturity—life cycle stage typified by steady state replacement of cells and cessation of growth

mean—the statistical average of a measurement of a population

megadont—"large-toothed," referring to the relatively large molars of hominids; Boaz (1983) has suggested that "megamylic" ("large-molared") is a more accurate term

meiosis—the process whereby eukaryote sex cells halve their DNA for combination with the sex cells of another individual

melanin—from Greek meaning "black"; a dark brown or black pigment that occurs in the skin and hair

membrane bone—bone formed by development from a connective tissue membrane, characteristic of vertebrate skull bones

meniscus—from Latin meaning "lens"; the cartilage rimming the articular surface of the tibia at the knee joint and which forms a basin for the articular end of the femur

menstruation–monthly, cyclic shedding of the lining of the uterus by nonpregnant female primates, particularly noticeable in humans

metabolic rate–the rate at which energy is expended in all the chemical reactions in an animal's cells and tissues

methanethiol–a chemical breakdown product of asparagus with a detectable odor, excreted by individuals heterozygous for the gene

microevolution–small-scale change in gene frequencies or other biological traits in a population or species over a relatively brief period of time

microfauna–the smallest members of a fauna, usually used in paleoanthropological research to refer to small mammals, such as rodents, insectivores, and prosimian primates

midfacial prognathism–forward projection of the bony nose region of the skull; characteristic of Neandertals

migration–the movement of a reproductively active individual into a population from a distant population, thus bringing new genes into that population

mitochondria–organelles within the cell with their own DNA that carry on energy metabolism for the cell

mitochondrial DNA–the DNA within the mitochondria, abbreviated as mt-DNA; mt-DNA evolves approximately 10 times faster than the DNA in the cell nucleus

mitosis–the duplication of the DNA during splitting of a cell and migration of each duplicated portion to a new cell

monogamous–referring to one male–one female pair bonding

monogenism–in the history of anthropology, relating to a single or unitary origin of the human species, connoting that all human races were part of one species; an early point of agreement between the Church and Darwinism

morbidity–showing evidence of disease or infection

morphology–the study of the form and anatomy of physical structures in the bodies of living or once living organisms

motor cortex–the part of the cerebral cortex located in the pre-central gyrus that controls voluntary movements of the body

Mousterian–a Middle Paleolithic stone tool culture characterized by prepared flakes struck off a core; *ca.* 250,000–40,000 years ago

multi-male groups–in reference to primate social organization, groups of primates where several dominant males live together in the same group

Multiregional Model–evolutionary hypothesis that suggests primary continuity from earlier to later human populations in each area of the world, with some gene exchange between populations

muscles of mastication–four paired muscles that connect the skull to the mandible and move the jaw upward and to the sides in chewing

mutation–any novel genetic change that may affect both genes and chromosomes. Such changes are spontaneous and random in occurrence. Mutations are the source of all variability in populations, and, if they occur in the sex cells usually during the formation of gametes, they hold the possibility of altering the Phenotypes in succeeding generations

natal residents–residents of a group that were born in the group

natural selection–the process of differential reproduction whereby individuals well-adapted to their environment will be "favored," that is, they will pass on more of their heritable attributes to the next generation than other, less well-adapted individuals

naturalistic fieldwork–the study of primates in their natural environment

Neandertal–a cave site in Germany, used to refer to a late Pleistocene human population in Europe and part of the Middle East; termed *Homo sapiens neanderthalensis*

Neo-Darwinism–the combined theory of evolution by natural selection and modern genetics

neocortex–the evolutionary "new" part of the cerebral cortex

neurocranium–that part of the skull holding the brain

neutral mutations–mutations that are not acted upon by selection; ones that do not affect the fitness of an organism in a particular environment. Neutral mutations accumulate at a more or less constant rate over time

observational learning–learning by seeing and hearing

occipital torus–a horizontal raised ridge of bone at the back of the *Homo erectus* skull

old age–life cycle stage typified by a greater rate of cell death than replacement

Olduvai Gorge–a site in northern Tanzania yielding remains of robust australopithecines and early *Homo*

Oldowan–earliest recognized stone tool tradition associated with the first members of the genus *Homo;* Mode I tools

Omo–a site in southern Ethiopia along the lower Omo River, with numerous hominids dating from about 3.4 to 1.0 million years ago

omomyids—tarsierlike prosimians, among the earliest haplorhines

optimal foraging theory—a predictive theory based on food-getting behavior selected to balance a group's needs to find food against the costs of getting it

orthogenesis—mistaken view of evolutionary change always proceeding in a "straight-line," directed course

osteology—study of bones

Out-of-Africa Model—evolutionary hypothesis that holds that modern humans evolved first in Africa and then spread out over the rest of the world, displacing or driving to extinction other populations

ovulation—release of a mature egg cell from the female's ovary after which time it can be fertilized by a male sperm cell

paleoanthropology—the study of the physical characteristics, evolution, and behavior of fossil humans and their relatives, incorporating parts of biological anthropology and archaeology

paleomagnetic dating—the matching of a sequence of strata with the dated pattern of changes in magnetic orientation through time, thereby dating the sediments

panmictic—"all mixing," referring to populations in which the breeding structure approximates the condition in which an individual male or female has the same probability of mating with another individual of the opposite sex anywhere in the population

paradigm—a framework for understanding and interpreting observations

parallelism—the evolution of similar traits in two closely related species, such as elongated hind legs for jumping in two small rodent species

paratypes—a group of specimens on which a taxonomic name is based

paromomyoids—plesiadapiform primates that had gliding adaptations

pedomorphosis—the retention of a juvenile stage in some part of a descendant species' morphology or behavior, in comparison with its ancestral species

perineal—relating to the area between the anus and the external genitalia, the perineum

peromorphosis—the extension of growth or "adultification" of some part of the morphology or behavior of a descendant species, in comparison with its ancestral species

pheromones—hormones that produce their effect by the sense of smell

phyletic gradualism—term coined by Stephen J. Gould to characterize Darwin's idea of evolutionary rate; slow, gradual change over long periods of time

phylogeny—the study of evolutionary relationships of organisms

pineal body—small, cone-shaped part of the brain located below the *corpus callosum;* synthesizes the hormone melatonin, which is important in mediating estrus cycling in mammals, and reacts to ambient light in the environment

pituitary gland—an endocrine gland at the base of the cerebral cortex

placentals—evolved mammals with a very efficient reproductive system, which includes a placenta, a structure that provides the developing embryo with well-oxygenated blood

placoderms—early fish with biting jaws

platyrrhines—New World monkeys

play—behavior that is not directed toward any clearly defined end result, such as food-getting, and which is frequently characteristic of young mammals

plesiadapiforms—archaic primates of the Paleocene and early Eocene Epochs

plesiadapoids—plesiadapiform primates that were generalized archaic primates and may have been ancestral to later primates

pliopithecid—medium-sized, folivorous hominoids known from the middle-late Miocene of Eurasia

polygenic—a trait controlled by interaction of genes at more than one locus

polygenism—in the history of anthropology, relating to a multiple origin of the human species, connoting that human races were different species; used by some to defend slavery and by others to justify colonial mistreatment of indigenous peoples

polypeptide chain—a molecule consisting of a long chain of amino acids joined together by peptide bonds

population—a geographically localized group of individuals in a species that more likely share a common gene pool among themselves than with other individuals in the species

potassium-argon method—dating technique pioneered by Garniss Curtis that measures the amount of radioactive potassium isotope (K^{40}) to its decay product, argon gas (Ar^{40}), found in rocks of volcanic origin

predation rate—frequency of killing and eating of individuals of a prey species by one or several predator species

primates—the zoological order of mammals that includes living and extinct monkeys, apes, and humans, as well as more primitive taxa

primatology—science that studies primates, usually primate behavior and ecology

proconsulids–family of early Miocene hominids known mostly from sites in eastern Africa

prognathism–forward-protruding jaws (maxilla plus mandible) or lower face

prokaryotes–organisms like bacteria that lack a differentiated cell nucleus

promiscuity–sexual relations with a number of partners

propliopithecoids–anthropoid (catarrhine) primates from the Oligocene of Egypt, sometimes considered the earliest hominoids

prosimians–primates typified by small body size and frequently nocturnal adaptations in the living forms

punctuated equilibrium–term coined by Stephen J. Gould and Niles Eldredge to characterize evolution typified by long periods of little or no change (stasis) interrupted by bursts of rapid change (punctuational events)

quantum evolution–stepwise evolutionary change

quantum theory of heredity–passing of traits as clear-cut quantifiable units not subject to subdivision; characteristic of Mendelian genetics

race–a biological term meaning subspecies, or a geographically defined population within a species; not synonymous with "ethnic group" or other sociopolitically or culturally defined terms referring to group identity

racism–a policy or opinion that unfairly generalizes real or perceived characteristics of a specific ethnic group, population, or "race" to every member of that group, and which may be used to deny resources or fair and equal treatment to an individual on the basis of their membership in that group

R-Complex–the most primitive, "reptilian" part of the "triune" brain model of Paul MacLean; the site of certain ritualistic, stereotypical, and social communication behaviors

replication–a duplication process requiring copying from a template, in this case the DNA molecule

reproductive fitness–relative reproductive success of certain individuals over others as measured by selection in a particular environment; the ability of one genotype to produce more offspring relative to this ability in other genotypes in the same environment

reproductive isolating mechanisms–genetic separation of populations by geography, ecology, behavior, physiology, or anatomy

retromolar space–a gap to be seen between the last upper molar and the ascending ramus of the mandible when articulated with the skull

Rh blood group–a complex system of blood antigens originally discovered by Landsteiner and Wiener in 1940 using blood from the rhesus monkey, which lent the first two letters of its name to the system. Rh antigens are controlled by 8 major genes or gene complexes yielding some 18 different phenotypes.

rickets–from Old English, meaning "twisted," a disease caused by deficiency of Vitamin D and characterized by the symptoms of poor calcification of bones, skeletal deformities, disturbance of growth, and generalized muscular weakness

RNA–ribonucleic acid, a molecule similar to DNA except that uracil (U) replaces thymine (T) as one of its four bases; the hereditary material in some viruses, but in most organisms a molecule that helps translate the structure of DNA into the structure of protein molecules

sagittal crest–a bony crest running along the length of the top of the skull, formed by the attachment areas of the *temporalis* muscles from opposite sides

sagittal keel–a low rounded elevation of bone along the midline of the top of the *Homo erectus* skull

sampling error–the degree that a sample of a population misrepresents or is not reflective of the composition in some trait of a larger population because of chance

sarcopterygians–lobe-finned fish capable of some support of the body on land

satellite DNA–DNA that consists of short sequences repeated many times in the genome; so named because it forms a subsidiary "satellite" band when DNA is spun in a laboratory centrifuge

segregation–the separation of recessive and dominant alleles during reproduction, allowing maintenance of their separate identities and later full expression of their traits; sometimes referred to as Mendel's First Law, or Law of Segregation

semi-free-ranging studies–in primatology, the study of primate groups that are in some way affected by or are dependent on humans, yet live more-or-less "normal" social lives

sensory cortex–the part of the cerebral cortex located in the post-central gyrus that senses touch, temperature, and pain on all parts of the body

serum cholesterol–cholesterol is a lipid (fat), deriving from the diet, that when in high concentrations in the blood serum causes lesions and plaque buildup in arteries

sexual dimorphism–presence of two distinctly different forms of male and female individuals in a species

sexual reproduction–reproduction resulting from the exchange of genetic material between two parent organisms

sexual selection–selection within a species based on mate choice or competition within the species, usually between males

sivapithecid–family of middle to late Miocene hominoids found mostly in Asia; species of this group may be ancestral to modern orangutan

social behavior–actions and interactions of animals within groups

social bond–linkage or tendency to associate between one or more individuals in a group

sociobiology–evolutionary study of social behavior emphasizing relative reproductive rates of success of individuals within a population

socioecology–evolutionary study of social behavior emphasizing the adaptation of species to their environment and ecological conditions

somatic mutation–a nonheritable change in the genetic material of the cells of the body

somatotrophin–pituitary or growth hormone, important in initiating the adolescent growth spurt

special creation–the nonevolutionary theory associated with catastrophism that held that totally new species, unrelated to prior species, were created after extinctions

species–an actually or potentially interbreeding group of organisms in nature

speech–the set of verbal sounds used by humans in language

splanchnocranium–that part of the skull holding the mouth and jaws

standard deviation–in statistics, a measure of variance about the mean within any population; defined as the square root of the average of the squares of the deviations from the mean

stereoscopic vision–the ability to perceive depth by virtue of the fact that the fields of vision of each eye partially overlap, thus giving the brain information sufficient to reconstruct an accurate impression of depth or distance

stereotypic–referring to repetitive behavior reproduced without significant variation

sternal glands–glands located near the sternum or breast bone

steroids–family of chemical substances that includes many hormones, constituents of the body, and Vitamin D

stone artifacts–stones broken or flaked by hominids in order to be used as tools, or unmodified stones found in geological circumstances indicating that hominids carried them and placed them at a site

subspecies–a geographically defined population within a species, the individuals of which tend to share certain physical and genetic traits but who are nevertheless interfertile with other members of the species; a race

Sudden Infant Death Syndrome–"crib death," or "cot death"; sudden and unexpected death of apparently healthy infants, usually between 3 weeks and 5 months of age

suspensory–positional behavior; ability of hominoids to hang (from branches) using one or both fully extended forelimbs

symbiosis–the theory that formerly free-living primitive organisms came together to form a single organism, capable of metabolism and reproduction as a unit

systematics–the science of classifying and organizing organisms

tanning–a response of lightly pigmented skin after exposure to sunlight that increases the amount of melanin in the cells of the skin; an example of acclimation

taphonomy–the paleontological study of burial processes leading to the formation and preservation of fossils

taxonomy–the science of naming different organisms

thalassemia–from Greek meaning "sea blood," in reference to the blood's "dilute" nature; genetic disorders affecting hemoglobin metabolism that can range from negligible clinical effects to fatal anemia

theory–usually a set of hypotheses that withstands attempts at disproof and continues to successfully explain observations as they are made, thus gaining scientific support over time

thermoregulation–controlling the body's temperature by a number of physiological and behavioral means

thrifty genotype–the adaptation of storing "excess calories" as fat, and then burning them during periods of famine or scarcity of food

thyroid hormone–also known as thyroxine, an iodine-containing hormone secreted by the thyroid gland and important in regulating the rate of tissue metabolism

tissue–literally meaning "woven"; in anatomy referring to an aggregate of cells of the same type, which form a structural unit of the body.

transcription–transfer of genetic information encoded in a DNA sequence to an RNA message

transformation–incorporation of another cell's DNA into a cell's own DNA structure

translation–synthesis of a polypeptide chain from an RNA genetic message

triune brain–the division of the human brain by Paul MacLean into three broad divisions based on phylogenetic and functional patterns

tuff—a geological deposit composed of volcanic ash

typology—"idealist" definition of an entire group by reference to a "type" that tends to ignore variation from that ideal

uniformitarianism—principle that processes observable today can account for past events in geological history

Upper Paleolithic—a series of late Pleistocene cultures typified by a diversification of traditions and stone tools made from blades struck from cores; associated with anatomically modern humans; *ca.* 40,000–10,000 years ago

variation—the range of differences in physical or genetic make-up across, within, and between populations of individuals of the same species

vasoconstriction—the contraction of small blood vessels next to the skin's surface; a response to cold

ventro-ventral position—two individuals facing each other with bodies in contact

vertebrates—animals with backbones and segmented body plans

vertical clinging and leaping—the method of locomotion characteristic of many living prosimians, and inferred to have been a method of locomotion in some early primates

Wernicke's Area—portion of the cerebral cortex (parts of the parietal and temporal lobes near the lateral sulcus, usually on the left) that is responsible for understanding and formulating coherent speech

Y-5 pattern—a pattern in the lower molars of five distinct cusps, separated by a backward (distally) facing Y-shaped groove; characteristic of hominoids, as well as of more primitive catarrhines

Zhoukoudian—middle Pleistocene cave site of *Homo erectus* near Beijing, China

References

Abbie, A. A. (1977). Multidisciplinary studies on Australian Aborigines. In *Human Adaptability: A History and Compendium of Research in the International Biological Programme* (K. J. Collins and J. S. Weiner, eds.), pp. 37–39. Taylor and Francis, Ltd., London.

Aiello, L. C., and Dunbar, R. I. M. (1993). Neocortex size, group size, and the evolution of language. *Curr. Anthropol.* **34:**184–193.

Alexander, R. D. (1974). The evolution of social behavior. *Ann. Rev. Ecol. Syst.* **5:**324–384.

Allman, W. F. (1994). *The Stone Age Present*. Simon & Schuster, New York.

Almquist, H. J. (1969). The future of animals as food producers. *Proc. West. Poul. Dis. Conf., 18th,* University of California, Davis, 1969.

Andrews, P. (1987). Aspects of hominoid phylogeny. In *Molecules and Morphology in Evolution: Conflict and Compromise* (C. Patterson, ed.), pp. 23–53. Cambridge Univ. Press, Cambridge, UK.

Andrews, P. (1995). Ecological apes and ancestors. *Nature (London)* **376:**555–556.

Andrews, P., and Cronin, J. E. (1982). The relationships of *Sivapithecus* and *Ramapithecus* and the evolution of the orangutan. *Nature (London)* **297:**541–546.

Ashton, E., and Oxnard, C. (1964). Locomotor patterns in primates. *Proc. Zool. Soc. London* **142:**1–28.

Badrian, A., and Badrian, N. (1984). Group composition and social structure of *Pan paniscus* in the Lomako Forest, Zaire. In *The Pygmy Chimpanzee: Evolutionary Biology and Behavior* (R. Susman, ed.), pp. 325–346. Plenum, New York.

Bailey, R., Head, G., Jenike, M., Owen, B., Rechtmann, R., and Zechenter, E. (1989). Hunting and gathering in tropical rain forest: Is it possible? *Am. Anthropol.* **91:**59–82.

Bailey, R. C. (1991). The comparative growth of Efe pygmies and African farmers from birth to age 5 years. *Ann. Hum. Biol.* **18:**113–120.

Bar Yosef, O., and Vandermeersch, B. (1993). Modern humans in the Levant. *Sci. Am.* **268:**94–100.

Barrett, J. M., Abramoff, P., Kumaran, A. K., and Millington, W. F. (1986). *Biology*. Prentice Hall, Englewood Cliffs, NJ.

Beard, K. C. (1990). Gliding behavior and paleoecology of the alleged primate family Paromomyidae (Mammalia, Dermoptera). *Nature (London)* **345:**340–341.

Begun, D. R. (1992). Miocene fossil hominids and the chimp-human clade. *Science* **257:**1929–1933.

Benefit, B., and McCrossin, M. (1993). New *Kenyapithecus* postcrania and other primate fossils from Moboko Island, Kenya. *Am. J. Phys. Anthropol.* **16**(Suppl.): 55–56.

Bianchi, N. O., Bianchi, M. S., Cleaver, J. E., and Wolff, S. (1985). The pattern of restriction enzyme-induced bonding in the chromosomes of chimpanzee, gorilla, and the orangutan and its evolutionary significance. *J. Mol. Evol.* **22:**323–333.

Biegert, J. (1963). The evolution of characteristics of the skull, hands, and feet for primate taxonomy. In *Classification and Human Evolution* (S. L. Washburn, ed.), pp. 116–145. Aldine, Chicago.

Binford, L. (1989). *Debating Archeology*. Academic Press, New York.

Binford, L. H., and Ho, C. K. (1985). Taphonomy at a distance: Zhoukoudian, "the cave home of Beijing Man?" *Curr. Anthropol.* **26:**413–442.

Binford, L. H., and Stone, N. M. (1986). Zhoukoudian: A closer look. *Curr. Anthropol.* **27:**453–468.

Birdsell, J. B. (1981). *Human Evolution: An Introduction of the New Physical Anthropology*. Houghton-Mifflin, Boston.

Blakemore, C. (1977). *Mechanics of the Mind*. Cambridge University Press, Cambridge, UK.

Blurton-Jones, N. (1987). Bushmen birth spacing: Direct tests of some simple predictions. *Ethol. Sociobiol.* **8:**183–203.

Boaz, N. T. (1979a). Early hominid population densities: New estimates. *Science* **206:**592–595.

Boaz, N. T. (1979b). Hominid evolution in eastern Africa during the Pliocene and early Pleistocene. *Ann. Rev. Anthropol.* **8:**71–85.

Boaz, N. T. (1983). Morphological trends and phylogenetic relationships from middle Miocene hominoids to late Pliocene hominids. In *New Interpretations of Ape and Human Ancestry* (R. L. Ciochon and R. S. Corruccini, eds.), pp. 705–720. Plenum, New York.

Boaz, N. T. (1985). Early hominid paleoecology in the Omo basin, Ethiopia. In *L'Environnement des Hominidés au Plio-Pléistocène,* Fondation Singer-Polignac, pp. 283–312. Masson, Paris.

Boaz, N. T. (1988). Status of *Australopithecus afarensis. Yearb. Phys. Anthropol.* **31:**85–113.

Boaz, N. T. (1993). *Quarry: Closing in on the Missing Link*. Free Press, New York.

Boaz, N. T. (1997). *Eco Homo*. Basic Books, New York.

Boaz, N. T., and Howell, F. C. (1977). A gracile hominid cranium from upper Member G of the Shungura Formation, Ethiopia. *Am. J. Phys. Anthropol.* **46:**93–108.

Bodmer, W. F., and Cavalli-Sforza, L. L. (1976). *Genetics, Evolution and Man*. Freeman, San Francisco.

Boesch-Ackermann, H., and Boesch, C. (1994). Hominization in the rainforest: The chimpanzee's piece of the puzzle. *Evol. Anthropol.* **3:**9–16.

Bogin, B. (1988). *Patterns of Human Growth*. Cambridge University Press, Cambridge, England.

Bogin, B. (1995). Growth and development: Recent evolutionary and biocultural research. In *Biological Anthropology: The State of the Science* (N. T. Boaz and L. D. Wolfe, eds.), pp. 49–70. International Institute for Human Evolutionary Research, Bend, OR.

Bogin, B., Wall, M., and MacVean, R. (1992). Longitudinal analysis of adolescent growth of Ladino and Mayan school children in Guatemala: Effects of environment and sex. *Am. J. Phys. Anthropol.* **89:**447–457.

Bolk, L. (1926). *Das Problem der Menschenwerdung*. G. Fischer, Jena.

Bonifay, E. (1989). Un site du très ancien Paléolithique de plus de 2 m.a. dans le massif central français: Saint-Eble-le-Coopeto (Haute-Loire). *C. R. Acad. Sci., Ser. 2* **308:** 1567–1570.

Bouchard, T. J., Lykken, D. T., McGue, M., Segal, N. L., and Tellegen, A. (1990). Sources of human psychological differences: The Minnesota study of twins reared apart. *Science* **250:**223–228.

Bowler, P. (1989). *Evolution: The History of an Idea,* rev. ed. Univ. of California Press, Berkeley.

Bown, T. M., Kraus, M. J., Wing, S. L., Fleagle, J. G., Tiffany, D., Simons, E. L., and Vondra, C. F. (1982). The Fayum primate forest revisited. *J. Hum. Evol.* **11:**603–632.

Brett, J., and Niemeyer, S. (1990). Neonatal jaundice: A disorder of transition or adaptive process. *Med. Anthropol. Q.* **4:**149–161.

Bromage, T. G., and Dean, M. C. (1985). Re-evaluation of the age of death of immature fossil hominids. *Nature* (*London*) **317:**525–527.

Brues, A. (1977). *People and Races*. Macmillan, New York.

Buffon, G. L., Compte de. (1767). *Nomenclature des Singes. Histoire Naturelle Générale et Particulaire*. Imprimerie Royale, Paris.

Butler, A. B., and Hodos, W. (1996). *Comparative Vertebrate Neuroanatomy: Evolution and Adaptation*. John Wiley and Sons, New York.

Caccone, A., and Powell, J. R. (1989). DNA divergence among hominoids. *Evolution* (*Lawrence, Kans.*) **43:**925–942.

Calvin, W. H. (1994). The emergence of intelligence. *Sci. Am.* October: 101–107.

Cann, R. L. (1988). DNA and human origins. *Ann. Rev. Anthropol.* **17:**127–143.

Cann, R. L., Stoneking, M., and Wilson, A. C. (1987). Mitochondrial DNA and human evolution. *Nature* (*London*) **325:**31–36.

Carbonell, V. M. (1963). Variations in the frequency of shovel-shaped incisors in different populations. In *Dental Anthropology* (D. R. Brothwell, ed.), pp. 211–234. Pergamon, Elmsford, NY.

Cardinali, D. P., and Wurtman, R. J. (1975). Methods for assessing the biological activity of the mammalian pineal organ. *Methods Enzymol,* **39:**376–397.

Carpenter, C. R. (1942). Sexual behavior of free-ranging rhesus monkeys, *Macaca mulatta. Comp. Psychol. Monogr.* **33:** 113–142.

Cartmill, M. (1974). Rethinking primate origins. *Science* **184:** 436–443.

Cartmill, M. (1982). Basic primatology and prosimian evolution. In *A History of American Physical Anthropology, 1930–1980* (F. Spencer, ed.), pp. 147–186. Academic Press, New York.

Cavalli-Sforza, L., and Edwards. (1967). Phylogenetic analysis: models and estimation procedures, *Am. J. Hum. Genet.* **19:**233–257.

Chagnon, N. (1983). *Yanomamo: The Fierce People,* 3rd ed. Holt, Rinehart & Winston, New York.

Chapman, C. A., Fedigan, L. M., Fedigan, L., and Chapman, L. J. (1989). Post-weaning resource competition and sex ratios in spider monkeys. *Oikos* **54:**315–319.

Charles-Dominique, C. (1977). *Ecology and Behavior of Nocturnal Primates*. Columbia Univ. Press, New York.

Chase, P. G. (1989). How different was Middle Paleolithic subsistence? A zooarchaeological perspective on the middle to upper Paleolithic transition. In *The Human Revolution* (P. Mellars and C. Stringer, eds.), pp. 321–337. Princeton University Press, Princeton, NJ.

Chomsky, N. (1957). *Syntactic Structures,* Ser. Janna Linguaram No. 11. 's-Gravenhage, Mouton.

Clark, W. E. LeGros. (1960). *The Antecedents of Man*. Quadrangle Books, Chicago.

Clark, W. E. LeGros. (1964). *The Fossil Evidence for Human Evolution*. Univ. of Chicago Press, Chicago.

Clark, W. E. LeGros. (1967). *Man-Apes or Ape-Men. The Story of Discoveries in Africa*. Holt, Rinehart & Winston, New York.

Clarke, R. J., and Tobias, P. V. (1995). Sterkfontein member 2 foot bones of the oldest South African hominid. *Science* **269:**521–524.

Clutton-Brock, T. H., and Harvey, P. H. (1977). Primate ecology and social organization. *J. Zool.* **183:**1–39.

Cohen, B. H. (1970a). ABO and Rh incompatibility. I. Fetal and neonatal mortality with ABO and Rh incompatibility: Some new interpretations. *Am. J. Hum. Genet.* **22:**412–440.

Cohen, B. H. (1970b). ABO and Rh incompatibility. II. Is there a dual interaction in combined ABO and Rh incompatibility? *Am. J. Hum. Genet.* **22:**441–452.

Conkey, M. (1980). The identification of prehistoric hunter-gatherer aggregation sites: The case of Altamira. *Curr. Anthropol.* **21:**609–629.

Conroy, G. C. (1990). *Primate Evolution*. Norton, New York.

Conroy, G. C., Pickford, M., Senut, B., et al. (1992a). *Otavipithecus namibiensis,* first Miocene hominoid from Southern Africa. *Nature* **356:**144–148.

Conroy, G. C., Pickford, M., Senut, B., VanCouvering, J., and Mein, P. (1992b). The Otavi Mountain land of Namibia yields Southern Africa's first Miocene hominoid. *Res. and Expl.* **8:**492–494.

Conroy, G. C., Senut, B., Gommery, D., Pickford, M., and Mein, P. (1996). Brief communication: New primate remains from the Miocene of Namibia, Southern Africa. *Am. J. Phys. Anthropol.* **99:**487–492.

Conroy, G. C., and Vannier, M. W. (1987). Dental development of the Taung skull from computerized tomography. *Nature* (*London*) **329:**625–627.

Cronin, H. (1992). Sexual selection: Historical perspectives. In *Keywords in Evolutionary Biology* (E. F. Keller and E. A. Lloyd, eds.), pp. 286–293. Harvard University Press, Cambridge, MA.

Cronin, J. E. (1983). Apes, humans and molecular clocks: A reappraisal. In *New Interpretations of Ape and Human Ancestry* (R. Ciochon and R. Corruccini, eds.), pp. 115–150. Plenum, New York.

Crook, J. H., and Gartlan, J. S. (1966). Evolution of primate societies. *Nature* **210**:1200–1203.

Darwin, C. R. (1839). *Journal of Researches into the Geology and Natural History of the Various Countries Visited by H. M. S. Beagle.* Colburn, London.

Darwin, C. R. (1859). *The Origin of Species by Natural Selection.* Murray, London.

Darwin, C. R. (1871). *The Descent of Man and Selection with Respect to Sex.* Murray, London.

Darwin, C. (1872). *The Expression of the Emotions in Man and Animals.* Reprinted in 1965. University of Chicago Press, Chicago.

Darwin, C. R. (1958). *The Autobiography of Charles Darwin and Selected Letters,* edited by Francis Darwin (1892). Dover Publications, Mineola, NY.

Dawkins, R. (1989) *The Selfish Gene,* 2nd ed. Oxford Univ. Press, Oxford.

Delson, E. (1977). Catarrhine phylogeny and classification: Principles, methods and comments. *J. Hum. Evol.* **6**:433–459.

Delson, E. (1988). Chronology of South African australopith site units. In *Evolutionary History of the "Robust" Australopithecines* (F. E. Grine, ed.), pp. 317–324. de Gruyter, New York.

Delson, E. (1989) Oldest Eurasian stone tools. *Nature (London)* **340**:96.

Dennell, R. (1989). Reply to Hemingway, "Early artefacts from Pakistan?—Some questions for the excavators." *Curr. Anthropol.* **30**:318–322.

DeVore, I., and Washburn, S. L. (1963). Baboon ecology and human evolution. In *African Ecology and Human Evolution.* (F. C. Howell and F. Bourliere, eds.), pp. 335–367. Aldine, Chicago.

Diamond, J. M. (1992). Diabetes running wild. *Nature* **357**:362–363.

Dickemann, M. (1985). Human sociobiology: The first decade. *New Sci.* **108**:38–42.

Di Lonardo, A. M., Darlu, P., Baur, M., et al. (1984). Human genetics and human rights: Identifying the families of kidnapped children. *Am. J. Foren. Med. Pathol.* **5**:339–347.

Dixon, A. F. (1981). *The Natural History of the Gorilla.* Columbia Univ. Press, New York.

Dohlinow, P. C., and Taff, M. A. (1993). Rivalry, resolution and the individual. Cooperation among male langur monkeys. In *Milestones in Human Evolution* (A. J. Almquist and J. A. Manyak, eds.), pp. 75–92. Waveland Press, Prospect Heights, IL.

DuMond, F. V., and Hutchinson, T. C. (1967). Squirrel monkey reproduction: The "fatted" male phenomenon and season spermatogenesis. *Science* **158**:1067–1070.

Dunbar, R. I. M. (1986). The social ecology of gelada baboons. In *Ecological Aspects of Social Evolution: Birds and Mammals* (D. I. Rubenstein and R. W. Wrangham, eds.). Princeton Univ. Press, Princeton, NJ.

Dunbar, R. I. M. (1992). Neocortex size as a constraint on group size in primates. *J. Hum. Evol.* **20**:469–493.

Dunbar, R. I. M. (1989). Reproductive strategies of female gelada baboons. In *Sociobiology of Reproductive Strategies* (A. E. Rasa, C. Vogel, and E. Voland, eds.), pp. 74–282. Chapman & Hall, New York.

Dyson-Hudson, R., and Smith, E. A. (1978). Human territoriality: An ecological reassessment. *Am. Anthropol.* **80**:21–41.

Eaton, S. B., Pike, M. C., Short, R. V., Lee, N. C., Trussell, J., Hatcher, R. A., Wood, J. W., Worthman, C. M., Blurton-Jones, N. G., Konner, M. J., Hill, K. R., Bailey, R., Hurtado, A. M. (1994). Women's reproductive concerns in evolutionary context. *Quart. Rev. Biol.* **69**:353–367.

Eaton, S. B., Shostak, M., and Konner, M. (1989). *The Paleolithic Prescription: A Program of Diet and Exercise and a Design for Living.* Harper & Row, New York.

Eckhardt, R. B. (1989). Matching molecular and morphological evolution. *Hum. Evol.* **4**:317–319.

Eibl-Eibesfeldt, I. (1975). *Ethology: The Biology of Behavior.* Holt, Rinehart & Winston, New York.

Eibl-Eibesfeldt, I. (1989). *Human Ethology.* de Gruyter, New York.

Eisenberg, J. F., Muckerhirn, N. A., and Rudran, R. (1972). The relation between ecology and social structure in primates. *Science* **176**:863–874.

Ewald, P. (1994). *Evolution of Infectious Diseases.* Oxford Univ. Press, London.

Fairbanks, L. A. (1988). Vervet monkey grandmothers: Interactions with infant offspring. *Int. J. Primatol.* **9**:425–441.

Falk, D. (1990). Brain evolution in Homo: The "radiator" theory. *Behav. Brain Sci.* **13**:333–381.

Fleagle, J. G. (1988). *Primate Adaptation and Evolution.* Academic Press, San Diego, CA.

Fleagle, J. G., Brown, T. M., Obradovich, J. D., and Simons, E. L. (1986). Age of the earliest African anthropoids. *Science* **234**:1247–1249.

Fleagle, J. G., and Kay, R. F. (1987). The phyletic position of the Parapithecidae. *J. Hum. Evol.* **16**:483–531.

Foley, R. (1990). The causes of brain enlargement in human evolution. *Behav. Brain Sci.* **13**:354–356.

Fossey, D. (1983). *Gorillas in the Mist.* Houghton-Mifflin, Boston.

Frayer, D. W. (1992). The persistence of Neanderthal features in post-Neanderthal Europeans. In *Continuity or Replacement?* (G. Brauer and F. H. Smith, eds.), pp. 179–188. A A Balkema, Rotterdam.

Frisancho, A. R. (1975). Functional adaptation to high hypoxia. *Science* **187**:313–319.

Gabriel, S. E., Brigman, K. N., Koller, B. H., Boucher, R. C., and Smuts, M. J. (1994). Cystic fibrosis heterozygote resistance to cholera toxin in the cystic fibrosis mouse model. *Science* **266**:107–109.

Galdikas, B. (1979). Orangutan adaptation at Tanjung Puting Reserve: Mating and ecology. In *The Great Apes* (D. A.

Hamburg and E. R. McCown, eds.), pp. 195–233. Benjamin/Cummings, Menlo Park, CA.

Gebo, D., MacLatchy, L., Kityo, R., Deino, A., Kingston, J., and Pilbeam, D. R. (1997). A hominoid genus from the early Miocene of Uganda. *Science* **276**:401–404.

Gebo, D. L. (1989a). Locomotor and phylogenetic considerations in anthropoid evolution. *J. Hum. Evol.* **18**:201–233.

Gebo, D. L. (1989b). Postcranial adaptation and evolution in Lorisidae. *Primates* **30**:347–367.

Gibson, K. R. (1993). Tool use, language and social behavior in relationship to information processing capacities. In *Tools, Language and Cognition in Human Evolution* (K. R. Gibson and T. Ingold, eds.), pp. 251–269. Cambridge University Press, Cambridge, UK.

Gibson, K. R. (1994). Continuity theories of human language origins versus the Lieberman model. *Language and Communication* **14**:97–114.

Gingerich, P. (1990). African dawn for primates. *Nature (London)* **346**:411.

Goodall, J. (1977). Infant killing and cannibalism in free-living chimpanzees. *Folia Primatol.* **28**:259–282.

Goodall, J. (1986). *The Chimpanzees of Gombe*. Harvard University (Belknap Press), Cambridge, MA.

Goodman, M. (1961). The role of immunochemical differences in the phyletic development of human behavior. *Hum. Biol.* **33**:131–162.

Goodman, M. (1962). Evolution of the immunologic species specificity of human serum proteins. *Hum. Biol.* **34**:105–150.

Goodman, M. (1973). The chronicle of primate phylogeny continued in proteins. *Symp. Zool. Soc. London* **33**:339–375.

Gordon, T. P., Rose, R. W., Grady, C. L., and Bernstein, I. S. (1979). Effects of increased testosterone secretion on the behavior of adult male rhesus living in a social group. *Folia Primatol.* **32**:149–160.

Goren-Inbar, N. (1986). A figurine from the Acheulean site of Berekhat Rom. *Mitakufat Haeven* **19**:7–12.

Gould, S. J., and Eldredge, N. (1993). Punctuated equilibrium comes of age. *Nature* **366**:223–227.

Grant, V. (1991). *The Evolutionary Process: A Critical Study of Evolutionary Theory,* 2nd ed. Columbia University Press, NY.

Greene, L. S. (1993). G6PD deficiency as protection against *falciparum* Malaria: An epidemiologic critique of population and experimental studies. *Yearb. Phys. Anthropol.* **36**:153–178.

Greenfield, L. O. (1980). Late divergence hypothesis. *Am. J. Phys. Anthropol.* **52**:351–365.

Grine, F. E. (ed.). (1988). *Evolutionary History of the "Robust" Australopithecines*. de Gruyter, New York.

Groves, C. P., and Mazek, V. (1975). An approach to the taxonomy of the Hominidae: Gracile Villafranchian hominids of Africa. *Cas. Mineral. Geol.* **20**:225–247.

Hafleigh, A. S., and Williams, C. A., Jr. (1966). Antigenic correspondence of serum albumins among the primates. *Science* **151**:1530–1535.

Hamilton, W. D. (1971). Selection of selfish or altruistic behaviors in some extreme models. In *Man and Beast: Comparative Social Behavior* (J. Eisenberg and W. Dillon, eds.). Smithsonian Institution Press, Washington, DC.

Harding, R. M. (1992). VNTR's in review. *Evol. Anthropol.* **1**(2):62–71.

Harding, R. M., and Teleki, G. (eds.). (1981). *Omnivorous Primates. Gathering and Hunting in Human Evolution*. Columbia Univ. Press, New York.

Harrison, T. (1986). A reassessment of the phylogenetic relationships of *Oreopithecus bambolii* Gervais. *J. Hum. Evol.* **15**:541–583.

Hausfater, G. (1976). Predatory behavior of yellow baboons. *Behaviour* **56**:44–68.

Henneberg, M., and Thackeray, J. F. (1995). A single-lineage hypothesis of hominid evolution. *Evol. Theory* **11**:31–38.

Herschel, J. F. W. (1831). *A Preliminary Discourse on the Study of Natural Philosophy*. Carey and Lea, Philadelphia.

Hewes, G. W. (1964). Hominid bipedalism: Independent evidence for food carrying theory. *Science* **146**:416–418.

Hill, A., and Ward, S. (1988). Origin of the Hominidae: The record of African large hominoid evolution between 14 my and 4 my. *Yearb. Phys. Anthropol.* **31**:49–83.

Hill, K., Kaplan, H., Hawkes, K., and Hurtado, A. M. (1987). Foraging decisions among Ache hunter-gatherers: New data and implications for optimal foraging models. *Ethol. Sociobiol.* **8**:1–36.

Hockett, C., and Ascher, R. (1964). The human revolution. *Curr. Anthropol.* **5**:135–168.

Hoffstetter, R. (1972). Relationships, origins and history of the ceboid monkeys and caviomorph rodents: A modern reinterpretation. In *Evolutionary Biology,* vol. 6 (T. Dobzhansky, M. K. Hecht, and W. C. Steere, eds.), pp. 323–347. Appleton-Century-Crofts, New York.

Holmquist, R., Miyamoto, M. M., and Goodman, M. (1988). Higher primate phylogeny. Why can't we decide? *Mol. Biol. Evol.* **5**:201–216.

Horai, S., et al. (1995). Recent African origin of modern humans revealed by complete sequences of hominoid mitochondrial DNAs. *Proc. Nat. Acad. Sci.* **92**:532–536.

Houghton, P. (1993). Neandertal supralaryngeal vocal tract. *Am. J. Phys. Anthropol.* **90**:139–146.

Hoyer, B. H., Van de Vilde, N. W., Goodman, M., and Roberts, R. B. (1972). Examination of hominoid evolution by DNA sequence homology. *J. Hum. Evol.* **1**:645–649.

Hrdy, S. B. (1979). Infanticide among animals: A review, classification, and examination of the implications for the reproductive strategies of females. *Ethol. Sociobiol.* **1**:13–40.

Hrdy, S. B., Janson, C., and Van Schaik, C. (1995). Infanticide: Let's not throw out the baby with the bath water. *Evol. Anthropol.* **3**:151–154.

Huang Wanpo, Ciochon, R., Gu Yumin, Larick, R., Fang Qiren, Schwarcz, H., Yonge, C., de Vos, J., and Rink, W. (1995). Early *Homo* and associated artifacts from Asia. *Nature* **378**:275–278.

Hull, D. L. (1973). *Darwin and His Critics: The Reception of Darwin's Theory of Evolution by the Scientific Community.* Harvard University Press, Cambridge, MA.

Isaac, G. L. (1978). The food sharing behavior of protohuman hominids. *Sci. Am.* **238:**90–109.

Isbell, L. A. (1991). Contest and scramble competition: patterns of female aggression and ranging behavior among primates. *Behav. Ecol.* **2:**143–155.

Iscan, M. Y., and Kennedy, K. A. R. (1989). *Reconstruction of Life from the Skeleton.* Alan R. Liss, New York.

Jensen, A. (1969). How much can we boost IQ and scholastic achievement? *Harv. Educ. Rev.* **39:**1–123.

Jensen, A. (1980). *Bias in Mental Testing.* Free Press, New York.

Jisaka, M., Kawanaka, M., Sugiyama, H., Takegawa, K., Huffman, M. A., Ohigashi, H., and Koshimizu, K. (1992). Antischistosomal activities of sesquiterpene lactones and steroid glucosides from *Vernonia amygdalina,* possibly used by wild chimpanzees against parasite-related diseases. *Biosci., Biotech., and Biochem.* **56:**845–846.

Johanson, D. C., Masao, F. T., Eck, G. G., White, T. D., Walter, R. C., Kimbel, W. H., Asfaw, B., Manega, P., Ndessokia, P., and Suwa, G. (1987). New partial skeleton of *Homo habilis* from Olduvai Gorge, Tanzania. *Nature (London)* **327:**205–209.

Johanson, D. C., and White, T. D. (1979). A systematic assessment of early African hominids. *Science* **203:**321–330.

Johanson, D. C., White, T. D., and Coppens, Y. (1978). A new species of the genus *Australopithecus* (Primates: Hominidae) from the Pliocene of eastern Africa. *Kirtlandia* **28:**1–14.

Jolly, A. (1985). *The Evolution of Primate Behavior,* 2nd ed. Macmillan, New York.

Joyce, C., and Stover, E. (1991). *Witnesses from the Grave: The Stories Bones Tell.* Ballantine Books, New York.

Jungers, W. L. (1988). New estimates of body size in australopithecines. In *Evolutionary History of the "Robust" Australopithecines* (F. E. Grine, ed.), pp. 115–125. de Gruyter, New York.

Jungers, W. L., and Stern, J. T. (1980). Telemetered electromyography of forelimb muscle chains in gibbons (*Hylobates lar*). *Science* **208:**617–619.

Kawamura, S. (1959). The process of sub-culture propagation among Japanese macaques. *Primates* **2:**43–60.

Kay, R. (1977). Diets of early Miocene African hominoids. *Nature (London)* **268:**628–630.

Keith, A. (1896). An introduction to the study of the anthropoid apes. *Nat. Sci.* **9:**316–326, 372–379.

Keith, A. (1899). On the chimpanzees and their relationship to the gorilla. *Proc. Zool. Soc. London,* pp. 296–312.

Keith, A. (1915). *The Antiquity of Man.* Williams & Norgate, London.

Kelley, J. (1987). Species recognition and sexual dimorphism in *Proconsul* and *Rangwapithecus. J. Hum. Evol.* **15:**461–495.

Kimbel, W. H., Walter, R. C., Johanson, D. C., Reed, K. E., Aronson, J. L., Assefa, Z., Marean, C. W., Eck, G. G., Bobe, R., Hovers, E., Rak, Y., Vondra, C., Yemane, T., York, D.,

Chen, Y., Evenson, N. M., and Smith, P. E. (1996). Late Pliocene *Homo* and Olduwan tools from the Hadar Formation (Kada Hadar Member), Ethiopia. *J. Hum. Evol.* **31:** 549–561.

King, B. (1994). *The Information Continuum: Evolution of Social Information Transfer in Monkeys, Apes, and Hominids.* SAR Press, Santa Fe, NM.

King, M.-C. (1974). Evolution at two levels: Molecular similarities and biological differences between humans and chimpanzees. *Am. J. Hum. Genet.* **26:**49A.

King, M.-C., and Wilson, A. C. (1975). Evolution at two levels in humans and chimpanzees. *Science* **188:**107–116.

Klug, W. S., and Cummings, M. R. (1994). *Concepts of Genetics,* 4th ed. Macmillan, New York.

Kohne, D. E. (1970). Evolution of higher organism DNA. *Quart. Rev. Biophys.* **3:**327–375.

Krings, M., Stone, A., Schmitz, R. W., Krainitzki, H., Stoneking, M., and Paabo, S. (1997). Neandertal DNA sequences and the origin of modern humans. *Cell* **90:**19–30.

Kuroda, S. (1980). Social behavior of the pygmy chimpanzee. *Primates* **21:**181–197.

Kuroda, S. (1984). Interaction over food among pygmy chimpanzees. In *The Pygmy Chimpanzee: Evolutionary Biology and Behavior* (R. Susman, ed.). Plenum, New York.

Kurten, B. (1972). *Not from the Apes.* Pantheon Books, New York.

Laidler, K. (1980). *The Talking Ape,* Stein & Day, New York.

Lancaster, J. (1978). Carrying and sharing in human evolution. *Hum. Nat.* **1:**32–89.

Lartet, E. (1856). Note sur un grand singe fossile qui se rattache au groupe des singes superieurs. *C. R. Hebd. Seances Acad. Sci.* **43:**219–223.

Lasker, G. W. (1991). Introduction. In *Applications of Biological Anthropology to Human Affairs* (C. G. N. Mascie-Taylor and G. W. Lasker, eds.), pp. 1–13. Cambridge Univ. Press, London.

Leakey, M. G., Feibel, C. S., McDougal, I., and Walker, A. (1995). New four-million-year-old hominid species from Kanapoi and Allia Bay, Kenya. *Nature (London)* **376:**565–571.

Leakey, M. G., and Leakey, R. E. (1978). *The Fossil Hominids and an Introduction to Their Context, 1968–1974.* Koobi Fora Res. Proj., Vol. 1. Oxford Univ. Press (Clarendon), Oxford.

Lee, R. B. (1980). Lactation, ovulation, infanticide, and women's work: A study of hunter-gatherer population regulation. In *Biosocial Mechanisms of Population Regulation* (M. Cohen, R. Malpass, and H. Klein, eds.), pp. 321–348. Yale Univ. Press, New Haven, CT.

Lee, R. B., and DeVore, I. (eds.). (1968). *Man the Hunter.* Aldine, Chicago.

Leutenegger, W. (1987). Neonatal brain size and neurocranial dimensions in Pliocene hominids: Implications for obstetrics. *J. Hum. Evol.* **16:**291–296.

Lieberman, L., and Kirk, R. (1996). The trial of Darwin is over: Religious voices for evolution and the "fairness" doctrine. *Creation/Evolution* **16:**1–9.

Lieberman, P., and Crelin, E. S. (1971). On the speech of Neanderthal man. *Linguistic Inquiry* **11**:203–222.

Linton, S. (1971). Woman the gatherer: Male bias in anthropology. In *Women in Perspective: A Guide for Cross-Cultural Studies* (S. Jacobs, ed.), pp. 9–21. Univ. of Illinois Press, Urbana.

Little, M. A., and Baker, R. T. (1988). Migration and adaptation. In *Biological Aspects of Human Migration* (C. G. N. Mascie-Taylor and G. W. Lasker, eds.), pp. 167–215. Cambridge University Press, Cambridge, UK.

Lopreato, J. (1984). *Human Nature and Biocultural Evolution*. Allen and Unwin, London.

Lorenz, K. (1965a). *On Aggression*. Harcourt, Brace, New York.

Lorenz, K. (1965b). *Evolution and Modification of Behavior*. University of Chicago Press, Chicago.

Loy, J. (1987). The sexual behavior of African monkeys and the question of estrus. In *Comparative Behavior of African Monkeys* (E. Zucker, ed.), pp. 175–195. Alan R. Liss, New York.

Loy, J. (1992). Behavioral dynamics among primates: An overview. *Perspect. Primate Biol.* **4**:79–94.

MacFadden, B. J. (1985). An overview of paleomagnetic chronology with special reference to the South African hominid sites. *Palaeontol. Afr.* **23**:35–40.

MacFadden, B. J., Campbell, K. E., Cifelli, R. L., Siles, O., Johnson, N., Naeser, C. W., and Zeitler, P. K. (1985). Magnetic polarity and mammalian biostratigraphy of the Deseadan (Late Oligocene–Early Miocene) Salla Beds of northern Bolivia. *J. Geol.* **93**:223–250.

MacKinnon, J. (1979). Reproductive behavior in the wild orangutan populations. In *The Great Apes* (D. A. Hamburg and E. R. McCown, eds.), pp. 257–273. Benjamin-Cummings, Menlo Park, CA.

MacLean, P. D. (1990). *The Triune Brain in Human Evolution*. Plenum, New York.

Malthus, T. R. (1798). An essay on the principle of population as it affects the future improvement of society. Reprinted in 1960 *On Population* (G. Himmelfarb, ed.). Random House Modern Library, New York.

Mann, A. (1975). *Some Paleodemographic Aspects of the South African Australopithecines*. University of Pennsylvania Publications in Anthropology, Vol. 1. 171 pp. Philadelphia.

Margulis, L., and Sagan, D. (1986a). *Microcosmos: Four Billion Years of Evolution from Our Microbial Ancestors*. Summit Press, New York.

Margulis, L., and Sagan, D. (1986b). *Origins of Sex: Three Billion Years of Genetic Recombination*. Yale Univ. Press, New Haven, CT.

Marks, J., Schmid, C. W., and Sarich, V. M. (1988). DNA hybridization as a guide to phylogeny: Relations of the Hominoidea. *J. Hum. Evol.* **17**:769–786.

Marler, P. (1973). A comparison of vocalizations of red-tailed monkeys and blue monkeys, *Cercopithecus ascanius* and *C. mitis,* in Uganda. *Z. Tierpsychol.* **33**:223–247.

Marshack, A. (1989). Evolution of the human capacity: Symbolic evidence. *Yearb. Phys. Anthropol.* **32**:1–34.

Mayr, E. (1963). *Animal Species and Evolution*. Harvard Univ. Press, Cambridge, MA.

McGrew, W. C. (1988). Parental division of infant care-taking varies with family composition in cotton-topped tamarins. *Anim. Behav.* **36**:285–286.

McGrew, W. (1992). *Chimpanzee Material Culture*. Cambridge Univ. Press, New York.

McHenry, H. M. (1984). The common ancestor: A study of the postcranium of *Pan paniscus, Australopithecus* and other hominids. In *The Pygmy Chimpanzee: Evolutionary Biology and Behavior* (R. Susman, ed.), pp. 201–230. Plenum, New York.

McHenry, H. M. (1988). New estimates of body weight in early hominids and their significance to encephalization and megadontia in "robust" australopithecines. In *Evolutionary History of the "Robust" Australopithecines* (F. E. Grine, ed.), pp. 133–148. de Gruyter, New York.

McKenna, J., Mosko, S., Dungy, C., and McAninch, J. (1990). Sleep and arousal patterns of co-sleeping human mother-infant pairs: A preliminary physiological study with implications for the study of sudden infant death syndrome. *Am. J. Phys. Anthropol.* **83**:331–347.

McKinney, M. L., and McNamara, K. J. (1991). *Heterochrony: The Evolution of Ontogeny*. Plenum Press, New York.

McKusick, V. A. (1989). *Mendelian Inheritance in Man*. Johns Hopkins Univ. Press, Baltimore.

Mitani, M. (1992). Preliminary results of the studies on wild western lowland gorillas and other sympatic diurnal primates in the Ndoki Forest, northern Congo. In *Topics in Primatology,* Vol. 2 (Itoigawa et al., eds.), pp. 215–224. University of Tokyo Press, Tokyo.

Morbeck, M. E. (1979). Forelimb use and positional adaptation in *Colobus guereza:* Integration of behavioral and anatomical data. In *Environment, Behavior and Morphology: Dynamic Interactions in Primates* (M. Morbeck, H. Preuschoft, and N. Gomberg, eds.), pp. 95–118. Fischer, New York.

Morbeck, M. E. (1983). Miocene hominoid discoveries from Rudabánya: Implications from the post-cranial skeleton. In *New Interpretations of Ape and Human Ancestry* (R. Ciochon and R. Corruccini, eds.), pp. 369–404. Plenum Press, NY.

Mourant, A. E., Kopec, A. C., and Domaniewska-Sobczak, K. (1976). *The Distribution of the Human Blood Groups and Other Polymorphisms*. Oxford Univ. Press, London.

Napier, J. R., and Napier, P. (1967). *Handbook of Living Primates*. Academic Press, New York.

Napier, J. R., and Walker, A. (1967). Vertical clinging and leaping: A newly recognized category of locomotor behavior in primates. *Folia Primatol.* **6**:204–219.

Neel, J. V. (1962). Diabetes mellitus: A "thrifty" genotype rendered detrimental by "progress." *Am. J. Hum. Genet.* **14**:353–362.

Newman, R. W. (1970). Why man is such a sweaty and thirsty naked animal: A speculative review. *Hum. Biol.* **42**:12–27.

Newman, R. W. (1975). Human adaptation to heat. In *Physiological Anthropology* (A. Damon, ed.), pp. 80–92. Oxford University Press, New York.

Nichols, J. (1994). Paper presented at the annual meeting of the American Association for the Advancement of Science, February 1994. San Francisco.

Nieuwenhuijsen, K., de Neef, K. J., and Slob, A. K. (1986). Sexual behaviour during ovarian cycles, pregnancy and lactation in group-living stump-tailed macaques (*Macaca arctoides*). *Hum. Reprod.* **1**:159–169.

Olivier, G. (1969). *Practical Anthropology.* Thomas, Springfield, IL.

Owen, R. (1859). *On the Classification and Geographical Distribution of the Mammalia.* Parker, London.

Painter, N. S., and Burkitt, D. P. (1975). Diverticular disease of the colon. In *Refined Carbohydrate Foods and Disease* (D. P. Burkitt and H. C. Trowell, eds.). Academic Press, London.

Parker, S. T. (1985). A social-technological model for the evolution of language. *Curr. Anthropol.* **27**:671–639.

Parker, S. T. (1987). A sexual selection model for hominid evolution. *Hum. Evol.* **2**:235–253.

Parker, S. T., and Gibson, K. R. (1979). A developmental model for the evolution of language and intelligence in early hominids. *Behav. Brain Sci.* **2**:367–408.

Partridge, T. (1986). Paleoecology of the Pliocene and lower Pleistocene hominids of southern Africa: How good is the chronological and paleoenvironmental evidence? *S. Afr. J. Sci.* **82**:80–83.

Pettigrew, J. D., Jamieson, B. G. M., Robson, S. K., Hall, L. S., Mcanally, K. I., and Cooper, H. M. (1989). Phylogenetic relations between microbats, megabats and primates (Mammalia: Chiroptera and Primates). *Philos. Trans. R. Soc. London, Ser. B* **325**:489–559.

Pickford, M., Senut, B., Ssemmanda, I., Elepu, D., and Obwona, P. (1988). Premiers résultats de la mission de l'Uganda. Palaeontology expedition à Nkondo (Pliocene du Bassin du Lac Albert, Ouganda). *C. R. Acad. Sci., Ser. 2* **306**:315–320.

Pilbeam, D. R. (1972). *The Ascent of Man.* Macmillan, New York.

Pilbeam, D. R. (1978). Rearranging our family tree. *Hum. Nat.* **1**(6):38–45.

Pilbeam, D. R. (1980). Major trends in human evolution. In *Current Argument on Early Man* (L. Konigsson, ed.), pp. 261–285. Pergamon, Oxford.

Pilbeam, D. R. (1996). Genetic and morphological records of the Hominoidea and hominid origins: A synthesis. *Molec. Phylogenet. Evol.* **5**:155–168.

Pilbeam, D. R., Rose, M. D., Badgley, C., et al. (1980). *Miocene Hominoids from Pakistan.* Postilla No. 181. Yale Peabody Museum, New Haven, CT.

Pilgrim, G. (1915). New Siwalik primates and their bearing on the questions of evolution of man and the Anthropoidea. *Rec. Geol. Surv. India* **XLV**:1–74.

Pinker, S. (1994). *The Language Instinct.* William Morrow, New York.

Ploog, D. W. (1964). Verhaltensforschung und Psychiatrie. In *Psychiatrie der Gegenwart* (H. Gruhle, R. Jung, W. Mayer-Gross, and M. Muller, eds.), pp. 291–443. Springer-Verlag, Berlin.

Pope, G. G. (1988a). Current issues in Far Eastern paleoanthropology. In *The Palaeoenvironments of East Asia from the Mid-Tertiary* (E. K. Y. Chen, ed.), Vol. 2, pp. 1097–1123.

Pope, G. G. (1988b). Recent advances in Far Eastern paleoanthropology. *Ann. Rev. Anthropol.* **17**:43–77.

Potts, R. (1988). *Early Hominid Activities at Olduvai.* de Gruyter, New York.

Potts, R., and Shipman, P. (1981). Cutmarks made by stone tools on bone from Olduvai Gorge. *Nature* **291**:557–580.

Pusey, A., Williams, J., and Goodall, J. (1997). The influence of dominance rank on the reproductive success of female chimpanzees. *Science* **277**:828–831.

Pusey, A. E., and Parker, C. (1987). Dispersal and philopatry. In *Primate Societies* (B. Smuts, D. Cheney, R. Seyfarth, T. Struhsaker, and R. Wrangham, eds.). Univ. of Chicago Press, Chicago.

Radetsky, P. (1997). Immune to a plague. *Discover* **18**:60–67.

Rak, Y. (1983). *The Australopithecine Face.* Academic Press, Orlando, FL.

Rasmussen, D. T. (1990). Primate origins: Lessons from a neotropical marsupial. *Am. J. Primatol.* **22**:263–277.

Rayner, R. J., Moon, B. P., and Masters, J. C. (1993). The Makapansgat australopithecine environment. *J. Hum. Evol.* **24**:219–231.

Reynolds, V., and Reynolds, F. (1965). Chimpanzees of the Budongo Forest. In *Primate Behavior* (I. DeVore, ed.), pp. 368–424. Holt, Rinehart & Winston, New York.

Richard, A. F. (1985a). *Primates in Nature.* Freeman, New York.

Richard, A. F. (1985b). Social boundaries in a Malagasy prosimian, the sifaka (*Propithecus verreauxi*). *Intl. J. Primatol.* **6**:553–568.

Rightmire, G. P. (1990). *The Evolution of Homo erectus.* Cambridge Univ. Press, Cambridge, UK.

Robins, A. H. (1991). *Biological Perspectives on Human Pigmentation.* Cambridge Univ. Press, Cambridge, UK.

Robinson, J. G. (1986). Seasonal variation in the use of time and space by the wedge-capped capuchin monkey, *Cebus olivaceus:* Implications for foraging theory. *Smithsonian Contrib. Zool.* **431**:1–60.

Rodman, P. S. (1984). Foraging and social systems of orangutans and chimpanzees. In *Adaptations for Foraging in Nonhuman Primates* (P. S. Rodman and J. G. H. Cant, eds.), pp. 134–160. Columbia University Press, New York.

Rodman, P. S. (1988). Resources and group size of primates. In *The Ecology of Social Behavior* (C. N. Slobodchikoff, ed.), pp. 83–108. Academic Press, San Diego, CA.

Rose, K. D., and Fleagle, J. G. (1981). The fossil history of non-human primates in the Americas. In *Ecology and Behavior of Neotropical Primates* (A. F. Coimbra-Filho and R. A. Mittermeier, eds.), Vol. 1, pp. 111–167. Academia Brasiliera de Ciencias, Rio de Janeiro, Brazil.

Rosenberger, A. L. (1992). Evolution of New World monkeys. In *The Cambridge Encyclopedia of Human Evolution* (S. Jones, R. Martin, and D. Pilbeam, eds.), pp. 209–216. Cambridge University Press, Cambridge, UK.

Rowell, T. E. (1993). Reification of social systems. *Evol. Anthropol.* **2**:135–137.

Rumbaugh, D. (1985). Comparative psychology: Patterns in adaptation. In *The G. Stanley Hall Lecture Series 5*

(A. Rogers and C. Scheirer, eds.), pp. 7–53. Psychological Assoc., Washington, DC.

Russel, M. J., Switz, G. M., and Thompson, K. T. (1980). Olfactory influences on the human menstrual cycle. *Pharmacol. Biochem. Behav.* **13:**737–738.

Sarich, V. M., and Wilson, A. C. (1967). Immunological time scale for hominid evolution. *Science* **158:**1200–1203.

Savage-Rumbaugh, S., Sevcik, R. A., Rumbaugh, D. M., and Rupert, E. (1985). The capacity of animals to acquire language: Do species differences have anything to say to us? *Phil. Trans. R. Soc. Lond.* **B308:**177–185.

Schaller, G. B. (1963). *The Mountain Gorilla: Ecology and Behavior.* Univ. of Chicago Press, Chicago.

Schell, L. M. (1991). Pollution and human growth: Lead, noise, polychlorobiphenyl compounds, and toxic wastes. In *Applications of Biological Anthropology to Human Affairs* (C. G. N. Mascie-Taylor and G. W. Lasker, eds.), pp. 83–116. Cambridge Univ. Press, Cambridge, UK.

Schell, L. M., and Ando, Y. (1991). Postnatal growth of children in relation to noise from Osaka International airport. *J. Sound Vibr.* **151:**371–382.

Schepartz, L. A. (1993). Language and modern human origins. *Yearb. Phys. Anthropol.* **36:**91–126.

Schoch, R. M. (1986). *Phylogeny Reconstruction in Paleontology.* Van Nostrand Reinhold Co., New York.

Schultz, A. H. (1924). Growth studies on primates bearing upon man's evolution. *Am. J. Phys. Anthropol.* **7:**149–164.

Schultz, A. H. (1936). Characters common to higher primates and characters specific to man. *Quart. Rev. Biol.* **11:**259–283, 425–455.

Schultz, A. H. (1969). *The Life of Primates.* Weidenfels & Nicolson, London.

Seyfarth, R. M., Cheney, D. L., and Marler, P. (1980). Monkey responses to three different alarm calls: Evidence of predator classification and semantic communication. *Science* **210:**801–803.

Shapiro, H. (1979). *Peking Man.* Simon & Schuster, New York.

Shea, B. T. (1990). In *Bone,* Vol. 6 (B. Hall, ed.). CRC Press, Boca Raton, FL.

Shipman, P. (1994). *The Evolution of Racism.* Simon & Schuster, New York.

Shreeve, J. (1996). Sunset on the Savanna. Why do we walk? *Discover* **17:**116–125.

Sibley, C. G., and Ahlquist, J. E. (1987). DNA hybridization evidence of hominoid phylogeny. Results from an expanded data set. *J. Mol. Evol.* **26:**99–121.

Sibley, C. G., Comstock, J. A., and Ahlquist, J. E. (1990). DNA hybridization evidence of hominoid phylogeny: A reanalysis of the data. *J. Mol. Evol.* **30:**202–236.

Sige, B., Jaeger, J. J., Sudre, J., and Vianey-Liaud, M. (1990). *Altiatlasius koulchii* n. gen. et sp., Primate Omomyidae du Paleocene superieur du Maroc, et les origenes des euprimates. *Palaeontographica Abt. A* **214:**31–56.

Sigmon, B. A. (1971). Bipedal behavior and the emergence of erect posture in Man. *Am. J. Phys. Anthropol.* **34:**55–60.

Simons, E. L. (1972). *Primate Evolution.* Macmillan, New York.

Simons, E. L. (1989). Human origins. *Science* **245:**1343–1350.

Simons, E. L. (1990). Discovery of the oldest known anthropoidean skull from the Paleogene of Egypt. *Science* **247:**1567–1569.

Simons, E. L., and Pilbeam, D. R. (1965). Preliminary revision of the Dryopithecinae (Pongidae, Anthropoidea). *Folia Primatol.* **3:**81–152.

Simpson, G. G. (1944). *Tempo and Mode in Evolution.* Columbia University Press, New York.

Small, M. F. (1989). MS monkey. *Nat. Hist.,* January:10–12.

Smith, B. H. (1986). Dental developments in *Australopithecus* and early *Homo. Nature* (London) **323:**327–330.

Smith, E. A. (1992). Human behavioral ecology. I. *Evol. Anthropol.* **1:**20–25.

Smith, H. M. (1960). *Evolution of Chordate Structure.* Holt, Rinehart & Winston, New York.

Smith, J. Maynard (1978). *The Evolution of Sex.* Cambridge Univ. Press, Cambridge, UK.

Smouse, P. E., and Li, W. H. (1987). Likelihood analysis of mitochondrial restriction-cleavage patterns for the human chimpanzee-gorilla trichotomy. *Evolution (Lawrence, Kans.)* **41:**1162–1176.

Smuts, B. (1987). What are friends for? *Nat. Hist.* **92:**36–45.

Sober, E. (ed.). (1984). *Conceptual Issues in Evolutionary Biology: An Anthology.* MIT Press, Cambridge, MA.

Southwick, C. H., and Smith, R. B. (1986). The growth of primate field studies. *Comp. Primate Biol.* **2A:**173–191.

Spuhler, J. N. (1989). Raymond Pearl memorial lecture, 1988: Evolution of mitochondrial DNA in human and other organisms. *Am. J. Hum. Biol.* **1:**509–528.

Steklis, H. D. (1985). Primate communication, comparative neurology, and the origin of language re-examined. *J. Hum. Evol.* **14:**157–173.

Stokes, W. L. (1988). *Essentials of Earth History.* Prentice Hall, Englewood Cliffs, NJ.

Stringer, C. B. (1990). The emergence of modern humans. *Sci. Am.* **263:**98–104.

Susman, R. L., Stern, J., Jr., and Jungers, W. (1984). Arboreality and bipedality in the Hadar hominids. *Folia Primatol.* **43:**113–156.

Sussman, R. W. (1991). Primate origins and the evolution of angiosperms. *Am. J. Primatol.* **23:**209–223.

Sussman, R. W., and Raven, P. H. (1978). Pollination by lemurs and marsupials: An archaic coevolutionary system. *Science* **200:**731–736.

Swisher, C. C., III, Curtis, G. H., Jacob, T., Getty, A. G., Suprijo, A., and Widiasmoro. (1994). Age of the earliest known hominids in Java, Indonesia. *Science* **263:**1118–1121.

Szalay, F. S. (1970). Late Eocene *Amphipithecus* and the origins of catarrhine primates. *Nature* (London) **227:**355–357.

Szalay, F. S. (1972). Paleobiology of the earliest primates. In *The Functional and Evolutionary Biology of Primates* (R. H. Tuttle, ed.), pp. 3–35. Aldine, Chicago.

Tague, R., and Lovejoy, O. C. (1986). The obstetric pelvis of A. L. 288–1 (Lucy). *J. Hum. Evol.* **15:**237–255.

Tanner, J. M. (1964). *The Physique of the Olympic Athlete.* George Allen and Unwin, London.

Tanner, J. M. (1981). *A History of the Study of Human Growth.* Cambridge Univ. Press, Cambridge, UK.

Tanner, J. M. (1989). *Foetus into Man,* rev. and enlarged ed. Harvard Univ. Press, Cambridge, MA.

Tanner, J. M., and Whitehouse, R. H. (1976). Clinical longitudinal standards for height, weight, height velocity and weight velocity and the stages of puberty. *Arch. Disease in Childhood* **51:**170–179.

Taub, D., and Mehlman, P. (1991). Primate paternalistic investment: A cross-species view. In *Understanding Behavior* (J. Loy and C. Peters, eds.), pp. 51–89. Oxford Univ. Press, Oxford.

Templeton, A. R. (1985). The phylogeny of the hominoid primates: A statistical analysis of the DNA-DNA hybridization data. *Mol. Biol. Evol.* **2:**420–433.

Templeton, A. R. (1986). Further comments on statistical analysis of DNA-DNA hybridization data. *Mol. Biol. Evol.* **3:**290–295.

Templeton, A. R. (1993). The "Eve" hypothesis: A genetic critique and reanalysis. *Am. Anthropol.* **95:**51–72.

Terbough, J. T., and Jansen, C. H. (1986). The socioecology of primate groups. *Ann. Rev. Ecol. Syste.* **17:**111–136.

Terrace, H. (1979). How Nim Chimpsky changed my mind. *Psychol. Today,* November:65–76.

Tobias, P. V. (1991). *The Skulls, Endocasts, and Teeth of Homo habilis. Olduvai Gorge,* Vol. 4. Cambridge Univ. Press, Cambridge, UK.

Toth, N., and Schick, K. D. (1993). Early stone industries and inferences regarding language and cognition. In *Tools, Language and Cognition in Human Evolution* (K. Gibson and T. Ingold, eds.), pp. 346–362. Cambridge Univ. Press, Cambridge, UK.

Trevathan, W. (1987). *Human Birth: An Evolutionary Perspective.* de Gruyter, New York.

Trivers, R. L. (1972). Parental investment and sexual selection. In *Sexual Selection and the Descent of Man* (B. Campbell, ed.). Aldine, Chicago.

Tutin, C., and McGinnis, P. (1981). Sexuality of the chimpanzee in the wild. In *Reproductive Biology of the Great Apes: Comparative and Biomedical Perspectives.* (C. Graham, ed.), pp. 239–264. Academic Press, New York.

Tuttle, R. (1975). Parallelism, brachiation, and hominid phylogeny. In *The Phylogeny of the Primates* (W. Luckett and F. S. Szalay, eds.), pp. 447–480. Plenum, New York.

Tuttle, R. H. (1967). Knucklewalking and the evolution of hominoid hands. *Am. J. Phys. Anthropol.* **26:**171–206.

Tyson, E. (1699). *Orang-Outang, sive Homo sylvestris: Or; The Anatomy of a Pygmie Compared with That of Monkey, an Ape, and a Man.* Bennet, London.

Ubelaker, D. H., (1995). Latest developments in skeletal biology and forensic anthropology. In *Biological Anthropology: The State of the Science* (N. T. Boaz and L. D. Wolfe, eds.), pp. 91–106. International Institute for Human Evolutionary Research, Bend, OR.

Ubelaker, D. H., and O'Donnell, G. (1992). Computer-assisted facial reconstruction. *J. Foren. Sci.* **37:**155–162.

Van Schaik, C. P. (1983). Why are diurnal primates living in groups? *Behaviour* **87:**120–143.

Van Schaik, C. P., and Dunbar, R. I. M. (1990). The evolution of monogram in large primates: A new hypothesis and some crucial tests. *Behaviour* **115:**30–62.

Vigilant, L., Pennington, R., Harpending, H., Kocher, T. D., and Wilson, A. C. (1989). Mitochondrial DNA sequences in single hairs from a southern African population. *Proc. Natl. Acad. Sci. U.S.A.* **86:**9350–9354.

Vogel, J. C. (1985). Further attempts at dating the Taung tufas. In *Hominid Evolution: Past, Present, and Future* (P. V. Tobias, ed.), pp. 189–194. Alan R. Liss, New York.

Vrba, E. S. (1988). Late Pliocene climatic events and hominid and hominid evolution. In *Evolutionary History of the "Robust" Australopithecines* (F. Grine, ed.), pp. 405–426. de Gruyter, New York.

Vrba, E. S. (1994). An hypothesis of heterochrony in response to climatic cooling and its relevance to early hominid evolution. In *Integrative Paths to the Past* (R. Corruccini and R. Ciochon, eds.), pp. 345–376. Prentice Hall, Upper Saddle River, NJ.

Walker, A., and Leakey, R. (eds.). (1993). *The Nariokotome Homo erectus Skeleton.* Harvard University Press, Cambridge, MA.

Ward, P., and Zahavi, A. (1973). The importance of certain assemblages of birds as "information-centres" for food-finding. *Ibis* **115**(4):517–534.

Washburn, S. L. (1960). Tools and human evolution. *Sci. Am.* **203:**63–75.

Washburn, S. L. (1963). Behavior and human evolution. In *Classification and Human Evolution* (S. L. Washburn, ed.), pp. 190–203. Aldine, Chicago.

Washburn, S. L. (1993). Evolution and education. In *Milestones in Human Evolution* (A. J. Almquist and J. A. Manyak, eds.), pp. 223–240. Waveland Press, Prospect Heights, IL.

Washburn, S. L., and Harding, R. S. O. (1975). Evolution and human nature. In *American Handbook of Psychiatry,* 2nd ed. Vol. 6, Chapter 1:3–13.

Washburn, S. L., and Lancaster, C. S. (1968). The evolution of hunting. In *Man the Hunter* (R. Lee and I. DeVore, eds.), pp. 292–303. Aldine, Chicago.

Washburn, S. L., and Moore, R. (1980). *Ape into Human,* 2nd ed. Little, Brown, Boston.

Watson, J. D. (1970). *Molecular Biology of the Gene,* 2nd ed. Benjamin, Menlo Park, CA.

Weinert, H. (1932). *Ursprung der Menschheit. Uber den engeren Anschluss des Menschengeschlechts an die Menschenaffen.* Enke, Stuttgart.

Watts, D. P. (1989). Infanticide in mountain gorillas: New cases and a reconsideration of the evidence. *Ethology* **81:**1–18.

Weidenreich, F. (1939). Did *Sinanthropus pekinensis* practice cannabalism? *Bull. Geol. Soc. China* **19:**49–63.

Wescott, R. W. (1967). The exhibitionistic origin of human bipedalism. *Man* **2:**630.

White, T. D., Suwa, G., and Asfaw, B. (1994). *Australopithecus ramidus,* a new species of early hominid from Aramis, Ethiopia. *Nature (London)* **371:**306–312.

White, T. D., Suwa, G., and Asfaw, B. (1995). *Australopithecus ramidus,* a new species of early hominid from Aramis, Ethiopia. *Nature (London)* **375:**88.

Wiessner, P. (1990). Is there a unity to style? In *Uses of Style in Archeology* (M. Conkey and C. Hasdorf, eds.), pp. 105–112. Cambridge Univ. Press, Cambridge, UK.

Williams, G. C., and Nesse, R. M. (1991). The dawn of Darwinian medicine. *Quart. Rev. Biol.* **66:**1–22.

Williams, R. J. (1951). Biochemical Institute Studies. IV. Individual metabolic patterns and human disease: An exploratory study utilizing predominantly paper chromatographic methods. *Univ. Tex. Publ.* **5109:**7–21.

Williams, S. A., and Goodman, M. (1989). A statistical test that supports a human/chimpanzee clade based on noncoding DNA sequence data. *Mol. Biol. Evol.* **6:**325–330.

Wilson, E. O. (1975). *Sociobiology: The New Synthesis.* Harvard Univ. Press, Cambridge, MA.

Wilson, E. O. (1996). Culture as a biological product. In *Search of Nature,* pp. 107–126. Island Press, Washington, DC.

Winchester, A. M. (1972). *Genetics: A Survey of the Principles of Heredity,* 4th ed. Houghton-Mifflin, Boston.

Wobst, H. M. (1977). Stylistic behavior and information exchange. In *For the Director: Research Essays in Honor of James B. Griffin* (C. E. Cleland, ed.), Anthropol. Pap. No. 61, pp. 317–342. Ann Arbor Museum of Anthropology, Ann Arbor, MI.

WoldeGabriel, G., White, T. D., Suwa, G., Renne, P., de-Heinzelin, J., Hart, W. K., and Helken, G. (1994). Ecological and temporal placement of early Pliocene hominids of Aramis, Ethiopia. *Nature* **371:**330–333.

Wolfe, L. D. (1981). Display behavior of three troups of Japanese monkeys. *Primates* **22:**24–32.

Wood, B. A. (1992). Taxonomy and evolutionary relationships of *Homo erectus. Cour. Forschungsint,* Senckenberg, Frankfurt, Germany.

Wrangham, R. (1997). Subtle, secret female chimpanzees. *Science* **277:**774–775.

Wrangham, R. W. (1980). An ecological model of female-bonded primate groups. *Behaviour* **75:**262–300.

Wrangham, R. W. (1983). Ultimate factors determining social structure. In *Primate Social Relationships: An Integrated Approach* (R. Hinde, ed.), pp. 255–262. Blackwell, Oxford.

Wrangham, R. W. (1987a). Evolution of social structure. In *Primate Societies* (B. B. Smuts, D. L. Cheny, R M. Seyfarth, R. W. Wrangham, and T. T. Struhsaker, eds.), pp. 282–296. Univ. of Chicago Press, Chicago.

Wrangham, R. W. (1987b). The significance of African apes for reconstructing human social evolution. In *The Evolution of Human Behavior: Primate Models* (W. Kinzey, ed.), pp. 51–71. SUNY Press, Albany, NY.

Wright, K. (1990). Cradle of mutation. *Discover,* September: 22–23.

Wynn, I. (1988). Tools and the evolution of human intelligence. In *Machiavellian Intelligence* (R. Byrne and A. Whiten, eds.), pp. 271–284. Oxford Univ. Press (Clarendon), Oxford.

Zihlman, A. L. (1981). Women as shapers of human adaptation. In *Woman the Gatherer* (F. Dahlberg, ed.), pp. 75–120. Yale Univ. Press, New Haven, CT.

Zihlman, A., Cronin, J. E., Cramer, D. L., and Sarich, V. M. (1978). Pygmy chimpanzee as a possible prototype for the common ancestor of humans, chimpanzees, and gorillas. *Nature* **275:**744–746.

Zuckerman, S. (1932). *The Social Life of Monkeys and Apes.* Routledge & Kegan Paul, London.

Illustration Credits

CHAPTER 1 **1-1** N. T. Boaz; **1-3** The Granger Collection; **1-5** Corbis-Bettmann; **1-6** ENP Images; **1-7** Dr. Gerhard Storch, Forschungsinstitut Senckenberg; **1-8, 1-9** From *Phylogeny Reconstruction in Paleontology* by Schoch, Robert M., © 1986. Reprinted by permission of the author; **1-10** Reproduced from Thomas Henry Huxley, *Evidence as to Man's Place in Nature.* London: Williams and Norgate, 1863. By permission of Burndy Library, Norwalk, Connecticut; **1-11** (left) Reprinted by permission of the publisher from *Promethean Fire* by C. J. Lumsden and E. O. Wilson, Cambridge, Mass.: Harvard University Press, copyright © 1983 by the President and Fellows of Harvard College. Illustration copyright © 1983 by Whitney Powell. (right) Chromosome diagrams reprinted with permission from "The Striking Resemblance of High Resolution G. Banded Chromosomes of Man and Chimpanzee," J. J. Yunis, et al., *Science*, Vol. 208, pp. 1145–1148, Copyright © 1980 American Association for the Advancement of Science. **1-13** California Academy of Sciences.

CHAPTER 2 **2-1, 2-6, 2-7, 2-16, 2-21** (right) From *Biology* by Barrett/Abramoff/Kumaran/Millington: © 1986. Reprinted by permission of Prentice Hall, Upper Saddle River, New Jersey. (d) Thomas Broker/Phototake NYC; **2-2** From *Molecular Biology of the Gene,* 3rd Ed. by J. D. Watson, et al. Copyright © 1976 by James D. Watson. Reprinted by permission of Benjamin/Cummings Publishing Company; **2-4** From *The Processing of RNA* by James E. Darnell, Jr., illustration by Jerome Kuhl, copyright © 1983. From Scientific American, Inc., 249(1):94. Reprinted by permission of Jerome Kuhl; **2-9, 2-11** Culver Pictures, Inc.; **2-10** North Wind Picture Archives; **2-13** (left) Galen Rowell/FPG International; (right) Frans Lanting/Photo Researchers, Inc.; **2-14** (left) The Stock Market; (right) Margot Conte/Animals Animals/Earth Scenes; **2-15** Archive Photos; **2-17** Klug/Cummings, *Concepts of Genetics,* 4/E, © 1994, p. 102. Reprinted by permission of Prentice Hall, Upper Saddle River, New Jersey; **2-18** Photo Researchers, Inc.; **2-20** Peter Menzel Photography; **2-21** (left) After Barrett/Abramoff/Kumaran/Millington, *Biology,* © 1986, p. 622. (right) Adapted from *Biology* by Barrett/Abramoff/Kumaran/Millington: © 1986. Reprinted by permission of Prentice Hall, Upper Saddle River, New Jersey.

CHAPTER 3 **3-3** Custom Medical Stock Photo, Inc.; **3-4** VU/Stanley Flegler/Visuals Unlimited; **3-5** Based on papers by Sewell Wright, *Statistical Theory of Evolution,* J. of American Statistical Association, March 1931, 201-208; **3-6** David Barritt/Gamma-Liaison, Inc.; **3-7** Illustration by Ian Worpole © 1990. Reprinted with permission of *Discover* Magazine; **3-8** M. W. Tweedie/Photo Researchers, Inc.; **3-9** From *Genetics: A Human Concern* by Sutton, H. Eldon, © 1985. Reprinted by permission of Prentice Hall, Upper Saddle River, New Jersey; **3-10** From *Population Genetics and Evolution,* 2/E by Mettler/Gregg/Schaffer, © 1988, p. 195. Reprinted by permission of Prentice Hall, Upper Saddle River, New Jersey; **3-11** (left) Tom McHugh/Photo Researchers, Inc.; (right) Michael Kevin Daly/The Stock Market; **3-12** Joe M. Macedonia; **3-13** Archive Photos; **3-14** (left) Frans Lanting/Minden Pictures; (center) Stan Osolinski/Tony Stone Images; (right) Joe M. Macedonia.

CHAPTER 4 **4-1** From *Biology* by Barrett/Abramoff/Kumaran/Millington, © 1986. Reprinted by permission of Prentice Hall, Upper Saddle River, New Jersey; **4-2** (left) Robert and Linda Mitchell Photography; (right) VU/Larry S. Roberts/Visuals Unlimited; **4-3** From *Human Anatomy*, 2/E by Martini/Timmons, © 1997. Adapted by permission of Prentice Hall, Upper Saddle River, New Jersey; **4-5** (bird embryo) Cabisco/Visuals Unlimited; (human embryo) Petit Format/Nestle/Science Source/Photo Researchers, Inc.; **4-8** Dorothy Norton/Simon & Schuster/PH College; **4-10** After *The Triune Brain* by P. D. MacLean, copyright © 1990 Plenum Publishing Corporation. Reprinted by permission of Plenum Publishing Corporation; **4-11** (left) Wayne Lynch/DRK Photo; (center) McGuire/Anthro-Photo; (right) European Picture Service/FPG International; **4-14** Rod Williams/Bruce Coleman, Inc.

CHAPTER 5 **5-1, 5-2, 5-3, 5-4, 5-12** From *Primate Adaptation and Evolution* by J. G. Fleagle, copyright © 1988, Academic Press. Reprinted by permission of Academic Press, Inc., a subsidiary of Harcourt Brace & Co., and the author; **5-5** From *The Human Odyssey: Four Million Years of Evolution* by I. Tattersall, © 1993 by I. Tattersall. Reprinted by permission; **5-6** Dorothy Norton/Simon & Schuster/PH College; **5-7** Jean-Philippe Varin/JACANA/Photo Researchers, Inc.; **5-8** Reproduced with permission of S. Karger AG, Basel; **5-10** (left) S. F. Kimbrough/from Steven M. Stanley, *Earth and Life Through Time,* p. 541, W. H. Freeman and Company. Reprinted by permission of Dr. Richard Kay. (right) R. F. Kay/Steven Stanley; **5-11, 5-14** From *Primate Adaptation and Evolution* by J. G. Fleagle, copyright © 1988 Academic Press, Inc. Reprinted by permission of Academic Press, Inc., Dr. John G. Fleagle, and Stephen Nash, artist; **5-13** Art Wolfe, Inc.

CHAPTER 6 **6-1** N. DeVore/Anthro-Photo; **6-2, 6-4** From *Primate Adaptation and Evolution* by J. G. Fleagle, copyright © 1988 Academic Press, Inc. Reprinted by permission of Academic Press, Inc., Dr. John G. Fleagle, and Stephen Nash, artist; **6-3** Anthro-Photo; **6-6** Irven DeVore/Anthro-Photo; **6-7** Dan McCoy/Rainbow; **6-8** Barbara Smuts/Anthro-Photo; **6-9** Bruce Coleman, Inc.; **6-10** R. Wrangham/Anthro-Photo; **6-11** From *Primate Behavior: Field Studies of Monkeys and Apes* by

Irven DeVore, 1965, Fig. 3-10, p. 70, Harcourt Brace & Co.; **6-12** (left) Rod Williams/Bruce Coleman, Inc.; (right) James H. Carmichael/Bruce Coleman, Inc.; **6-13** Peter Veit/DRK Photo; **6-14** K. & K. Ammann/Bruce Coleman, Inc.; **6-15** Martin Rogers/Stock Boston; **6-16** Paul Simonds.

CHAPTER 7   7-3 Dieter & Mary Plage/Bruce Coleman, Inc.; **7-4** Courtesy of The National Geographic Society; **7-5** From John Buettner-Janusch, *Origins of Man: Physical Anthropology,* p. 298, John Wiley & Sons, Inc.; **7-6, 7-11** (top) From *Human Anatomy,* 2/E by Martini/Timmons, © 1997. Adapted by permission of Prentice Hall, Upper Saddle River, New Jersey; **7-7, 7-12, 7-15** Adapted from *Primate Adaptation and Evolution* by J. G. Fleagle, copyright © 1988 Academic Press, Inc. Reprinted by permission of Academic Press, Inc., John G. Fleagle, and Stephen Nash, artist; **7-8, 7-10** Art Wolfe, Inc.; **7-9** VU/Joe McDonald/Visuals Unlimited; **7-11** (bottom) From Beard, K. C., and Godinot, M. 1988, *Journal of Human Evolution* 17:71–92. Reprinted by permission of Academic Press, Ltd., London; **7-14** From *New Interpretations of Ape and Human Ancestry* by Walker & M. Pickford, copyright © 1983 Plenum Publishing Corp., pp. 325–52. Reprinted by permission; **7-16** From *Yearbook of Physical Anthropology* by D. R. Begun, copyright © 1994 John Wiley & Sons, Inc. Reprinted by permission; Dorothy Norton/Simon & Schuster/PH College; **7-17** From *Human Evolution, Third Edition* by R. Lewis, Copyright © 1993 Blackwell Science Ltd. Reprinted by permission; **7-18** Philbeam/Peabody Museum, Harvard University.

CHAPTER 8   8-1, 8-6 N. T. Boaz; **8-2, 8-13** Brill Atlanta; **8-3** Adapted from *Encyclopedia of Human Evolution and Prehistory,* Tattersall, I., et al., Garland Publishing Co.; **8-4** Nanci Kahn/Institute of Human Origins; **8-5** From *Primitive Adaptation and Evolution* by J. G. Fleagle, copyright © 1988 Academic Press, Inc. Reprinted by permission of Academic Press, Inc., Dr. John G. Fleagle, and Stephen Nash, artist; **8-7** From *Nature* 371:306–312, T. D. White et al., 1994, *Australopithecus ramidus,* a new species of early hominoid from Aramis, Ethiopia, copyright © 1994, Macmillan Magazines Limited; **8-8** (left) John Reader/Science Photo Library/Photo Researchers, Inc.; (center) N. T. Boaz; (right) D. Finnin/C. Chesek/American Museum of Natural History; **8-9** Institute of Human Origins; **8-10** W. H. Kimbel/Institute of Human Origins; **8-11** Adapted from Cooke, 1983, Human Evolution: The Geological Framework, *Can. J. of Anthropology* 3:143–161; **8-14** (left) Cannon-Bonventure/Anthro-Photo; (right) Brill Atlanta.

CHAPTER 9   9-1 (left) Phillip V. Tobias, Medical School, University of the Witwatersrand, South Africa; (right) K. Cannon-Bonventure/Anthro-Photo; **9-2, 9-4** N. T. Boaz; **9-7** John Reader/Science Photo Library/Photo Researchers, Inc.; **9-8** From *Human Evolution,* 3rd Ed., by R. Lewin, p. 152, © 1993. Reprinted by permission of Blackwell Science, Inc.; **9-9** (left) Paris Pavlakis, Ph.D., University of Ioannina, Greece; (center, right) Willard Whitson/American Museum of Natural History; **9-12** Rota/American Museum of Natural History; **9-13** Eric Trinkaus/Washington University; **9-14** C. M. Dixon; **9-15** Gamma-Liaison, Inc.

CHAPTER 10   10-1 From "Bonobo Sex and Society," by Frans B. M. de Waal, illustration by Laurie Grace, *Scientific American,* March 1995. Reprinted by permission of Laurie Grace; **10-2** The Zoological Society of San Diego; **10-3** Bruce Coleman, Inc.; **10-4** From *The Mountain Gorilla* by George B. Schaller, Fig. 6-6, p. 285. Copyright © 1963 George B. Schaller. Reprinted by permission; Dorothy Norton/Simon & Schuster/PH College; **10-5** Gerry Ellis/ENP Images; **10-6** Jim Moore/Anthro-Photo; **10-7** (left) Wrangham/Anthro-Photo; (right) Nancy Nicolson/Anthro-Photo; **10-8** Peter Davey/Bruce Coleman, Inc.; **10-9** Tenace/Anthro-Photo; **10-10** R. Van Nostrand/Photo Researchers, Inc.; **10-11** Rose A. Sevcik/Shelly Williams, Georgia State University; **10-12** (left) Petit Format/J. Da Cunha/Photo Researchers, Inc.; (right) Suzanne Szasz/Photo Researchers, Inc.; **10-13** Reprinted with permission from Eibl-Eibesfeldt, Irenaus. *Human Ethology.* (New York: Aldine de Gruyter). © 1989 Irenaus Eibl-Eibesfeldt; **10-14** Scottish Media Newspapers, Ltd.; **10-15** M. Shostak/Anthro-Photo; **10-16** From Tague, R., & Lovejoy, O. C., *Journal of Human Evolution,* Vol. 15, pp. 237–55, 1986. Copyright © 1986, by permission of the publisher, Academic Press Limited, London; **10-17** From An Hypothesis of Heterochrony in Response to Climatic Cooling . . ." by E. S. Vrba in *Integrative Paths to the Past* edited by Corricini/Ciochon, © 1994. Adapted by permission of Prentice Hall, Upper Saddle River, New Jersey; **10-18** From *Human Anatomy,* 2/E by Martini/Timmons, © 1997. Adapted by permission of Prentice Hall, Upper Saddle River, New Jersey; **10-19** Reprinted by permission of the Estate of Bunji Tagawa; **10-20, 10-21** Courtesy of Mrs. J. Desmond Clark; **10-22** Peabody Museum, Harvard University.

CHAPTER 11   11-1 Bill Losh/FPG International; **11-2** Alan Mann/University of Pennsylvania Museum; **11-7** Hanna Schreiber/Photo Researchers, Inc.; **11-8** D. Gorton/Time Inc., NJ.

CHAPTER 12   12-1 From *Patterns of Human Growth* by Barry Bogin. Copyright © 1988. Reprinted with the permission of Cambridge University Press; **12-2, 12-7, 12-8** Adapted from *Growth and Development* by R. Malina, copyright © 1975, by Burgess Publishing Co., an imprint of Burgess International Group, Inc., Edina, MN; **12-3** From Georges Olivier, *Practical Anthropology,* copyright © 1969. Courtesy of Charles C. Thomas, Publisher, Springfield, Illinois; **12-4** "Prolongation of life phases and gestation in primates" by C. O. Lovejoy. Copyright © 1977. American Association for the Advancement of Science; **12-5** From Tanner, J. M. Human Growth, 1962, *Growth at Adolescence, with a general consideration to the effect of heredity and environmental factors upon growth and maturation from birth to maturity,* 2nd Ed., Blackwell Scientific Publications, Oxford, England; **12-6** From *Biology* by Barrett/Abramoff/Kumaran/Millington, © 1986, p. 302. Reprinted by permission of Prentice Hall, Upper Saddle River, New Jersey; **12-9** (a) From Eveleth, P. B., and Tanner, J. M. (1976) *Worldwide Variation in Human Growth,* IBP Synth. Ser. No. 8. Cambridge University Press, Cambridge, UK; **12-10** Peacock/Anthro-Photo; **12-11** From *The Paleolithic Prescription* by S. Boyd Eaton, Marjorie Shostak, and Melvin Konner. Copyright © 1988 by S. Boyd Eaton, M.D., Marjorie Shostak, and Melvin Konner, M.D., Ph.D. Reprinted by permission of HarperCollins Publishers, Inc.; **12-12** Reprinted with permission from *Science*, Vol. 269, July 1995, J. Cohen. Copyright © 1995 American Association for the Advancement of Science.

CHAPTER 13 **13-1** National Archives; **13-3** (left) Ursula Markus/Photo Researchers, Inc.; (right) Dick Lauria/Photo Researchers, Inc.; **13-4** (top) James Sugar/Black Star; (bottom) Tom McHugh/Photo Researchers, Inc.; **13-5** James Stevenson/Science Photo Library/Photo Researchers, Inc.; **13-6** Biophoto Associates/Photo Researchers, Inc.; **13-8** John Karapelou/© 1997. Reprinted with permission of *Discover* Magazine;

13-10 Dr. Melissa McDonnell/United States National Zoo Park; **13-11** (left) Long Photography, Inc.; **13-12** Gene O'Donnell/FBI; **13-13** EAAF archives.

Tables

3-1 From *Genetics*, 4/E by A. M. Winchester, © 1972, p. 423; **12-2, 12-3, 12-4** From *The Paleolithic Prescription* by S. Boyd Eaton, Marjorie Shostak, and Melvin Konner. Copyright © 1988 by S. Boyd Eaton, M.D., Marjorie Shostak, and Melvin Konner, M.D., Ph.D. Reprinted by permission of HarperCollins Publishers, Inc.

Index